THE COMPLETE
AIR NAVIGATOR

THE COMPLETE
AIR NAVIGATOR

COVERING THE SYLLABUS FOR THE
FIRST CLASS AIR NAVIGATOR'S LICENCE

BY

D. C. T. BENNETT
A.F.R.Ae.S.

SECOND EDITION

LONDON
SIR ISAAC PITMAN & SONS, LTD.
1940

SIR ISAAC PITMAN & SONS, Ltd.
PITMAN HOUSE, PARKER STREET, KINGSWAY, LONDON, W.C.2
THE PITMAN PRESS, BATH
PITMAN HOUSE, LITTLE COLLINS STREET, MELBOURNE

ASSOCIATED COMPANIES
PITMAN PUBLISHING CORPORATION
2 WEST 45TH STREET, NEW YORK
205 WEST MONROE STREET, CHICAGO

SIR ISAAC PITMAN & SONS (CANADA), Ltd.
(INCORPORATING THE COMMERCIAL TEXT BOOK COMPANY)
PITMAN HOUSE, 381–383 CHURCH STREET, TORONTO

MADE IN GREAT BRITAIN AT THE PITMAN PRESS, BATH
D—(A.31)

"Eternal Vigilance is the Price of Safety."

LY

PREFACE

THE general standard of air navigation in the British Commonwealth is high and is on sound lines. But if the prestige and authority of the profession is to be maintained at this high level it behoves all air navigating officers to do all they can to maintain the standard of the First Class Navigator's Licence and to induce more of their numbers to obtain this essential qualification. Moreover, navigating officers should constantly endeavour to increase the extent of their professional knowledge and ability.

In presenting the second edition a large number of alterations and additions have been included—necessitated by improvements and developments in air navigation. In a few cases the requirements of the First Class Navigator's syllabus have been exceeded slightly, but every effort has been made to avoid redundancy.

An index has been added in the hope that the value of this volume as a reference book will thereby be enhanced.

1940   D. C. T. B.

PREFACE
TO THE FIRST EDITION

THE term "Air Navigation" is used in a general sense in this book. Its meaning corresponds with the more distinctive American word "Avigation."

Briefly, Air Navigation includes any or all of the three different methods of observation (astronomical navigation, air pilotage, and D/F wireless), together with, in all cases, a certain amount of calculation (dead reckoning). Then, with this, it is necessary to ally knowledge of the weather, the tides, signals, law and regulations, etc. *But common sense is a vital factor.*

In this book an effort has been made to cover the whole syllabus of the Air Ministry First Class Navigator's examination. Much, therefore, has had to be sacrificed for the sake of brevity.

Navigators, particularly those who are studying with a view to taking the First Class Navigator's examination, are reminded that it is not sufficient that they understand all the matters in this book, but also that, in order to obtain the necessary speed and accuracy, they must be thoroughly exercised in working problems, in chart work, and taking observations, etc. And those taking the examination must also be practised in answering examination questions, in producing synoptic charts, and must develop a thorough background of theory in addition to their practical knowledge.

It must be remembered that the First Class Navigator's Licence is the highest available air navigation qualification. The First Class Navigator should therefore be a person having both practical and theoretical navigational knowledge of the very highest order.

D. C. T. B.

July, 1936

CONTENTS

CHAPTER VIII

CHAPTER IX

APPENDICES

ABBREVIATIONS

A	= Temperature Absolute.
A	= Coef. *A* = (Dev. on N + NE + E + SE + S + SW + W + NW) ÷ 8.
A	= In W/R Code, the amount and characteristic of barometric tendency.
a	= Parameter *a*.
a	= In W/R Code, the characteristic of barometric tendency in preceding three hours.
A.A.	= Air Almanac.
A/C	= Alter Course; or altered course.
A.I.T.	= Air Intake Temperature.
A/S	= Air Speed.
A.S.I.	= Air Speed Indicator; also the actual reading of the Air Speed Indicator before Instrument and Position Errors corrections have been applied.
a.m.	= ante meridian, or morning.
Az.	= Azimuth.
Alt.	= Altitude.
A. Alt.	= Apparent Altitude.
Ac. Posn.	= Accepted Position.
B	= Coef. *B* = (Dev. on E − W) ÷ 2.
B	= Magnetic Induction.
b	= Parameter *b*.
BB	= In W/R Code, the pressure in whole mbs. omitting the "hundreds" figure(s).
BBB	= In W/R Code, the pressure in mbs. and tenths omitting the "hundreds" figure(s).
bb	= In W/R Code, the amount in fifths of mbs. of barometric tendency in preceding three hours.
C	= Temperature Centigrade.
C	= Compass.
C	= Coef. *C* = (Dev. on N − S) ÷ 2.
C	= In W/R Code, the form of predominating cloud.
c	= Parameter *c*.
C_L	= In W/R Code, the form of Low Cloud.
C_M	= In W/R Code the form of Medium Cloud.
C_H	= In W/R Code the form of High Cloud.
Co	= Course, or Heading.

Calc. Alt. or C. Alt. = Calculated Altitude.
C.D.C.   = Course and Distance Calculator, or like computer.
Coef.   = Coefficient
Colat.   = Colatitude = 90° — Latitude.
Corr.   = Correction.
Cos   = Cosine.
Cosec   = Cosecant.
Cot   = Cotangent.
C.Z.D.   = Calculated Zenith Distance.

D = Coef. D = (Dev. on NE + SW — SE — NW) ÷ 4.
d = Parameter d.
d = In W/R Code, the direction from which swell comes
              (1 — 8, where 8 = N).
d_s = In W/R Code, the direction of movement of a ship
              (1 — 8, where 8 = N).
DD = In W/R Code, the Wind direction (01 — 32, where
              32 = N).
dd = In W/R Code, the upper Wind direction (01 — 36,
              where 36 = 360 T).
D/F   = Direction Finding wireless.
D/R   = Dead Reckoning navigation.
D.W.T.   = Deck Watch Time.
Dec.   = Declination.
Dep.   = Departure.
Dev.   = Deviation.
Dist.   = Distance.
d. Lat.   = Difference of Latitude.
d. Long.   = Difference of Longitude.
d. M.P.   = Difference of Meridianal Parts.

E.   = East.
E   = Estimate, or Estimated.
E = Factor E = Equation of Time + 12 hours.
E = Coef. E = (Dev. on N + S — E — W) ÷ 4.
E = In W/R Code, the state of ground.
e = Parameter e.
E.T.   = Equation of Time.
E.T.A.   = Estimated Time of Arrival.
E.T.D.   = Estimated Time of Departure.

F = Temperature Fahrenheit.
F = In W/R Code, the force of the wind on the Beaufort
              scale.

F	= Fast (Watch or Chronometer).
F/T	= Full Throttle.
f	= Parameter f.
f	= In W/R Code, the speed of ship.
ft.	= Feet.
f.p.s.	= Feet per second.
g	= The force of Gravity.
G.D.	= Greenwich Date.
G.A.T.	— Greenwich Apparent Time.
G.H.A.	= Greenwich Hour Angle, measured W from Greenwich.
G.H.A.♈.	= Greenwich Hour Angle of Aries, measured W from Greenwich.
G.L.	= Ground Level.
G.M.T.	= Greenwich Mean Time.
G.P.	= Geographical Position.
G.Sid.T.	= Greenwich Sidereal Time.
G/S	= Ground Speed.
Gt. C.	= Great Circle.
Gr. or Green	= To starboard.
GG	= In W/R Code, the G.M.T. of observation (01 — 24, where 24 = midnight).
H	= Field strength, or the horizontal component of the Earth's Magnetic Field.
h	= In the W/R Code, the height of base of cloud.
h_1	= In the W/R Code, the height at which upper wind is reported.
HA	= Hour Angle.
HAMS	= Hour Angle of the Mean Sun.
HATS	= Hour Angle of the True Sun.
Hav.	= Haversine or half versine.
Hd.	= Heading, or course.
H.P.	= Horizontal Parallax.
Hr.	= Hour.
Ht.	= Height.
HWFC	= High Water Full and Change.
HWLI	= High Water Lunitidal Interval.
I	= Intensity of Magnetization.
I.A.S.	= Indicated Air Speed—generally taken to mean the A.S.I. reading + or — Instrument Error and Position Error corrections, but before Height and Temperature corrections have been applied.
IE	= Index Error.

ICAN = International Committee of Air Navigation.
Int. = Intercept.

K = Moment of Inertia.
K = In W/R Code, the state of swell in the open sea.
K_1 = Luni-Solar Declinational Diurnal tidal constituent.
K_2 = Luni-Solar Declinational Semidiurnal tidal constituent.
k = Magnetic Susceptibility.
km. = Kilometres.
k.p.h. = Kilometres per hour.
Kts. = Knots.

L = Logarithm.
l = Length.
L.A.N. = Local Apparent Noon.
LD = Local Date.
L.H.A. = Local Hour Angle.
LL = Lower Limb.
LAT = Local Apparent Time.
LMT = Local Mean Time.
LST = Local Standard Time.
L.Sid.T. = Local Sidereal Time.
LLL = In W/R Code, the Latitude in degrees and tenths of a degree.
lll = In W/R Code, the Longitude in degrees and tenths of a degree.
Lat. = Latitude.
Long. = Longitude.
LWFC = Low Water Full and Change.
λ = Coef. λ (Lambda).

M (or Mag.) = Magnetic.
M = Magnetic moment = ml.
M_2 = Mean Lunar Semidiurnal tidal constituent.
M_4 = Frictional and shallow water effect tidal constituent.
MS_4 = Frictional and shallow water effect tidal constituent.
m. = Metres.
m = Magnetic pole strength.
mb. = Millibar.
ml. = Statute mile.
ML = Mean Level.
MHW = Mean High Water.
MLW = Mean Low Water.

MNR   = Mean Neap Range.
M.P.   = Meridional Parts.
M.S.A.   = Mean Sextant Altitude.
MSL   = Mean Sea Level.
MSR   = Mean Spring Range.
MTL   = Mean Tide Level.
MHWI   = Mean High Water Lunitidal Interval.
MHWN   = Mean High Water Neaps.
MHWS   − Mean High Water Springs.
MLWI   = Mean Low Water Lunitidal Interval.
MLWN   = Mean Low Water Neaps.
MLWS   = Mean Low Water Springs.
m.p.h.   = Miles per hour.
Met.   = Meteorology or Meteorological.
Mer.   = Meridian, or meridional.
Min.   = Minute.
Mid. Lat. = Middle Latitude.
μ = Magnetic Permeability.
μ = Coef. μ (Mu).

N.   = North.
N = In W/R Code, the amount of cloud.
N_L = In W/R Code, the amount of Low cloud.
N_2 = Lunar Elliptical tidal constituent.
NA   = Nautical Almanac.
Nat.   = Natural.
Np.   = Neap Tide.
Naut.   = Nautical.

O   = Observed.
O.A.T.   = Outside Air Temperature.
O_1 = Lunar Declinational Diurnal tidal constituent.
OZD   = Observed Zenith Distance.
O. Alt. (or Obs. Alt.) = Observed Altitude.

P   = Pole.
P = Parameter P.
P = In W/R Code, the day of the week. (1 = Sunday.)
P_1 = Solar Declinational Diurnal tidal constituent.
P.E.   = Position Error correction to an A.S.I.
P.L.   = Position Line.
p.m.   = Post meridian; Afternoon.
Plx.   = Parallax.
P. in A.   = Parallax in Altitude.

Posn.   = Position.
P. Dist.   = Polar Distance.
P.T.   = Point of Tangency.
P.V.   = Prime Vertical.

Q = Parameter Q.
Q = In W/R Code, the octant of the globe (1 — 8, East from Greenwich, N then S).

R = Earth's radius.
R = Factor R = RAMS + 12 hours.
R = Parameter R.
r   = Radius of curvature (in map projections).
R or red   = To port.
R/T   = Radio Telephony.
RA   = Right Ascension.
RAMS   = Right Ascension of the Mean Sun.
RATS   = Right Ascension of the True Sun.
RA*   = Right Ascension of a Heavenly Body.
Red.   = Reduction.
Ref.   = Refraction.

S.   = South.
S = In W/R Code, the state of sea.
S_2 = Mean Solar Semidiurnal tidal constituent.
S/C   = Set course.
S.D.   = Semidiameter.
Sl   = Slow (Watch or chronometer).
Sp.   = Spring tide.
SAT   = Ship's Apparent Time.
S.H.A.   = Sidereal Hour Angle = 360 — R.A.
S.L.   = Sea Level.
SMT   = Ship's Mean Time.
Sec   = Secant.
Sid.   = Sidereal.
Sin   = Sine.
Stbd.   = Starboard.

T   = True.
T   = Total Strength of Earth's Magnetic Field at a place.
t_d = In W/R Code, the difference between sea and air temperature.
TT   = In W/R Code, the temperature in degrees Fahrenheit or Centigrade.

Tab.   = Tabulated.
T.A.S.   = True Air Speed.
Tr.   = Track.
Tan   = Tangent.
T. Alt.   = True Altitude.
Temp.   = Temperature.
T.Z.D.   = True Zenith Distance.

U   ▬ In W/R Code, the humidity of the air.
U.L.   = Upper Limb.

Varn.   = Variation.

W.   = West
W/R   = Weather report.
W/S   = Wind speed.
W/T   = Wireless telegraphy.
W.T.   = Watch Time.
WSD (or WS and D) = Wind Speed and Direction.

X   = Celestial position of a body.

Z   = Observer's Zenith.
Z   = Vertical component of the Earth's Magnetic Field at
                a place.
ZD   = Zenith Distance.
Z.T.   = Zone Time.

SYMBOLS

° = Degrees of Arc (should not be used in the air.).
′ = Minutes of Arc, and Nautical Miles.
″ = Seconds of Arc.
☉ = Sun.
☉̄ = Upper Limb of the Sun.
⊕ = Sun's centre.
☉̲ = Lower Limb of the Sun.
☾ = The Moon.
☾̄ = Upper Limb of the Moon.
☾̲ = Lower Limb of the Moon.
✳ = A Heavenly Body, usually a star or planet.
♈ = First Point of Aries.
♎ = First Point of Libra.
∼ = Difference between.

THE COMPLETE
AIR NAVIGATOR

CHAPTER I

SUMMARIZED MATHEMATICS AND FORM OF THE EARTH

THE most complete and excellent air navigator need not be an expert in higher mathematics. All that is necessary is that the navigator be of a mentality capable of following the development and proofs of the formulæ given in this book, and then, having accepted them, being able above all to apply them correctly to *any* workable problem.

It is assumed that the reader already has some knowledge of mathematics. The more elementary matter is covered only briefly.

(*Note.*—Of the three mathematical tables, Norie's, Inman's, and Burton's, which are the most generally accepted, Inman's have been used in the calculations in this book.)

SECTION 1

GENERAL

1. (a) Notes on the Conventions of **Signs, Brackets,** etc.

Plus and Plus give a Plus;   e.g. $+(+a) = +a$

Plus and Minus give a Minus; e.g. $+(-a) = -a$

Minus and Plus give a Minus; e.g. $-(+a) = -a$

Minus and Minus give a Plus; e.g. $-(-a) = +a$.

When there is no sign before a quantity it is positive (plus). The above examples indicate the procedure when brackets are removed. The signs of *all* quantities inside the brackets which are being removed are changed only when the sign outside the brackets is negative (minus).

Thus $+(a+b-c) = a+b-c$, but $-(a+b-c) = -a-b+c$.

(b) An "**Identity**" is the algebraic statement of equality existing between two expressions for *all* values of the quantities involved.

An "**Equation**" is the algebraic statement of equality existing between two expressions for *certain* values of the quantities involved.

(c) In an equation (or identity) quantities may be moved from

1

one side to the other without changing the state of equality, thus—

> To each side may be added an equal quantity.
> From each side may be subtracted an equal quantity.
> Each side may be multiplied by an equal quantity.
> Each side may be divided by an equal quantity.

Thus, if
$$\frac{a+b+c}{12x} + 5 = \frac{3}{x} + 5$$

then
$$\frac{a+b+c}{12x} = \frac{3}{x} + 5 - 5 = \frac{3}{x}$$

$$\frac{(a+b+c)x}{12x} = 3$$

$$\frac{a+b+c}{12} = 3$$

$$a+b+c = 3 \times 12 = 36.$$

2. INDICES

(a) An index placed near to the top and to the right of a quantity is the power to which the quantity is raised. The conventions and rules governing the use of indices are shown in the following examples—

(i) $a^2 \times a^3 \times a^2 = (a \times a)(a \times a \times a)(a \times a) = a^{(2+3+2)} = a^7$, i.e. when multiplying different powers of a quantity add the indices.

(ii) $(a^2)^3 = (a \times a)(a \times a)(a \times a) = a^{(2 \times 3)} = a^6$, i.e. when a power of a quantity is raised to a further power multiply the indices.

(iii) $(abcd)^3 = a^3b^3c^3d^3$, i.e. when a product is raised to a power, raise each of its factors to that power.

(b) Conventional methods of writing indices. Thus

(i) $\dfrac{1}{a} = a^{-1}$

(ii) $\sqrt{a} = a^{\frac{1}{2}}$; or $\sqrt[3]{a} = a^{\frac{1}{3}}$

(iii) $\left(\dfrac{a^2 \times \sqrt[5]{a}}{a^3}\right)^2 = a^{(2+\frac{1}{5}-3)2} = a^{-\frac{8}{5}} = \dfrac{1}{a^{\frac{8}{5}}} = \dfrac{1}{\sqrt[5]{a^8}}$

3. (a) LOGARITHMS

The logarithm (or log) of a given number is the power to which a certain base (i.e. basic number) must be raised to equal the given number. The base used is indicated by a small suffix after the word "log." In "common logarithms" where the base is 10, this is omitted. Now $100 = 10^2$,

$$\therefore \quad \text{Log}_{10} \text{ of } 100 = 2 \cdot 00000, \text{ or Log } 100 = 2 \cdot 00000.$$

A log consists of two parts: (i) the Characteristic which is the whole number portion, and (ii) the Mantissa which is the decimal portion of the power to which the base has been raised. Thus above in log 100, the Characteristic is 2, and the Mantissa zero. It is clear that if the number is less than the base but more than unity, then the characteristic is 0; and so on. When using common logs (i.e. to base 10) the Characteristic is obtainable by sight and therefore only the decimal part or Mantissa is printed in log tables. The Mantissa is always positive.

In common logarithms—

(i) The Characteristic of a number greater than unity is positive and is less by 1 than the number of figures to the left of the decimal. Thus log 12545 has Characteristic of 4.

(ii) The Characteristic of a number less than unity is negative and is greater by 1 than the number of 0's (noughts) which consecutively follow the decimal point. Thus log ·00032 has Characteristic of $\bar{4}$ (called "bar 4" which is often written as 6, i.e. 10 is added: $10-4 = 6$).

To use logarithms—

(i) By inspection of maths. tables it will be obvious how the following examples were taken out.

Log 597·1 = 2·7761.   Log ·01874 = $\bar{2}$·2727 or 8·2727.

Or using five-figure logs (for greater accuracy) as in Inman's Tables—

Log 597·1 = 2·77605.   Log ·01874 = $\bar{2}$·27277.

Or using six-figure logs as in Norie's Tables—

Log 597·1 = 2·776047.   Log ·01874 = $\bar{2}$·272770.

(ii) To multiply numbers, add their logs and "antilog" the result.

Thus $125 \times 0.35 =$ Log 125   2·09691
                          + Log 0·35 $\bar{1}$·54407
                          ————————
                                         1·64098   antilog = 43·75.

(In antilogging, the Mantissa only is entered in the table.)

(iii) To divide numbers their logs are subtracted.

(iv) To raise a number to a power, multiply its log by the index of the power, and antilog. Remember that Mantissa is always positive, and therefore if the characteristic is negative the two parts must be multiplied separately.

Thus, to find $\cdot23^3$; Log $\cdot23 = \bar{1}\cdot36173$

multiplied by $3 = \bar{3} + 1\cdot08519 = \bar{2}\cdot08519$

antilog $= \cdot01217$.

(v) To find root of a number, divide its log by the root required and antilog. A complication arises when dividing with a negative Characteristic (Mantissa being always positive). The procedure is as follows—

To find $\cdot00003^{\frac{1}{4}}$ i.e. $\sqrt[4]{\cdot00003}$

Log $\cdot00003 = \bar{5}\cdot47712$

$\frac{1}{4}$ Log $\cdot00003 = 4)\overline{\bar{5}\cdot47712} = 4)\overline{\bar{8} + 3\cdot47712}$

$\overline{\bar{2}\cdot86928}$

antilog $= 0\cdot07401$.

(b) **Cologarithms.** When a combined multiplication and division problem is worked by logs the sum of the logs of the quantities forming the denominator has to be subtracted from the sum of the logs of quantities forming the numerator, thus entailing possibly three stages of working. By taking the cologs of the quantities of the denominator and adding them to the logs of the numerator, the working comprises addition only, thus saving time. Unfortunately cologs are not often included in tables. The colog of a number is the log of its reciprocal.

Thus Log $\frac{1}{55}$ = Log $0\cdot018182 = \bar{2}\cdot25964 =$ Colog 55.

The colog is the arithmetic complement of the log; thus—

Log $55 = 1\cdot74036$.

Colog $55 = \bar{2}\cdot25964$.

This colog is obtained without colog tables as follows: (a) The Characteristic if positive is increased by one and made negative (thus 1· becomes $\bar{2}$·); if negative it is decreased by one and made positive (thus $\bar{2}$·, "bar 2" becomes 1·). (b) The Mantissa is subtracted from $\cdot00000$. The quickest way of doing this in practice is, instead of starting with the right-hand figure, to start from the left and subtract each figure from 9, except the last figure, which is taken from 10.

(c) **Slide Rules.** Whether of the circular type used so often on Course and Distance Calculators or of the straight type commonly used by all "x chasers" a slide rule is simply a means of adding (for multiplication) and subtracting (for division) different lengths which are in proportion to the logs of the numbers written beside them on the scale.

They may also include trigonometrical ratios, etc.

4. MEASUREMENT OF ANGLES. The magnitude of an angle is measured by the number of times it contains a Unit Angle.

(i) **The Sexagesimal System.** The unit which concerns us in this book is the degree (°), which is $\frac{1}{360}$th of a circle. $90° = 1$ right angle. Each degree $= 60$ minutes ('). Each minute $= 60$ seconds (").

(ii) **Circular Measure,** a more fundamental system, has the "radian" as its unit. A radian $= \frac{1}{2\pi}$ of a circle; i.e. $3\cdot14159$ radians $= 180°$.

(iii) **The Centesimal System** has the grade (G) as its unit—which is $\frac{1}{400}$ of a circle. Each grade $= 100$ minutes (') and each minute $= 100$ seconds (").

(iv) **Time.** Arc can be measured in time units by making 1 hour $= \frac{1}{24}$ of a circle. Then the conversion between sexagesimal units and time units is simple: thus 24 hours $= 360°$; 1 hour $= 15°$; 4 minutes of time $= 1°$; 1 minute of time $= 15'$; and 1 second of time $= 15"$. The conversion between centesimal units and time units consists of extremely awkward fractions: 1 minute of time $= \cdot278$ G. approximately.

SECTION 2

PLANE TRIGONOMETRY

5. (a) Trigonometry is the mathematics of triangles, both plane and spherical. The basic principles are contained in right-angled plane trigonometry, that is, trigonometry of plane triangles in which one angle is a right angle (i.e. of 90°). This section deals with plane trigonometry—of right-angled triangles and all other plane triangles.

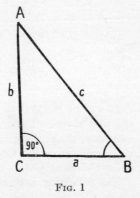

FIG. 1

In any plane triangle the sum of any two sides is greater than the third side, and the sum of the angles equals 180°. (Simply geometric facts.) Also in a right-angled triangle the side opposite the right angle (the hypotenuse) squared equals the sum of the squares on the two other sides; that is, in triangle ABC (Fig. 1) the square of $AB =$ sum of squares of AC and BC. It is conventional practice to call angles by single capital letters, and sides by single small letters thus: The angle $CAB = A$;

angle $ABC = B$; the side AB (i.e. the side opposite the angle C) $= c$; and the side $AC = b$, etc.

Now, in establishing trigonometrical ratios with relation to one of the angles other than the right angle in a right-angled triangle it is customary to name the sides as follows—

The side opposite the right angle is called the "Hypotenuse."

The side opposite the angle referred to is called the "Perpendicular" or the "Opposite."

The side adjacent to the angle referred to is called the "Base" or the "Adjacent."

Thus, in Fig. 1 in relation to the angle B,

$$c = \text{Hypotenuse}, \ a = \text{Base or Adjacent},$$
$$\text{and } b = \text{Perpendicular or Opposite}.$$

The names Hypotenuse (Hyp.), Opposite (Opp.), and Adjacent (Adj.), will be used in this book.

(b) Trigonometrical Ratios. In the right-angled triangle ABC (in Fig. 1) the ratios of—

(i) $\dfrac{b}{c} = \dfrac{\text{Opp.}}{\text{Hyp.}} = \text{Sine } B.$

(ii) $\dfrac{a}{c} = \dfrac{\text{Adj.}}{\text{Hyp.}} = \text{Cosine } B.$

(iii) $\dfrac{b}{a} = \dfrac{\text{Opp.}}{\text{Adj.}} = \text{Tangent } B.$

(iv) $\dfrac{c}{b} = \dfrac{\text{Hyp.}}{\text{Opp.}} = \text{Cosecant } B = \dfrac{1}{\text{Sine } B}.$

(v) $\dfrac{c}{a} = \dfrac{\text{Hyp.}}{\text{Adj.}} = \text{Secant } B = \dfrac{1}{\text{Cos } B}.$

(vi) $\dfrac{a}{b} = \dfrac{\text{Adj.}}{\text{Opp.}} = \text{Cotangent } B = \dfrac{1}{\text{Tan } B}.$

It will be noticed that the last three ratios are the reciprocals of the first three. The names of the Ratios are abbreviated for convenience, thus: Sine = Sin (still pronounced "Sine"); Cosine = Cos (pronounced "Cos"); Tangent = Tan; Cosecant = Cosec; Secant = Sec; Cotangent = Cot.

The following may help as an aid to memory—

$$\text{Sin} = \frac{\text{Opp.}}{\text{Hyp.}} = \frac{\text{O}}{\text{H}} = \frac{\text{Old}}{\text{Hands}}.$$

$$\text{Cos} = \frac{\text{Adj.}}{\text{Hyp.}} = \frac{A}{H} = \frac{\text{Always}}{\text{Help}}.$$

$$\text{Tan} = \frac{\text{Opp.}}{\text{Adj.}} = \frac{O}{A} = \frac{\text{Other}}{\text{Aviators}}.$$

(c) *Examples.* (i) When steering due East at 90 knots with wind from due North, drift is 14° to starboard (which may be called "14 green"). Find, trigonometrically, ground speed and wind speed.

Difference between wind direction and course

$$= 90° = \text{angle } ABC \text{ in Fig. 2.}$$

Then $\qquad\qquad \dfrac{c}{a} = \text{Tan } C = \text{Tan } 14°$

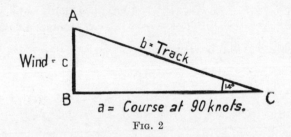

FIG. 2

and $\qquad$ Wind Speed $= c = a$ Tan 14 $= 90$ Tan 14

$$= 90 \times 0\cdot2493 = 22\cdot437$$

i.e. $\qquad$ Wind Speed $= 22\frac{1}{2}$ *knots approx.*

Ground Speed $= b = a$ Sec 14 $= 90$ Sec 14

$$= 90 \times 1\cdot0306 = 92\cdot754$$

i.e. $\qquad$ Ground Speed $= 92\frac{3}{4}$ *knots.*

(ii) In still air, steering a steady course at 110 knots, a lighthouse bore 33° on the port bow and 10 minutes later was dead abeam (i.e. bearing 90° red). How far is aircraft from the lighthouse when it is abeam?

In 10 minutes distance covered $= 18\cdot3$ nautical miles.

∴ Side x in triangle XYZ in Fig. 3 $= 18\cdot3$.

Distance from lighthouse when abeam $= y$

$$= x \text{ Tan } 33 = 18\cdot3 \times \cdot6496 = 11\cdot9 \text{ *miles.*}$$

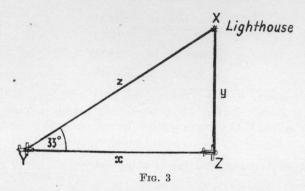

FIG. 3

(**d**) Logarithms of trigonometrical ratios are tabulated in Nautical Tables for logarithmic working.

Thus,

Log Cos 43° = Log 0·73135 = $\bar{1}$·86413 (which is value given in Tables for Log Cos 43°).

(**e**) In Fig. 1 it can be seen that

$$\text{Sin } A = \frac{a}{c}; \qquad \text{Cos } A = \frac{b}{c}; \text{ and Tan } A = \frac{a}{b}.$$

$$\text{But Cos } B = \frac{a}{c}; \qquad \text{Sin } B = \frac{b}{c}; \text{ and Cot } B = \frac{a}{b}.$$

∴ Sin A = Cos B, and Cos A = Sin B, etc.

Now, the three angles of a triangle together = 180°. The angle C in Fig. 1 = 90°, therefore $A + B = 90°$, that is, they are "Complementary."

Then, as we have just shown that Sin A = Cos B = Cos $(90 - A)$; etc.—

Sin A = Cos $(90° - A)$	Cosec A = Sec $(90° - A)$
Cos A = Sin $(90° - A)$	Sec A = Cosec $(90° - A)$
Tan A = Cot $(90° - A)$	Cot A = Tan $(90° - A)$.

(**f**) Now in Fig. 1, since $a^2 + b^2 = c^2$ (simply a geometric fact!) then $\qquad$ Sin$^2 A$ + Cos$^2 A$ = 1

$$\left(\text{Proof: } \text{Sin}^2 A + \text{Cos}^2 A = \frac{a^2}{c^2} + \frac{b^2}{c^2} = \frac{a^2 + b^2}{c^2}.\right.$$

$$\text{But } a^2 + b^2 = c^2 \qquad \therefore \frac{a^2 + b^2}{c^2} = 1.\Big)$$

Similarly— $\underline{\text{Sec}^2 A = 1 + \text{Tan}^2 A}$

(Proof: $\text{Sec}^2 A = \dfrac{c^2}{b^2} = \dfrac{a^2 + b^2}{b^2} = \dfrac{a^2}{b^2} + \dfrac{b^2}{b^2} = \text{Tan}^2 A + 1.$)

and $\underline{\text{Cosec}^2 A = 1 + \text{Cot}^2 A}$

(Proof: $\text{Cosec}^2 A = \dfrac{c^2}{a^2} = \dfrac{a^2 + b^2}{a^2} = \dfrac{a^2}{a^2} + \dfrac{b^2}{a^2} = 1 + \text{Cot}^2 A.$)

6. (a) Trigonometrical Ratios of Angles 60° and 30°. It is helpful at times to remember these values, and the easiest method of doing so is to picture mentally the angles of 30° and 60° in a triangle and deduce the ratios, as follows—

If an equilateral triangle ABC in Fig. 4 is divided by AD which is perpendicular to BC, then the angle $ABD = 60°$ and angle $BAD = 30°$. Let the sides AB and AC each equal 2 units.

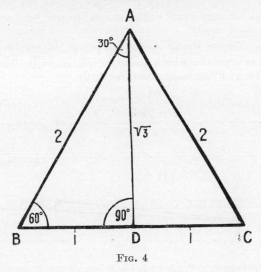

Fig. 4

Then,

$BD = 1$ and $DC = 1$. Then, as $BD^2 + DA^2 = BA^2$, $AD = \sqrt{3}$

$\text{Sin } BAD = \dfrac{DB}{BA} = \tfrac{1}{2}$,   i.e. Sin 30 $= \tfrac{1}{2}$.

Similarly $\text{Cos } 30 = \dfrac{\sqrt{3}}{2}$, and Tan 30 $= \dfrac{1}{\sqrt{3}}$.

Also, $\text{Sin } 60 = \dfrac{\sqrt{3}}{2}$, Cos 60 $= \tfrac{1}{2}$, and Tan 60 $= \sqrt{3}$.

(b) Trigonometrical Ratios of Angle 45°. As with 60° and 30° the ratios should be remembered. In Fig. 5, a right-angled triangle has AB and AC each unit length. Then AC will equal $\sqrt{2}$.

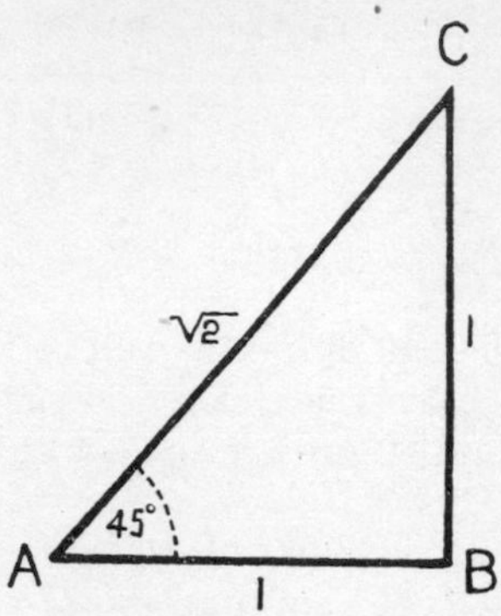

The angle $CAB = 45°$.

$$\text{Sin } 45 = \frac{1}{\sqrt{2}}, \text{ Cos } 45 = \frac{1}{\sqrt{2}}, \text{ Tan } 45 = 1.$$

Fig. 5

7. RATIOS OF SMALL ANGLES

(a) Accuracy. In Sines and Tangents, the *rate of change* of value in very small angles is very large. To avoid errors in working special tables giving values for every 10″ of arc, or less, are printed. It is obvious that for very small angles the difference between Sines and Tangents is very small.

Example. From a flying boat at moorings the vertical angle subtended by a flagstaff, which is known to be 65 ft. high, is 54·4′. Find distance of flying boat from flagstaff.

$$\text{Distance} = \frac{65}{\text{Tan } 54·4'}$$

$$\text{Log } 65 = 1·81291$$
$$\text{L Tan } 54'24'' = \overline{2}·19895$$
$$\overline{ 54'24'' = } 3·61396$$
$$\text{Antilog} = 4111 \text{ ft.}$$

i.e. Distance = 4111 ft.

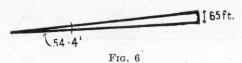

Fig. 6

(*Note.*—In Inman's Tables log tangents of small angles are taken from the log sine table for small angles. A column in this table gives the difference to be added for log tangents.)

(b) Approximation. For small angles (of less than about 8°) the following method of approximation is useful. If the length of the side adjacent to the angle is 60, then the number of degrees in the angle equals the length of the side opposite the angle. Or, the number of degrees in the angle equals the length of the opposite side multiplied by $\dfrac{\text{the side adjacent}}{60}$. (Based on the fact that for small angles sin $A = A$ where A is measured in radians. A radian equals $57°\ 17'\ 45''$ or $57\cdot3$ approximately, which is nearly 60.) Thus according to this rule a wind of 5 knots on the beam of an aircraft flying at 60 knots gives a drift of $5°$; or if the airspeed was 90 knots a drift of about $3°$; or if the airspeed was 120 knots a drift of $2\frac{1}{2}°$. Actually results obtained by this rule compared to accurate results are as follows—

By Rule	Correct Answer
$1°$	$1\cdot0476$
$3°$	$3\cdot1446$
$5°$	$5\cdot2494$
$8°$	$8\cdot4324$
$10°$	$10\cdot5798.$

Thus it can be seen that at an angle of $10°$ the answer is over $\frac{1}{2}°$ in error. This rule may be helpful for mental approximations by a pilot.

8. (a) Angles greater than 90°. With angles of less than $90°$, the trigonometrical ratios are positive, but this may or may not be the case in angles greater than $90°$. The conventional way of dealing

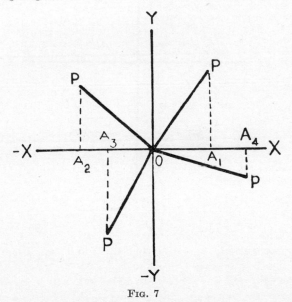

FIG. 7

with ratios of angles greater than $90°$ is to have a line OP (see Fig. 7) revolving anti-clockwise through $360°$ starting from OX.

The line OP (which is the hypotenuse) is always positive. All vertical lines above the $-XX$ line are positive, and below the $-XX$ line are negative. All horizontal lines to the right of the $-YY$ line are positive, and to the left of the $-YY$ line are negative.

The 360° are divided by the lines $-XX$ and $-YY$ into four quadrants, numbered 1 to 4 as in Fig. 8.

Now referring to Figs. 7 and 8—

Ratios in First Quadrant

$$\text{Sin} = \frac{A_1P}{OP} = \frac{+}{+} = +$$

$$\text{Cos} = \frac{OA_1}{OP} = \frac{+}{+} = +$$

$$\text{Tan} = \frac{A_1P}{OA_1} = \frac{+}{+} = +$$

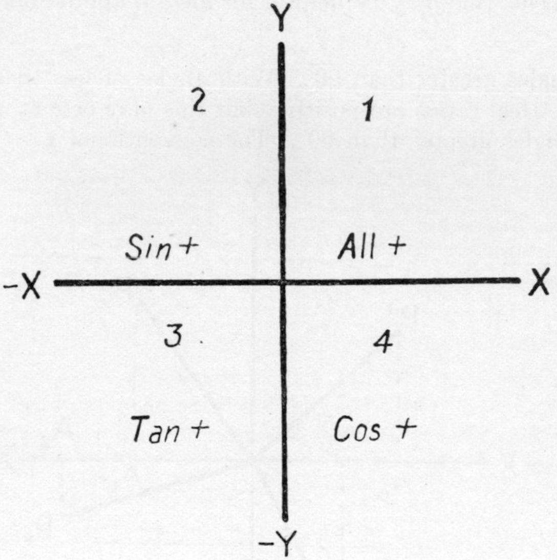

FIG. 8

Ratios in Second Quadrant

$$\text{Sin} = \frac{A_2P}{OP} = \frac{+}{+} = +$$

$$\text{Cos} = \frac{OA_2}{OP} = \frac{-}{+} = -$$

$$\text{Tan} = \frac{A_2P}{OA_2} = \frac{+}{-} = -$$

Ratios in Third Quadrant

$$\text{Sin} \ = \frac{A_3P}{OP} = \frac{-}{+} = -$$

$$\text{Cos} \ = \frac{OA_3}{OP} = \frac{-}{+} = -$$

$$\text{Tan} = \frac{A_3P}{OA_3} = \frac{-}{-} = +$$

Ratios in Fourth Quadrant

$$\text{Sin} \ = \frac{A_4P}{OP} = \frac{-}{+} = -$$

$$\text{Cos} \ = \frac{OA_4}{OP} = \frac{+}{+} = +$$

$$\text{Tan} = \frac{A_4P}{OA_4} = \frac{-}{+} = -$$

Thus it can be seen that the ratios which are positive are—

All	in the First Quadrant
Sin (and Cosec)	in the Second Quadrant
Tan (and Cot)	in the Third Quadrant
Cos (and Sec)	in the Fourth Quadrant.

All the remainder are negative. The sequence "All, Sin, Tan, Cos" must be remembered.

(b) Supplementary Angles. In para. 5(e) the comparison of ratios of Complementary Angles (i.e. two angles which together equal 90°) was given. Now, two angles which together equal 180° are said to be "Supplementary" to each other; and each is the supplement of the other.

By studying Fig. 7 the following can be deduced—

$$\text{Sin} \ (180-B) = \text{Sin} \ B \qquad \text{Cosec} \ (180-B) = \text{Cosec} \ B$$
$$\text{Cos} \ (180-B) = -\text{Cos} \ B \quad \text{Sec} \quad (180-B) = -\text{Sec} \ B$$
$$\text{Tan} \ (180-B) = -\text{Tan} \ B \quad \text{Cot} \quad (180-B) = -\text{Cot} \ B.$$

That is, the ratios of an angle and its supplement are equal in value but each has a sign depending on the quadrant in which the triangle may lie.

9. Ratios of the Sum or Difference between Two Angles. (a) In Fig. 9 the angle DOC equals A, and the angle DOK equals B. At any point F a line FK is drawn at right angles to OD on to OE at K.

Perpendiculars KJ and FH are dropped from K and F on to OC, and GF is drawn parallel to OC. Now as GF is parallel to OC, the angle $GFO = DOC = A$ and as KFO is a right angle, the angle GFO is complementary to GFK. But angle GKF is also complementary to angle GFK.

$\therefore$ Angle GKF = angle $GFO = A$.

Then $\text{Sin}\,(A+B) = \text{Sin}\,COK = \dfrac{JK}{OK} = \dfrac{JG+GK}{OK} = \dfrac{FH+GK}{OK}$

$$= \frac{FH}{OK} + \frac{GK}{OK} = \left(\frac{FH}{OF} \times \frac{OF}{OK}\right) + \left(\frac{KF}{OK} \times \frac{GK}{KF}\right)$$

i.e. $\underline{\text{Sin}\,(A+B) = \text{Sin}\,A\,\text{Cos}\,B + \text{Sin}\,B\,\text{Cos}\,A.}$

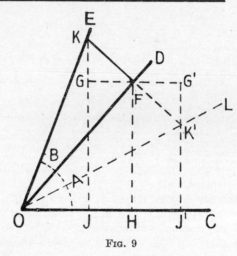

FIG. 9

By a similar procedure it can be shown that

$$\underline{\text{Cos}\,(A+B) = \text{Cos}\,A\,\text{Cos}\,B - \text{Sin}\,A\,\text{Sin}\,B}$$

and $\underline{\text{Tan}\,(A+B) = \dfrac{\text{Tan}\,A + \text{Tan}\,B}{1 - \text{Tan}\,A\,\text{Tan}\,B}.}$

(b) To find the ratios of the difference between the two angles A and B in Fig. 9, the line OL is drawn so that angle $DOL = B$, then angle $COL = (A - B)$. Drop FK' at right angles to OD on to OL. Draw FG' parallel to OC. Drop a perpendicular $K'J'$ on to OC and produce it to meet FG' at G'. The angle $DFG' = DOC = A$. The angles DFG' and $G'K'F$ are both complementary to $G'FK'$.

$\therefore$ $DFG' = G'K'F = A.$

Then

$$\text{Sin } (A - B) = \frac{K'J'}{OK'} = \frac{FH - G'K'}{OK'} = \frac{FH}{OK'} - \frac{G'K'}{OK'}$$

$$= \frac{FH}{FO} \times \frac{FO}{OK'} - \frac{FK'}{OK'} \times \frac{G'K'}{FK'}$$

i.e. $\text{Sin } (A - B) = \text{Sin } A \text{ Cos } B - \text{Sin } B \text{ Cos } A.$

And similarly

$$\text{Cos } (A - B) = \text{Cos } A \text{ Cos } B + \text{Sin } A \text{ Sin } B$$

and $\text{Tan } (A - B) = \dfrac{\text{Tan } A - \text{Tan } B}{1 + \text{Tan } A \text{ Tan } B}$

(c) When $A = B$ in the first three formulæ given in this paragraph, we get by substitution—

$$\text{Sin } 2A = 2 \text{ Sin } A \text{ Cos } A.$$

$$\text{Cos } 2A = 2 \, (\text{Cos}^2 A) - 1 = 1 - (2 \text{ Sin}^2 A).$$

$$\text{Tan } 2A = \frac{2 \text{ Tan } A}{1 - \text{Tan}^2 A}.$$

10. The Sum or Difference of Two Similar Ratios.

By adding $\text{Sin } (A + B) = \text{Sin } A \text{ Cos } B + \text{Cos } A \text{ Sin } B$
and $\text{Sin } (A - B) = \text{Sin } A \text{ Cos } B - \text{Cos } A \text{ Sin } B$,
we have $\text{Sin } (A + B) + \text{Sin } (A - B) = 2 \text{ Sin } A \text{ Cos } B.$

Now if we replace $(A + B)$ by P, and $(A - B)$ by Q, then by simple algebra $2A = P + Q$, and $2B = P - Q$, i.e. $A = \dfrac{P + Q}{2}$, and $B = \dfrac{P - Q}{2}$, and the above expression becomes—

$$\text{Sin } P + \text{Sin } Q = 2 \text{ Sin } \frac{P + Q}{2} \text{ Cos } \frac{P - Q}{2}.$$

And similarly it may be shown that

$$\text{Sin } P - \text{Sin } Q = 2 \text{ Cos } \frac{P + Q}{2} \text{ Sin } \frac{P - Q}{2}$$

$$\text{Cos } P + \text{Cos } Q = 2 \text{ Cos } \frac{P + Q}{2} \text{ Cos } \frac{P - Q}{2}$$

$$\text{Cos } P - \text{Cos } Q = - 2 \text{ Sin } \frac{P + Q}{2} \text{ Sin } \frac{P - Q}{2}.$$

11. GENERAL FORMULÆ OF THE TRIANGLE. Up to the present stage the trigonometrical ratios have been applied in right-angled triangles. We now go on to the general application of the ratios to all triangles.

(a) The Sine Formulæ. In *any* plane triangle ABC (see Fig. 10) drop a perpendicular AD ($= p$) on to BC (or BC produced).

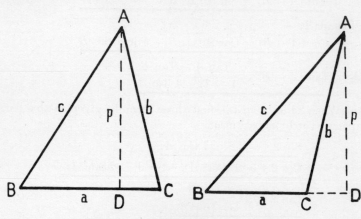

FIG. 10

Then in right-angled triangle ADB, $p = c$ Sin B and in right-angled triangle ADC, $p = b$ Sin C.

(*Note.*—In right figure, it must be remembered that Sin $(180 - C)$ $=$ Sin C.)

$\therefore$ c Sin $B = b$ Sin C

i.e. $$\frac{b}{\text{Sin } B} = \frac{c}{\text{Sin } C}.$$

Similarly by dropping a perpendicular on to another side it can be shown that $\dfrac{a}{\text{Sin } A} = \dfrac{b}{\text{Sin } B} = \dfrac{c}{\text{Sin } C}$, which is the Sine Formula, i.e. the sides of a triangle are in proportion to the sines of their opposite angles.

This formula may be used to solve the triangle (i.e. to find its unknown side(s) and/or angle(s)) when—

(i) Two angles and one opposite side are known;

(ii) Two sides and the angle opposite one of them are known;

or (iii) The perimeter and the ratios of the angles to each other are known.

(b) The Cosine Formula. In *any* plane triangle ABC (Fig. 10) drop AD perpendicular to BC at D.

In right-angled triangle ADB, $p^2 = c^2 - BD^2$
and in the right-angled triangle ADC,

$$b^2 = p^2 + CD^2$$
$$= c^2 + CD^2 - BD^2$$
$$= c^2 + (a - BD)^2 - BD^2$$
$$= c^2 + a^2 - (2a \times BD) + BD^2 - BD^2$$
$$= c^2 + a^2 - 2ac \text{ Cos } B.$$

Thus we have, $\underline{b^2 = c^2 + a^2 - 2ac \text{ Cos } B.}$

Similarly it can be shown that

$$a^2 = b^2 + c^2 - 2bc \text{ Cos } A$$

and $$c^2 = a^2 + b^2 - 2ab \text{ Cos } C.$$

This is the Cosine Formula. It is expressed in words thus—

The square on one side of a triangle equals the sum of the squares on the other two sides minus twice the product of one of those sides and the projection of the other upon it.

When using it to find the value of angles, its form should be twisted round. Thus $\text{Cos } A = \dfrac{b^2 + c^2 - a^2}{2bc}$ for the angle A. And similarly for B and C.

The Cosine Formula may be used to solve the triangle when—

(i) Two sides and the included angle are known.

(ii) All sides are known.

(c) The Haversine Formula. The Haversine is a ratio which is very useful in navigational problems. It is Half a Versed Sine, i.e.

Versine or Vers $= (1 - \text{Cos})$.

But $1 - \text{Cos } A = 2 \text{ Sin}^2 \dfrac{A}{2}$. (See para. 9 sub-para. (c)—making $2A$ equal to A.)

$\therefore$ Haversine $A = \frac{1}{2}(1 - \text{Cos } A) = \text{Sin}^2 \dfrac{A}{2}.$

Now, from Cosine Formula

$$\text{Cos } A = \frac{b^2 + c^2 - a^2}{2bc}$$

$$1 - \text{Cos } A = \frac{2bc - b^2 - c^2 + a^2}{2bc}$$

$$= \frac{a^2 - (b^2 - 2bc + c^2)}{2bc}$$

$$= \frac{a^2 - (b - c)^2}{2bc}$$

$$= \frac{(a - b + c)(a + b - c)}{2bc}.$$

Now if $\qquad$ $s = $ Semiperimeter, i.e. $\dfrac{a + b + c}{2}$

then $\qquad a - b + c = 2s - 2b,$

and $\qquad a + b - c = 2s - 2c$

and $\qquad 1 - \text{Cos } A = \dfrac{(2s - 2b)(2s - 2c)}{2bc} = \dfrac{2(s - b)2(s - c)}{2bc}$

$\therefore \qquad \dfrac{1 - \text{Cos } A}{2} = \dfrac{(s - b)(s - c)}{bc}$

i.e. $\qquad$ **Haversine A** $= \dfrac{(s - b)(s - c)}{bc}$

Similarly $\qquad$ Hav. $B = \dfrac{(s - a)(s - c)}{ac}$

and $\qquad$ Hav. $C = \dfrac{(s - a)(s - b)}{ab}$

The Haversine Formula can be used to solve the triangle when three sides are known, or when the perimeter is known and the ratios of the sides to each other.

12. CO-ORDINATES. (a) When the position of a given point on a plane surface with reference to point of origin is required to be expressed, co-ordinates are used. Co-ordinates are of two kinds, "Rectangular" and "Polar."

(b) In **Rectangular** co-ordinates the position is given by distance horizontally and a distance vertically. The horizontal axis is usually called the "x" axis, and the vertical axis is the "y" axis.

Thus, in Fig. 11, the co-ordinates of position A in relation to O are x and y. It must be remembered that vertical distances (i.e. along y axis) *below* the x axis are negative and horizontal distances (i.e. along x axis) to *left* of the y axis are negative.

(c) In **Polar** co-ordinates the position is expressed as an angle and a distance. Thus in Fig. 12 the polar co-ordinates of position B in relation to O, are the angle A and the distance d. The Polar co-ordinates of P are Z and g.

13. EXAMPLES IN PLANE TRIGONOMETRY. (a) In a triangular landing-ground ABC, the side $a = 600$ yds., the angle $B = 72° 55'$,

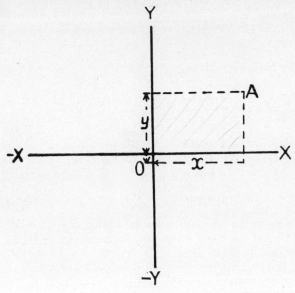

FIG. 11

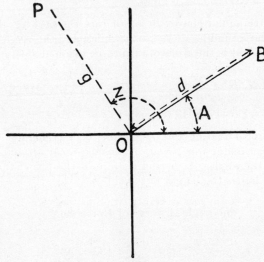

FIG. 12

and the angle $C = 52°\,25'$. Find length of the sides b and c of the landing-ground.

Now if $B = 72°\,55'$ and $C = 52°\,25'$ then $A = (180° - 125°\,20')$ $= 54°\,40'$.

Then by Sine Formula—

$$\frac{600}{\text{Sin } 54\cdot40} = \frac{b}{\text{Sin } 72\cdot55} = \frac{c}{\text{Sin } 52\cdot25}$$

600 log	$= 2\cdot77815$		600 log	$= 2\cdot77815$
72° 55′ log Sin	$= \bar{1}\cdot98040$		52° 25′ log Sin	$= \bar{1}\cdot89898$
54° 40′ log Cosec	$= 0\cdot08842$		54° 40′ log Cosec	$= 0\cdot08842$
	$2\cdot84697 = \log b$			$= 2\cdot76555 = \log c.$

$$\therefore b = 703 \text{ yds.} \qquad\qquad \therefore c = 582\cdot8 \text{ yds.}$$

(b) If a mountain A is 30 miles, mountain B is 22 miles from an observer C, and the angle which they subtend at C is $18°\,45'$. What is the distance between them?

By Cosine Formula—

$$c^2 = a^2 + b^2 - 2ab \text{ Cos } C$$

$$= 22^2 + 30^2 - 2 \times 22 \times 30 \text{ Cos } 18°\,45' = 1384 - 1250$$

$$\therefore \quad c = \sqrt{134} = 11\cdot576 \text{ miles.}$$

(c) In a triangular course for an air race the first leg $AB(= c)$ is $5\cdot2$ miles, the second leg $BC(= a)$ $3\cdot8$ miles, and the last leg $CA(= b)$ is 3 miles. What is the angle of turn to be made at B?

$$\text{Hav. } B = \frac{(s - a)(s - c)}{ac} = \frac{2\cdot2 \times 0\cdot8}{3\cdot8 \times 5\cdot2} = 0\cdot08906$$

$$\therefore \qquad B = 34°\,43'.$$

(d) In approximating the dimensions of a triangular aerodrome ABC, the perimeter was found, by driving a car around it, to be 2 miles, and the angles A, B, and C were in the proportion $0\cdot4$, $0\cdot5$, and $1\cdot1$. What is the length of the side b?

$$\text{The angle } A = \frac{0\cdot4}{2} \text{ of } 180 = 36°$$

$$\text{,, ,, } B = \frac{0\cdot5}{2} \text{ of } 180 = 45°$$

$$\text{,, ,, } C = \frac{1\cdot1}{2} \text{ of } 180 = 99°$$

By Sine Formula—

$$a : b : c \text{ is as Sin } A : \text{Sin } B : \text{Sin } C$$

$$\therefore \qquad \frac{b}{a + b + c} = \frac{\text{Sin } B}{\text{Sin } A + \text{Sin } B + \text{Sin } C}$$

Now, $\qquad \text{Sin } A = 0{\cdot}58779$

$\qquad\qquad \text{Sin } B = 0{\cdot}70711$

$\qquad\qquad \text{Sin } C = 0{\cdot}98769$

$$\text{Sum} = 2{\cdot}28259$$

i.e. $\qquad \dfrac{b}{1760 \times 2} = \dfrac{0{\cdot}70711}{2{\cdot}28259}$

$$0{\cdot}70711 \ \text{Log } \bar{1}{\cdot}84949$$
$$3520 \ \text{Log } 3{\cdot}54654$$
$$2{\cdot}28259 \ \text{Colog } \bar{1}{\cdot}64158$$

$$3{\cdot}03761 = \log b$$

$$\therefore \qquad b = 1090\tfrac{1}{2} \text{ yds.}$$

Similarly the sides $a + c$ may be found.

SECTION 3

SPHERICAL TRIGONOMETRY

14. (a) SPHERICAL DEFINITIONS. In spherical trigonometry the ratios used with plane triangles are applied to triangles on the surface of a sphere. It is essential to comprehend accurate definitions of the various parts or accessories of the sphere.

(i) A **Sphere** is a solid body bounded by a surface on which all points are an equal distance from a fixed centre point; this centre point is the Centre of the Sphere. (Point O in Fig. 13.)

(ii) A **Radius** is a straight line joining the centre of the sphere and any point on the surface (e.g. OC in Fig. 13).

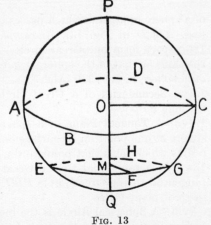

FIG. 13

(iii) An **Axis** of a circle lying on the surface of a sphere is the straight line passing through the centre of the sphere, at right angles to the plane in which the circle lies. The points where its extremities cut the surface of the sphere are the *Poles* of the circle. In Fig. 13, *PQ* is the axis to circles *ABCD* and *EFGH*. *P* and *Q* are its Poles.

(iv) A **Small Circle** is a circle lying on the surface of a sphere in a plane which does not pass through the centre of the sphere. *EFGH* in Fig. 13. (*Example*—All parallels of Lat. but not the Equator.) The radius of a small circle is a straight line measured in the plane of the circle between its axis and its circumference (e.g. *MF* in Fig. 13).

(v) A **Great Circle** or orthodrome is a circle lying on the surface

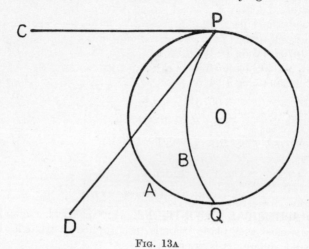

FIG. 13A

of a sphere in a plane which passes through the Centre of the Sphere (e.g. *ABCD* in Fig. 13). (*Example*—Equator; or two meridians 180° apart form one Great circle.) The radius of a Great circle is the same as that of the sphere (e.g. *OC* in Fig. 13). Two Great circles on a sphere bisect each other.

(vi) **Secondaries** of a Great circle are Great circles which pass through its poles.

(vii) A **Tangent Plane** of a sphere is a plane which touches the sphere at one point on its surface only and lies at right angles to the radius which joins that point to the centre of the sphere, e.g. in Fig. 13A *CP* is tangential to the Great circle *PAQ* at *P*; and *DP* is tangential to the Great circle *PBQ*. Both these tangents lie in the tangent plane *CPD*.

(viii) A **Spherical Angle** is the inclination at their point of intersection of two arcs of Great circles on the surface of a sphere, and equals the angle between two tangents drawn at the point of intersection, one to each Great circle measured in the tangent plane at the point of intersection. Thus in Fig. 13A the spherical angle between the Great circles QAP and QBP equals the angle between their tangents CP and DP, i.e. it equals CPD.

(ix) The **length of an arc** of a Great circle is measured as the angle which it subtends at the centre of the sphere (e.g. arc $AB =$ angle AOB, in Fig. 14). The length of an arc of a small circle is measured as the angle which it subtends at the point where the axis of the circle passes through the plane of the circle (e.g. arc $CD =$ angle CMD, in Fig. 14).

(b) **Actual Length of Arc of Small Circle.** It must be clearly understood that a given angular quantity indicates a smaller actual linear distance along the arc of a small circle than the same angular quantity would indicate along the arc of a Great circle.

In Fig. 14 the Great circle ABE and the small circle CDF are parallel to each other and PQ is the axis to both (i.e. perpendicular to the planes of both). The arc AB of the Great circle ABE, and the arc CD of the small circle CDF are cut off by two Great circles PAQ and PBQ and are thus equal arcs.

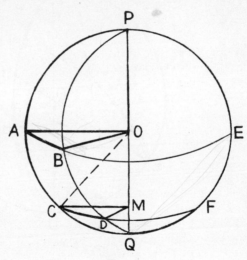

Fig. 14

Also the radii $AO(= R)$ and $CM(= r)$ are parallel, and OB and MD are parallel.

Now the arc $AB = R \times$ angle AOB in *radians* (obvious from definition of a radian) and the arc $CD = r \times$ angle CMD in *radians* but angle $AOB =$ angle CMD

$$\therefore \quad \frac{CD}{AB} = \frac{r}{R} = \frac{CM}{CO} = \text{Cos } OCM = \text{Cos } AOC$$

i.e. $\quad\quad CD = AB \text{ Cos } AOC$, or $AB \times$ Cos arc AC.

This, incidentally, is the relationship between Departure and difference of Longitude referred to later. Then $CD =$ Departure, $AB =$ difference of Longitude (see para. 25 (b)).

$$\text{Dep.} = \text{d. Long. Cos Lat.}$$

or $\quad\quad\quad\quad$ d. Long. = Dep. Sec Lat.

(c) **A Spherical Triangle** is a figure on the surface of a sphere enclosed by three arcs of Great circles. In Fig. 15 *ABC* is a spherical triangle made up of arcs of the three Great circles *AB*, *AE*, and *BE*.

The following properties, etc., of a spherical triangle are important—

(i) Notation is the same as for plane triangles; thus, in Fig. 15, in triangle *ABC*, the angle *ABC* = *B*, angle *BAC* = *A*, angle *BCA* = *C*, the side *AC* = *b*, *CB* = *a* and *AB* = *c*. The length of each side is measured as explained in sub-para. (*a* (ix)) above for arcs of Great circles.

Thus, length of side *AC* in spherical triangle *ABC* = *b* = angle

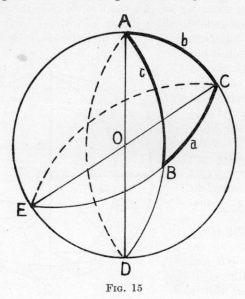

Fig. 15

AOC at centre of sphere. The actual length of a side may of course be found when the radius is known, but it is usual for all practical purposes to use the measure of the angle it subtends at the centre of the sphere.

(ii) It is conventional to restrict the length of any one side to a semicircle (180°) or less.

(iii) It follows that each angle must be less than 180°.

(iv) Any two sides are greater than the third side.

(v) The sum of the three sides is less than 360°. (This follows from (ii) above.)

(vi) The sum of the three angles is more than two right angles and less than six right angles. (This follows from (iii) above.)

(vii) When two sides are equal the angles opposite them are equal, and conversely.

(viii) The greatest side is always opposite the greatest angle.

15. THE POLAR TRIANGLE.

(a) In Fig. 16, ABC is a spherical triangle. The point A_1, is the pole of the Great circle of which a is an arc lying on the same side of a as A. Similarly, B_1 is the pole of the Great circle of b and lies on the same side of it as B. And C_1. is the pole of the Great circle of c and lies on the same side of it as C. Then $A_1B_1C_1$ is the Polar Triangle of the triangle ABC. ABC is called the Primitive Triangle of which $A_1B_1C_1$ is the Polar triangle. Of course, if $A_1B_1C_1$ is the polar triangle of ABC, then ABC is also the polar triangle of $A_1B_1C_1$.

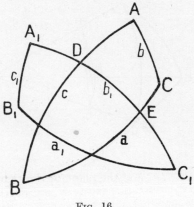

Fig. 16

(b) To prove the relationship between sides and angles in primitive and polar triangles : In Fig. 16, let the side A_1C_1 of the polar triangle cut the sides AB and BC of the primitive triangle at D and E. Now since B is a pole of A_1C_1 then arc DE = angle B.

$$\left.\begin{array}{l}\text{Also since } A_1 \text{ is a pole of } BC, \\ \quad \text{the arc } A_1E = 90° \\ \text{Also since } C_1 \text{ is a pole of } AB, \\ \quad \text{the arc } C_1D = 90° \end{array}\right\} \text{i.e. } A_1E + C_1D = 180°$$

But $A_1E + C_1D = A_1C_1 + DE = 180°.$

i.e. $A_1C_1 = 180 - DE$

$$b_1 = 180 - B$$

$$B = 180 - b_1.$$

Similarly A and a_1, C and c_1, A_1 and a, B_1 and b, C_1 and c may be found.

Then $A = 180 - a_1$. $B = 180 - b_1$. $C = 180 - c_1$.

$A_1 = 180 - a$. $B_1 = 180 - b$. $C_1 = 180 - c$.

These relationships are useful (see para. 23 (f)) when it is found necessary to solve the polar triangle and apply the results to the primitive triangle.

16. THE SINE FORMULA for spherical triangles. **(a)** In the spherical triangle ABC, in Fig. 17, the points A, B, and C are joined

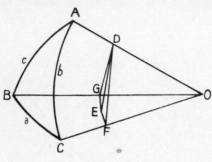

to the centre of the sphere, O. Then from a point D on AO drop DE perpendicular to the plane OBC. Then from E, on the plane OBC, draw EG perpendicular to OB, and EF perpendicular to OC. Then join DG and DF. We then have OC perpendicular to EF, DF and the plane of the right-angled triangle DEF; also we have OB perpendicular to

Fig. 17

GE, DG and the plane of the right-angled triangle DEG.

Then $\quad$ $\mathrm{Sin}\ c = \mathrm{Sin}\ AOB = \mathrm{Sin}\ DOG = \dfrac{DG}{DO}$

and similarly $\quad$ $\mathrm{Sin}\ b = \dfrac{DF}{DO}$

$\therefore \quad \dfrac{\mathrm{Sin}\ b}{\mathrm{Sin}\ c} = \dfrac{DF}{DG}$

Then $\quad$ $\mathrm{Sin}\ C = \mathrm{Sin}$ of angle between planes ACO and

$BCO = \mathrm{Sin}\ DFE = \dfrac{DE}{DF}$

and similarly $\quad$ $\mathrm{Sin}\ B = \dfrac{DE}{DG}$

$\therefore \quad \dfrac{\mathrm{Sin}\ B}{\mathrm{Sin}\ C} = \dfrac{DF}{DG}$

So $\quad \dfrac{\mathrm{Sin}\ b}{\mathrm{Sin}\ c} = \dfrac{\mathrm{Sin}\ B}{\mathrm{Sin}\ C},\left(\text{as each equal }\dfrac{DF}{DG}\right)$, or $\dfrac{\mathrm{Sin}\ b}{\mathrm{Sin}\ B} = \dfrac{\mathrm{Sin}\ c}{\mathrm{Sin}\ C}$

Similarly by dropping another perpendicular on to the planes AOB or AOC the relation with $\mathrm{Sin}\ a$ and $\mathrm{Sin}\ A$ can be proved, and the complete result is

$$\dfrac{\mathrm{Sin}\ a}{\mathrm{Sin}\ A} = \dfrac{\mathrm{Sin}\ b}{\mathrm{Sin}\ B} = \dfrac{\mathrm{Sin}\ c}{\mathrm{Sin}\ C}$$

The Sine Formula for spherical triangles can be used when (i) given any two sides and the angle opposite one of them, and (ii) when given two angles and a side opposite one of them. As, in this Sine Formula for spherical triangles, we must always derive the answer from the sine of an angle, ambiguity arises. That is Sin A also equals Sin $(180 - A)$, which means that the answer may be A or its Supplement. In practice doubt will probably not exist as to which is the correct answer, but for guidance it should be remembered that in a spherical triangle the smallest side is opposite the smallest angle, and conversely.

(b) *Example.* In the spherical triangle PAB, if the angle $P = 72°\ 30'$, the angle $A = 104°$, and the side $a = 126°$; find the length of the side p, in minutes of arc.

From Sine Formula, $\dfrac{\text{Sin } p}{\text{Sin } P} = \dfrac{\text{Sin } a}{\text{Sin } A}$

That is $\qquad \text{Sin } p = \dfrac{\text{Sin } a \text{ Sin } P}{\text{Sin } A} = \dfrac{\text{Sin } 126 \text{ Sin } 72°\ 30'}{\text{Sin } 104}$

$$= \dfrac{\text{Sin } 54 \text{ Sin } 72°\ 30'}{\text{Sin } 76}$$

$$- \text{ Sin } 54 \text{ Sin } 72°\ 30' \text{ Cosec } 76$$

L Sin 54 $\qquad = \bar{1}\cdot 90796$

L Sin 72° 30′ $= \bar{1}\cdot 97942$

L Cosec 76 $\quad = 0\cdot 01310$

$\qquad\qquad \overline{\bar{1}\cdot 90048} = \text{L Sin } p$

$\therefore \qquad\qquad p = 52°\ 40\tfrac{1}{2}'$

$\qquad\qquad\quad = 3160\tfrac{1}{2}'$

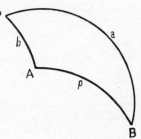

Fig. 18

(*Note.*—The answer could not be the supplement of 52° 40′, i.e. 127° 20′ for P is less than A, and therefore p must be less than a.)

17. THE COSINE FORMULA for Spherical Triangles. Let ABC be a spherical triangle on the surface of the sphere whose centre is O (Fig. 19). AD is a tangent to BA at A, and EA is a tangent to CA at A. The radii of the sphere, OB and OC are produced to meet AD and AE respectively in D and E. Then D and E are joined.

In triangle ADE—

$$DE^2 = AD^2 + AE^2 - 2\ AD{\cdot}AE \text{ Cos } EAD$$

In triangle *ODE*—

$$DE^2 = OE^2 + OD^2 - 2\,OD{\cdot}OE\,\mathrm{Cos}\,EOD$$

(from Cosine formula for plane triangles).

Then subtracting we get

$$OE^2 - AE^2 + OD^2 - AD^2 + 2\,AD{\cdot}AE$$
$$\mathrm{Cos}\,EAD - 2\,OD{\cdot}OE\,\mathrm{Cos}\,EOD = \mathrm{Nil}.$$

But as *OAE* is a right angle,

$$OE^2 - AE^2 = AO^2$$

and as *DAO* is a right angle,

$$OD^2 - AD^2 = AO^2$$

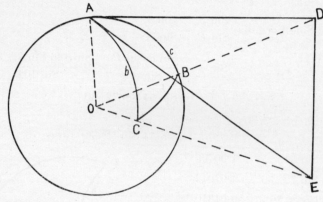

FIG. 19

then substituting these,

$$AO^2 + AO^2 + 2\,AD{\cdot}AE\,\mathrm{Cos}\,EAD$$
$$- 2\,OD{\cdot}OE\,\mathrm{Cos}\,EOD = \mathrm{Nil}$$

or $2\,OD{\cdot}OE\,\mathrm{Cos}\,EOD = 2\,AO^2 + 2\,AD{\cdot}AE\,\mathrm{Cos}\,EAD.$

$$OD{\cdot}OE\,\mathrm{Cos}\,EOD = AO^2 + AD{\cdot}AE\,\mathrm{Cos}\,EAD$$

$$\mathrm{Cos}\,EOD = \frac{AO}{OD}\cdot\frac{AO}{OE} + \frac{AD}{OD}\cdot\frac{AE}{OE}\,\mathrm{Cos}\,EAD.$$

But $\qquad EOD = a; \quad \dfrac{AO}{OD} = \mathrm{Cos}\,c; \quad \dfrac{AO}{OE} = \mathrm{Cos}\,b;$

$$\frac{AD}{OD} = \mathrm{Sin}\,c; \quad \frac{AE}{OE} = \mathrm{Sin}\,b; \quad \text{and}\ EAD = A.$$

Then, substituting these values, we have

$$\underline{\mathrm{Cos}\,a = \mathrm{Cos}\,b\,\mathrm{Cos}\,c + \mathrm{Sin}\,b\,\mathrm{Sin}\,c\,\mathrm{Cos}\,A.}$$

Similarly it can be shown that

$$\text{Cos } b = \text{Cos } a \text{ Cos } c + \text{Sin } a \text{ Sin } c \text{ Cos } B$$

and $\qquad \text{Cos } c = \text{Cos } a \text{ Cos } b + \text{Sin } a \text{ Sin } b \text{ Cos } C$

This, the Cosine Formula, is the fundamental formula of spherical trigonometry. From it are evolved further formulæ.

18. NATURAL HAVERSINE FORMULA. (a) From Cosine Formula

$$\text{Cos } a = \text{Cos } b \text{ Cos } c + \text{Sin } b \text{ Sin } c \text{ Cos } A.$$

Now Hav. $A = \dfrac{1 - \text{Cos } A}{2}.$

$\therefore \qquad \text{Cos } A = 1 - 2 \text{ Hav. } A.$

Then $\quad \text{Cos } a = \text{Cos } b \text{ Cos } c + \text{Sin } b \text{ Sin } c \, (1 - 2 \text{ Hav. } A)$

$\qquad \text{Cos } a = (\text{Cos } b \text{ Cos } c + \text{Sin } b \text{ Sin } c) - 2 \text{ Sin } b \text{ Sin } c \text{ Hav. } A$

$\qquad \text{Cos } a = \text{Cos } (b \sim c) - 2 \text{ Sin } b \text{ Sin } c \text{ Hav. } A. \text{ (See Para. 9 } (b).)$

(*Note.*—The sign $\sim$ indicates the "difference between," the result being positive.)

Then substituting for Cos a

$$1 - 2 \text{ Hav. } a = 1 - 2 \text{ Hav. } (b \sim c) - 2 \text{ Sin } b \text{ Sin } c \text{ Hav. } A$$

$$2 \text{ Hav. } a = 2 \text{ Hav. } (b \sim c) + 2 \text{ Sin } b \text{ Sin } c \text{ Hav. } A$$

i.e. $\quad$ Hav. $a = $ Hav. $(b \sim c) + \text{Sin } b \text{ Sin } c \text{ Hav. } A$

which is the Natural Haversine Formula, one of the most used formulæ in navigation.

Similarly

Hav. $b = $ Hav. $(a \sim c) + \text{Sin } a \text{ Sin } c \text{ Hav. } B.$
and
Hav. $c = $ Hav. $(a \sim b) + \text{Sin } a \text{ Sin } b \text{ Hav. } C.$

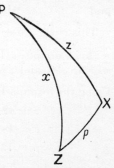

FIG. 20

The Natural Haversine Formula is the most convenient formula to find the side of a spherical triangle when two other sides and the included angle are known.

(b) *Example.* In Fig. 20, $x = 48° \, 50'$, $z = 42° \, 32'$, and $P = 19° \, 55'$.

Find p.

Hav. $p = $ Hav. $(x \sim z) + \text{Sin } x \text{ Sin } z \text{ Hav. } P$

The most convenient form of working is as follows—

$$
\begin{array}{ll}
\text{L Sin } 48°\ 50' & \bar{1}\text{·}87668 \\
\text{L Sin } 42°\ 32' & \bar{1}\text{·}82996 \\
\text{L Hav. } 19°\ 55' & \bar{2}\text{·}47575 \\
\hline
& \bar{2}\text{·}18239 = \text{Log product}
\end{array}
$$

$$
\begin{array}{rl}
\text{antilog} = & 0\text{·}01522 \\
x \sim z = 6°\ 18',\ \text{Nat. Hav.} = & 0\text{·}00302 \\
\hline
& 0\text{·}01824 = \text{Hav. } p \\
\therefore \qquad\qquad p = & 15°\ 31\tfrac{1}{2}'
\end{array}
$$

(*Note.*—In antilogging the log of the product of the Sin x, Sin y, and Hav. P the ordinary log table was not used, but the Haversine table. Thus in this case the value $\bar{2}$·18239 (i.e. 8·18239) was found in the Log Hav. column and the Natural Hav. beside it, 0·01522 taken out. This is more convenient than looking up a separate table of logs.)

19. THE COSECANT FORMULA. (a) The Natural Haversine Formula may be altered slightly to give a more convenient form for finding an angle when given three sides.

Thus $\qquad$ Hav. $a =$ Hav. $(b \sim c) +$ Sin b Sin c Hav. A

i.e. Hav. A Sin b Sin $c =$ Hav. $a -$ Hav. $(b \sim c)$

$$
\text{Hav. } A = \frac{\text{Hav. } a - \text{Hav. } (b \sim c)}{\text{Sin } b \ \text{Sin } c}
$$

Hav. $A =$ (Hav. $a -$ Hav. $(b \sim c)$) Cosec b Cosec c.

Similarly $\qquad$ Hav. $B =$ (Hav. $b -$ Hav. $(a \sim c)$) Cosec a Cosec c.

and $\qquad$ Hav. $C =$ (Hav. $c -$ Hav. $(a \sim b)$) Cosec a Cosec b.

This is the Cosecant Formula.

(**b**) *Example.* In the spherical triangle PZX, $p = 15°\ 31\tfrac{1}{2}'$, $x = 48°\ 50'$ and $z = 42°\ 32'$. Find Z.

Using the formula Hav. $Z =$ (Hav. $z -$ Hav. $(x \sim p)$) Cosec x Cosec p.

$$
\begin{array}{ll}
z = 42°\ 32' & \text{Hav.} = \ \ \cdot 13156 \\
x = 48°\ 50' & \\
p = 15°\ 31\tfrac{1}{2}' & \\
\hline
x \sim p = 33°\ 18\tfrac{1}{2}' & \text{Hav.} = 0\text{·}08214 \\
\hline
& \text{Diff.} = \underline{0\text{·}04942}
\end{array}
$$

of which $\qquad$ Log $= \bar{2}\cdot 69392$

$x = 48° 50'$ $\qquad$ Log Cosec $= 0\cdot 12332$

$p = 15° 31'$ $\qquad$ Log Cosec $= 0\cdot 57232$

$$\overline{1}\cdot 38956 = \text{Log Hav. } Z$$

$\therefore \qquad\qquad Z = 59° 22'.$

20. THE LOG HAVERSINE FORMULA.

(a) Another method of finding an angle when given three sides, if $\frac{1}{2}$ Log Hav. tables are available, is to use this formula. (Inman's Tables give $\frac{1}{2}$ Log Havs.)

From the Cosine Formula for spherical triangles

$\text{Cos } a = \text{Cos } b \text{ Cos } c + \text{Sin } b \text{ Sin } c \text{ Cos } A$

$\text{Cos } a = \text{Cos } b \text{ Cos } c + \text{Sin } b \text{ Sin } c \,(1 - 2 \text{ Hav. } A)$

$$\text{for Hav. } A = \frac{1 - \text{Cos } A}{2}, \quad \therefore \text{ Cos } A = 1 - 2 \text{ Hav. } A$$

$\text{Cos } a = \text{Cos } b \text{ Cos } c + \text{Sin } b \text{ Sin } c - 2 \text{ Sin } b \text{ Sin } c \text{ Hav. } A$

$\qquad = \text{Cos } (b \sim c) - 2 \text{ Sin } b \text{ Sin } c \text{ Hav. } A$

or

$2 \text{ Sin } b \text{ Sin } c \text{ Hav. } A = \text{Cos } (b \sim c) - \text{Cos } a$

$$= - 2 \text{ Sin } \frac{(b \sim c) + a}{2} \text{ Sin } \frac{(b \sim c) - a}{2}$$

(see para. 10),

$$= 2 \text{ Sin } \frac{a + (b \sim c)}{2} \text{ Sin } \frac{a - (b \sim c)}{2}$$

or

$\text{Hav. } A = \text{Cosec } b \text{ Cosec } c \text{ Sin } \dfrac{a + (b \sim c)}{2} \text{ Sin } \dfrac{a - (b \sim c)}{2}$

$\qquad = \text{Cosec } b \text{ Cosec } c \,\sqrt{\text{Hav. } (a + (b \sim c)) \text{ Hav. } (a - (b \sim c))}$

(for if Hav. $x = \text{Sin}^2 \dfrac{x}{2}$, then $\text{Sin } \dfrac{x}{2} = \sqrt{\text{Hav. } x}$).

Converting to Log form,

$\text{Log Hav. } A = \text{L Cosec } b + \text{L Cosec } c + \frac{1}{2} \text{ L Hav. } (a + (b \sim c))$

$\qquad\qquad + \frac{1}{2} \text{ L Hav. } (a - (b \sim c))$

Similarly

$\text{Log Hav. } B = \text{L Cosec } a + \text{L Cosec } c + \frac{1}{2} \text{ L Hav. } (b + (a \sim c))$

$\qquad\qquad + \frac{1}{2} \text{ L Hav. } (b - (a \sim c))$

and

$\text{Log Hav. } C = \text{L Cosec } a + \text{L Cosec } b + \frac{1}{2} \text{ L Hav. } (a + (a \sim b))$

$\qquad\qquad + \frac{1}{2} \text{ L Hav. } (c - (a \sim b))$

which is the Log Haversine Formula. It is also called the Half Log Haversine Formula.

(b) *Example.* (The same as in para. 19 (*b*).) In spherical triangle PZX, $p = 15° 31\frac{1}{2}'$, $x = 48° 50'$, and $z = 42° 32'$. Find Z.

Using the formula

$$\text{L Hav. } Z = \text{L Cosec } p + \text{L Cosec } x + \tfrac{1}{2} \text{ L Hav. } (z + (p \sim x)) + \tfrac{1}{2} \text{ L Hav. } (z - (p \sim x))$$

$$x = 40° 50' \qquad \text{L Cosec} = 0{\cdot}12332$$

$$p = 15° 31\tfrac{1}{2}' \qquad \text{L Cosec} = 0{\cdot}57232$$

$$x \sim p = 33° 18\tfrac{1}{2}'$$

$$z = 42° 32'$$

$$z + (x \sim p) = 75° 50\tfrac{1}{2}' \ \tfrac{1}{2} \text{ L Hav.} \ = \overline{6}{\cdot}78857$$

$$z - (x \sim p) = \ 9° 13\tfrac{1}{2}' \ \tfrac{1}{2} \text{ L Hav.} \ = \overline{7}{\cdot}90534$$

$$\overline{1}{\cdot}38955 = \text{L Hav. } Z$$

$$\therefore \qquad\qquad\qquad Z = 59° 22'.$$

(*Note.*—Comparing example worked in para. 19(*b*) it can be seen that there is very little in either over the other. In the latter (Log Hav. Formula) there is *slightly* less table reference, but also slightly more computation. Then, of course, $\frac{1}{2}$ L Hav. tables are not always available.)

(c) The Log Haversine Formula is sometimes given in the form

$$\text{Hav. } A = \frac{\text{Sin } (s - b) \text{ Sin } (s - c)}{\text{Sin } b \text{ Sin } c},$$

for if

$$\text{Hav. } A = \text{Cosec } b \text{ Cosec } c \sqrt{\text{Hav. } \frac{a + (b \sim c)}{2} \text{ Hav. } \frac{a - (b \sim c)}{2}}$$

$$\text{Hav. } A = \frac{\text{Sin } \dfrac{a + (b \sim c)}{2} \text{ Sin } \dfrac{(a - (b \sim c))}{2}}{\text{Sin } b \text{ Sin } c}$$

i.e. $\text{Hav. } A = \dfrac{\text{Sin } (s - c) \text{ Sin } (s - b)}{\text{Sin } b \text{ Sin } c}$, for $s = \dfrac{a + b + c}{2}$

Incidentally as

$$\text{Hav. } A = \text{Sin}^2 \frac{A}{2}$$

$$\text{Sin } \frac{A}{2} = \sqrt{\frac{\text{Sin } (s-b) \text{ Sin } (s-c)}{\text{Sin } b \text{ Sin } c}}$$

$$= \sqrt{\frac{\text{Sin } \dfrac{a+(b \sim c)}{2} \text{ Sin } \dfrac{a-(b \sim c)}{2}}{\text{Sin } b \text{ Sin } c}}$$

Also it can be shown by working from the Cosine Formula in a manner similar to sub-para. (a) of this para., that

$$\text{Cos } \frac{A}{2} = \sqrt{\frac{\text{Sin } s \text{ Sin } (s-a)}{\text{Sin } b \text{ Sin } c}}$$

and

$$\text{Tan } \frac{A}{2} = \sqrt{\frac{\text{Sin } (s-b) \text{ Sin } (s-c)}{\text{Sin } s \text{ Sin } (s-a)}}$$

21A. FOUR-PART FORMULA. (a) This formula can be used to find the side of a spherical triangle when two angles are known and the side between them (which can also be found by Napier's Analogies). It is developed from the Cosine formula, thus—

Cos a = Cos b Cos c + Sin b Sin c Cos A

and Cos b = Cos a Cos c + Sin a Sin c Cos B

Substituting for Cos a in the second formula, we have

Cos b = (Cos b Cos c + Sin b Sin c Cos A) Cos c
    + Sin a Sin c Cos B

Cos b = Cos b Cos^2 c + Sin b Sin c Cos c Cos A
    + Sin a Sin c Cos B

Cos b = Cos b (1 − Sin^2 c) + Sin b Sin c Cos c Cos A
    + Sin a Sin c Cos B

Cos b = Cos b − Cos b Sin^2 c + Sin b Sin c Cos c Cos A
    + Sin a Sin c Cos B

Transposing, we have

Cos b Sin^2 c = Sin b Sin c Cos c Cos A + Sin a Sin c Cos B

Dividing by Sin c

Cos b Sin c = Sin b Cos c Cos A + Sin a Cos B

Dividing by Sin b

$$\frac{\text{Cos } b}{\text{Sin } b} \text{ Sin } c = \text{Cos } c \text{ Cos } A + \frac{\text{Sin } a}{\text{Sin } b} \text{ Cos } B$$

$$\text{Cot } b \text{ Sin } c = \text{Cos } c \text{ Cos } A + \frac{\text{Sin } A \text{ Cos } B}{\text{Sin } B}$$

by sine formula, $\dfrac{\text{Sin } a}{\text{Sin } b} = \dfrac{\text{Sin } A}{\text{Sin } B}$

Transposing, we have the final form

$$\text{Cos } c \text{ Cos } A = \text{Cot } b \text{ Sin } c - \text{Cot } B \text{ Sin } A,$$

which is the Four-part Formula.

Similarly,

$$\text{Cos } a \text{ Cos } B = \text{Cot } c \text{ Sin } a - \text{Cot } C \text{ Sin } B$$
$$\text{etc.}$$

This formula is best expressed in words, thus: If four consecutive parts (an angle, a side, an angle, and a side adjoining each other) of a spherical triangle are named so that the side between the two angles is called the "Included Side," the angle between the two sides is called the "Included Angle," and the other two (outer) parts are called the "Other Side" and "Other Angle," then the Cos of the Included Side by the Cos of the Included Angle = Cot of the Other Side by the Sin of the Included Side — Cot of the Other Angle by the Sin of the Included Angle.

(b) *Example.* In the spherical triangle PZX, given $P = 33° 15'$, $Z = 78° 10'$, and $x = 68° 05'$. Find p. (Draw a diagram.)

By the Four-part formula—

$$\text{Cos } x \text{ Cos } Z = \text{Cot } p \text{ Sin } x - \text{Cot } P \text{ Sin } Z$$

or $\qquad \text{Cot } p \text{ Sin } x = \text{Cos } x \text{ Cos } Z + \text{Cot } P \text{ Sin } Z$

i.e. $\qquad \text{Cot } p = \dfrac{\text{Cos } x \text{ Cos } Z}{\text{Sin } x} + \dfrac{\text{Cot } P \text{ Sin } Z}{\text{Sin } x}$

$$= \text{Cot } x \text{ Cos } Z + \text{Cot } P \text{ Sin } Z \text{ Cosec } x$$

$x = 68° 05' \qquad$ Cot $\bar{1}{\cdot}60459$

$Z = 78° 10' \qquad$ Cos $\bar{1}{\cdot}31189$

Sum $= \bar{2}{\cdot}91648$ Antilog $= 0{\cdot}08251$

$P = 33° 15' \qquad$ Cot $0{\cdot}18334$

$Z = 78° 10' \qquad$ Sin $\bar{1}{\cdot}99067$

$x = 68° 05'$ Cosec $0{\cdot}03258$

Sum $= 0{\cdot}20659$ Antilog $= \dfrac{1{\cdot}60911}{1{\cdot}60162}$ = Nat. Cot. p.

$\therefore p = 30° 35{\cdot}3'$.

21B. NAPIER'S ANALOGIES. (a) Four formulæ known as Napier's Analogies which are useful in navigation problems, are given hereunder. Although it is not unduly difficult, it is considered unnecessary to give the proof here.

The formulæ are—

$$\text{Tan } \tfrac{1}{2} (A + B) = \frac{\text{Cos } \tfrac{1}{2} (a - b)}{\text{Cos } \tfrac{1}{2} (a + b)} \text{ Cot } \frac{C}{2}$$

$$= \text{Cos } \tfrac{1}{2} (a - b) \text{ Sec } \tfrac{1}{2} (a + b) \text{ Cot } \frac{C}{2}$$

$$\text{Tan } \tfrac{1}{2} (A - B) = \frac{\text{Sin } \tfrac{1}{2} (a - b)}{\text{Sin } \tfrac{1}{2} (a + b)} \text{ Cot } \frac{C}{2}$$

$$= \text{Sin } \tfrac{1}{2} (a - b) \text{ Cosec } \tfrac{1}{2} (a + b) \text{ Cot } \frac{C}{2}$$

$$\text{Tan } \tfrac{1}{2} (a + b) = \frac{\text{Cos } \tfrac{1}{2} (A - B)}{\text{Cos } \tfrac{1}{2} (A + B)} \text{ Tan } \frac{c}{2}$$

$$= \text{Cos } \tfrac{1}{2} (A - B) \text{ Sec } \tfrac{1}{2} (A + B) \text{ Tan } \frac{c}{2}$$

$$\text{Tan } \tfrac{1}{2} (a - b) = \frac{\text{Sin } \tfrac{1}{2} (A - B)}{\text{Sin } \tfrac{1}{2} (A + B)} \text{ Tan } \frac{c}{2}$$

$$= \text{Sin } \tfrac{1}{2} (A - B) \text{ Cosec } \tfrac{1}{2} (A + B) \text{ Tan } \frac{c}{2}.$$

The best form for the right-hand side of the equation when using logs is given below in each case (i.e. the form in which the Cos or Sin of the denominator is converted to the Sec or Cosec of the numerator).

This then entails addition only of the logs.

(b) *Example.* In spherical triangle PZX, given $P = 33° 15'$, $Z = 78° 10'$, and $x = 68° 05'$. Find p and z.

(i) $\text{Tan } \tfrac{1}{2} (z + p) = \text{Cos } \tfrac{1}{2} (Z - P) \text{ Sec } \tfrac{1}{2} (Z + P) \text{ Tan } \dfrac{x}{2}.$

(ii) $\text{Tan } \tfrac{1}{2} (z - p) = \text{Sin } \tfrac{1}{2} (Z - P) \text{ Cosec } \tfrac{1}{2} (Z + P) \text{ Tan } \dfrac{x}{2}.$

		(i)	(ii)
$P =$	$33° 15'$		
$Z =$	$78° 10'$		
$Z - P =$	$44° 55' \times \tfrac{1}{2} = 22° 27\tfrac{1}{2}'$	L Cos $\bar{1}\cdot96575$	L Sin $\bar{1}\cdot58208$
$Z + P =$	$111° 25' \times \tfrac{1}{2} = 55° 42\tfrac{1}{2}'$	L Sec $0\cdot24918$	L Cosec $0\cdot08293$
$x =$	$68° 05' \times \tfrac{1}{2} = 34° 02\tfrac{1}{2}'$	L Tan $\bar{1}\cdot82967$	L Tan $\bar{1}\cdot82967$
		$0\cdot04460$	$\bar{1}\cdot49468$

$\therefore \qquad \tfrac{1}{2}(z + p) = 47° 56'$ and $\tfrac{1}{2}(z - p) = 17° 21'.$

Then by addition $\qquad z = 65° 17'$

by subtraction $\qquad p = 30° 35'.$

22. NAPIER'S MNEMONIC RULES. (Napier's Rules of Circular Parts.) A series of formulæ giving the relationship between ratios for right-angled and right-sided (Quadrantal) spherical triangles are best remembered with the help of "Napier's Rules of Circular Parts."

(a) In Right-angled Spherical Triangles. Being a spherical triangle the Cosine formula applies. Then if in a spherical triangle ABC the angle $C = 90°$, we have

$$\text{Cos } c = \text{Cos } a \text{ Cos } b + \text{Sin } a \text{ Sin } b \text{ Cos } 90, \text{ but Cos } 90 = 0$$

(i) i.e. $\text{Cos } c = \text{Cos } a \text{ Cos } b.$

(*Note.*—This indicates that Pythagoras's Theorem (i.e. hyp.^{2} = adjacent^2 + opp.^{2}) for plane right-angled triangles does not apply to spherical right-angled triangles.)

(ii)　　　　Now $\text{Cos } a = \text{Cos } b \text{ Cos } c + \text{Sin } b \text{ Sin } c \text{ Cos } A.$

Then, substituting for Cos c as in (i) above.

$$\text{Cos } a = \text{Cos}^2 b \text{ Cos } a + \text{Sin } b \text{ Sin } c \text{ Cos } A$$

$$\text{Cos } a - (\text{Cos } a \text{ Cos}^2 b) = \text{Sin } b \text{ Sin } c \text{ Cos } A$$

$$\text{Cos } a (1 - \text{Cos}^2 b) = \text{Sin } b \text{ Sin } c \text{ Cos } A$$

$$\text{Cos } a \text{ Sin}^2 b = \text{Sin } b \text{ Sin } c \text{ Cos } A$$

or　　　　$$\text{Cos } A = \frac{\text{Cos } a \text{ Sin } b}{\text{Sin } c},$$

but from (i) above　$\text{Cos } a = \dfrac{\text{Cos } c}{\text{Cos } b}$

$$\therefore \text{ Cos } A = \frac{\text{Cos } c}{\text{Cos } b} \times \frac{\text{Sin } b}{\text{Sin } c}$$

$$\text{Cos } A = \frac{\text{Tan } b}{\text{Tan } c}.$$

Similarly it can be deduced that, where $C = 90°$,

$$\text{Cos } B = \frac{\text{Tan } a}{\text{Tan } c}$$

$$\text{Sin } A = \frac{\text{Sin } a}{\text{Sin } c} \text{ and Sin } B = \frac{\text{Sin } b}{\text{Sin } c}$$

$$\text{Tan } A = \frac{\text{Tan } a}{\text{Sin } b} \text{ or Sin } b = \text{Tan } a \text{ Cot } A$$

$$= \text{Tan } a \text{ Tan } (90 - A)$$

$$\text{Tan } B = \frac{\text{Tan } b}{\text{Sin } a} \text{ or Sin } a = \text{Tan } b \text{ Cot } B$$

$$= \text{Tan } b \text{ Tan } (90 - B).$$

Now Napier's Rules for remembering these formulæ operate as follows—

Draw a circle and divide it into five parts (sectors). Then in each write in order the following parts of the right-angled spherical triangle—working *around* the triangle from the right angle—the adjacent side, the complement of the next angle, the complement of

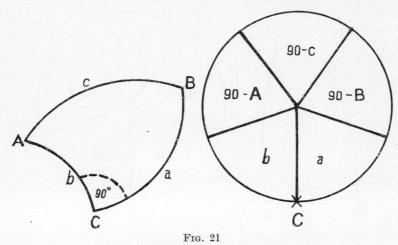

Fig. 21

the next side, the complement of the next angle, and the remaining (adjacent) side.

Thus in Fig. 21, where $C = 90°$, the parts in order are: a, $90 - B$, $90 - c$, $90 - A$, and b. Each part has two adjacent parts and two opposite parts in the circle. Then Napier's Rules of Circular Parts are—

Sine of middle Part = Product of Tangents of Adjacent Parts.

Sine of middle Part = Product of Cosines of Opposite Parts.

For example, $\operatorname{Sin} a = \operatorname{Tan} b \operatorname{Tan} (90 - B) = \operatorname{Cos} (90 - A) \operatorname{Cos} (90 - c)$ and $\operatorname{Sin} (90 - c) = \operatorname{Tan} (90 - A) \operatorname{Tan} (90 - B) = \operatorname{Cos} b \operatorname{Cos} a$ and so on (in Fig. 21).

(b) **Quadrantal Spherical Triangles.** When one side of a spherical triangle equals one right angle the triangle is called a Quadrantal (as the side equal one quadrant) or right-sided spherical triangle.

The relationships of the ratios, as for right-angled triangles in sub-para. (a), may be conveniently remembered by Napier's Rules.

In this case the parts taken in order are: an adjacent angle, the complement of the next side, the complement of the next angle, the complement of the next side, and the remaining angle. Thus in Fig. 22 if in the spherical triangle ABC, the side $c = 90°$, the parts, in order, are: B, $90 - a$, $90 - C$, $90 - b$, A. Then Napier's Rules, as in sub-para. (a) apply.

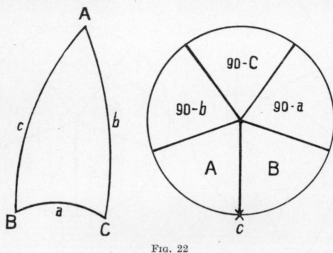

FIG. 22

(*Note.*—Many methods of solving the spherical triangle in navigation are based on the formulæ given in Napier's Rules, the oblique-angled triangle being divided into two right-angled (or right-sided) triangles.)

(c) *Examples.* (i) In the spherical triangle PZX, the angle Z is a right angle; the angle $P = 51° 15'$, and the side $p = 39° 03'$. Find side x. See Fig. 23.

Now $\text{Sin } x = \text{Tan } (90 - P) \text{ Tan } p = \text{Cot } P \text{ Tan } p$

$\qquad\qquad P = 51° 15' \text{ L Cot } \quad \bar{1}\cdot90449$

$\qquad\qquad p = 39° 03' \text{ L Tan} = \underline{\bar{1}\cdot90914}$

$\qquad\qquad\qquad\qquad\qquad\qquad \overline{\bar{1}\cdot81363}$

∴ $x = 40° 37'.$

But, from Fig. 23 it is obvious that two right-angled triangles, namely P_1ZX and P_2ZX, are possible with given p and P. Therefore the answer is either $\underline{\underline{40° 37'}}$ or $(180° - 40° 37') = \underline{\underline{139° 23'}}$.

This ambiguity would not normally cause trouble in practice as it would be obvious which triangle was applicable.

(ii) In spherical triangle PAB, the side $b = 90°$, the angle P

$= 44° 38'$ and the side $a = 72° 30'$. Find p (or to put the question in a more practical form: Find distance between place A on the

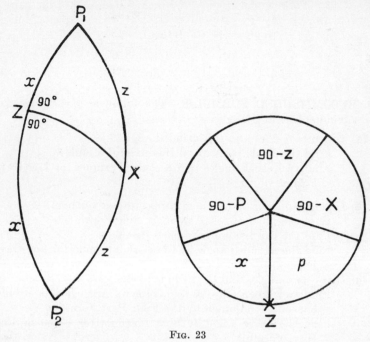

Fig. 23

Equator and place B situated $17° 30'$ South Lat., when their difference of longitude is $44° 38'$). See Fig. 24.

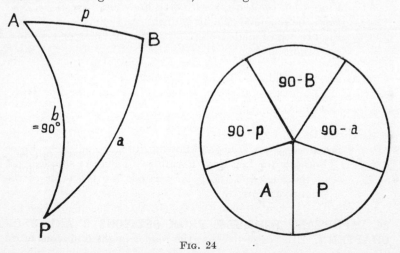

Fig. 24

$$\text{Sin} (90 - p) = \text{Cos } P \text{ Cos } (90 - a).$$

i.e. $\text{Cos } p = \text{Cos } P \text{ Sin } a$

$$a = 72° 30' \text{ L Sin } \bar{1}·97942$$
$$P = 44° 38' \text{ L Cos } \bar{1}·85225$$
$$\overline{ \bar{1}·83167}$$

∴ $p = 47° 15\frac{1}{2}'$ (or $2835\frac{1}{2}'$).

23. RECOMMENDED FORMULÆ. The following are suggested for solving spherical triangles—

(a) Given two sides and the included angle—
Find third side by Natural Haversine Formula.
Find two other angles by Cosecant Formula (or Log Hav. Formula).

(b) Given two sides and an angle opposite one of them—
Find the other opposite angle by Sine Formula.
Find the third side by Napier's Analogy.
Find the included angle by Cosecant Formula (or Log Hav. Formula).

(c) Given two angles and the included side—
Find two other sides by two Napier's Analogies, or if only one side is required, by the Four-Part Formula.
Find the other angle by Sine Formula (or Cosec or Log Hav. Formula).

(d) Given two angles and a side opposite one of them—
Find other opposite side by Sine Formula.
Find the included side by Napier's Analogy.
Find the third angle by Sine Formula (or Cosec or Log Hav. Formula).

(e) Given three sides—
Find each other angle by Cosecant Formula (or Log Hav. Formula).

(f) Given the three angles—
Solve the polar triangle, knowing its three sides, by Cosec Formula (or Log Hav. Formula). Then the supplements of the angles of the polar triangle are the sides of the primitive triangle.

24. IMPORTANT FORMULÆ FROM SECTIONS 2 AND 3 OF CHAPTER I. It is suggested that the reader might find it useful to have these formulæ copied into the front of his Nautical Tables, for reference. Of course they should be known, but to rely on memory is sometimes dangerous.

Identities

$$\text{Sin}^2\, A + \text{Cos}^2\, A = 1 \qquad\qquad\qquad\qquad \text{Para. 5 } (f)$$

$$\text{Sec}^2\, A = 1\, \text{Tan}^2\, A$$

$$\text{Cosec}^2\, A = 1\, \text{Cot}^2\, A.$$

$$\text{Sin}\, (A + B) = \text{Sin}\, A\, \text{Cos}\, B + \text{Sin}\, B\, \text{Cos}\, A \qquad \text{Para. 9 } (a)$$

$$\text{Cos}\, (A + B) = \text{Cos}\, A\, \text{Cos}\, B - \text{Sin}\, A\, \text{Sin}\, B$$

$$\text{Tan}\, (A + B) = \frac{\text{Tan}\, A + \text{Tan}\, B}{1 - \text{Tan}\, A\, \text{Tan}\, B}.$$

$$\text{Sin}\, (A - B) = \text{Sin}\, A\, \text{Cos}\, B - \text{Sin}\, B\, \text{Cos}\, A \qquad \text{Para. 9 } (b)$$

$$\text{Cos}\, (A - B) = \text{Cos}\, A\, \text{Cos}\, B + \text{Sin}\, A\, \text{Sin}\, B$$

$$\text{Tan}\, (A - B) = \frac{\text{Tan}\, A - \text{Tan}\, B}{1 + \text{Tan}\, A\, \text{Tan}\, B}.$$

$$\text{Sin}\, 2\, A = 2\, \text{Sin}\, A\, \text{Cos}\, A \qquad\qquad\qquad \text{Para. 9 } (c)$$

$$\text{Cos}\, 2\, A = 2\, \text{Cos}^2\, A - 1 = 1 - 2\, \text{Sin}^2\, A$$

$$\text{Tan}\, 2\, A = \frac{2\, \text{Tan}\, A}{1 - \text{Tan}^2\, A}.$$

$$\text{Sin}\, A + \text{Sin}\, B = 2\, \text{Sin}\, \tfrac{1}{2}\, (A + B)\, \text{Cos}\, \tfrac{1}{2}\, (A - B) \qquad \text{Para. 10}$$

$$\text{Sin}\, A - \text{Sin}\, B = 2\, \text{Cos}\, \tfrac{1}{2}\, (A + B)\, \text{Sin}\, \tfrac{1}{2}\, (A - B)$$

$$\text{Cos}\, A + \text{Cos}\, B = 2\, \text{Cos}\, \tfrac{1}{2}\, (A + B)\, \text{Cos}\, \tfrac{1}{2}\, (A - B)$$

$$\text{Cos}\, A - \text{Cos}\, B = 2\, \text{Sin}\, \tfrac{1}{2}\, (A + B)\, \text{Sin}\, \tfrac{1}{2}\, (A - B).$$

Solution of Plane Triangles

$$\frac{a}{\text{Sin}\, A} = \frac{b}{\text{Sin}\, B} = \frac{c}{\text{Sin}\, C}. \qquad\qquad \text{Para. 11 } (a)$$

$$a^2 = b^2 + c^2 - 2bc\, \text{Cos}\, A. \qquad\qquad \text{Para. 11 } (b)$$

$$\text{Hav.}\, A = \frac{(s - b)(s - c)}{bc}. \qquad\qquad \text{Para. 11 } (c)$$

Solution of Spherical Triangles

$$\frac{\text{Sin}\, a}{\text{Sin}\, A} = \frac{\text{Sin}\, b}{\text{Sin}\, B} = \frac{\text{Sin}\, c}{\text{Sin}\, C}. \qquad\qquad \text{Para. 16 } (a)$$

$$\text{Cos } a = \text{Cos } b \text{ Cos } c + \text{Sin } b \text{ Sin } c \text{ Cos } A.$$ Para. 17

$$\text{Hav. } a = \text{Hav. } (b \sim c) + \text{Sin } b \text{ Sin } c \text{ Hav. } A.$$ Para. 18

$$\text{Hav. } A = [\text{Hav. } a - \text{Hav. } (b \sim c)] \text{ Cosec } b \text{ Cosec } c.$$

$$\text{L Hav. } A = \text{L Cosec } b + \text{L Cosec } c + \tfrac{1}{2} \text{ L Hav. } (a + (b \sim c)$$
$$+ \tfrac{1}{2} \text{ L Hav. } (a - (b \sim c)).$$ Para. 20

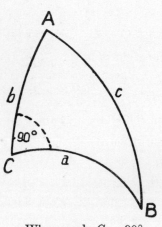
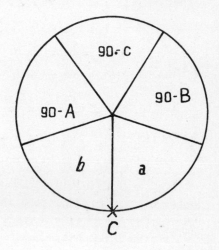

When angle $C = 90°$

Fig. 24a

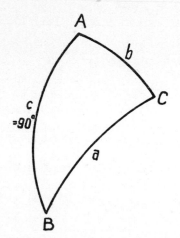
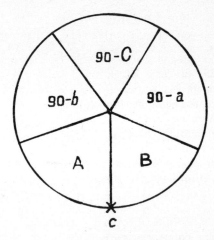

When side $c = 90°$

Fig. 24b

$$\text{Cos } c \text{ Cos } A = \text{Cot } b \text{ Sin } c - \text{Cot } B \text{ Sin } A \qquad \text{Para. 21 } (A)$$

$$\text{Tan } \tfrac{1}{2}(A + B) = \frac{\text{Cos } \tfrac{1}{2}(a - b)}{\text{Cos } \tfrac{1}{2}(a + b)} \text{ Cot } \frac{C}{2}$$

$$= \text{Cos } \tfrac{1}{2}(a - b) \text{ Sec } \tfrac{1}{2}(a + b) \text{ Cot } \frac{C}{2} \qquad \text{Para. 21 } (B)$$

$$\text{Tan } \tfrac{1}{2}(A - B) = \frac{\text{Sin } \tfrac{1}{2}(a - b)}{\text{Sin } \tfrac{1}{2}(a + b)} \text{ Cot } \frac{C}{2}$$

$$= \text{Sin } \tfrac{1}{2}(a - b) \text{ Cosec } \tfrac{1}{2}(a + b) \text{ Cot } \frac{C}{2}$$

$$\text{Tan } \tfrac{1}{2}(a + b) = \frac{\text{Cos } \tfrac{1}{2}(A - B)}{\text{Cos } \tfrac{1}{2}(A + B)} \text{ Tan } \frac{c}{2}$$

$$= \text{Cos } \tfrac{1}{2}(A - B) \text{ Sec } \tfrac{1}{2}(A + B) \text{ Tan } \frac{c}{2}$$

$$\text{Tan } \tfrac{1}{2}(a - b) = \frac{\text{Sin } \tfrac{1}{2}(A - B)}{\text{Sin } \tfrac{1}{2}(A + B)} \text{ Tan } \frac{c}{2}$$

$$= \text{Sin } \tfrac{1}{2}(A - B) \text{ Cosec } \tfrac{1}{2}(A + B) \text{ Tan}\frac{c}{2}.$$

Right-angled and Quadrantal Spherical Triangles   Para. 22

Napier's Rules of Circular Parts for right-angled and right-sided spherical triangles—

The Sine of a middle part = Product of Tangents of Adjacent parts

The Sine of a middle part = Product of Cosines of Opposite parts;
                            when the parts are as in Fig. 24.

SECTION 4

FORM OF THE EARTH, AND SAILINGS

25. (a) The Earth. Generally, for most practical navigational purposes, the earth is assumed to be a sphere. But it must be remembered that for accurate work it is sometimes necessary to take into account the fact that the earth is almost exactly an oblate spheroid (which is the figure traced out by an ellipse in a complete revolution about its smaller axis). The earth has its smallest radius at the poles and its greatest radius at the Equator. Then the "ellipticity" or "compression" of the earth

$$= \frac{\text{Equatorial Radius} - \text{Polar Radius}}{\text{Equatorial Radius}}.$$

The equatorial radius is about 20,925,871 ft., and the polar radius is about 20,855,721 ft.

The difference = 70,150 ft.

$$\text{Then compression} = \frac{70{,}150}{20{,}925{,}871} = \frac{1}{293 \cdot 3} = \frac{1}{300} \text{ approx.}$$

Although this "compression" will be referred to again, for most practical purposes the Earth is treated as if a sphere. For approximate working the Earth's radius may be taken as 3960 statute miles (or, more accurately, 3957 statute miles) = 3436 nautical miles.

(b) Now the Earth rotates towards the East about an axis through the North and South poles.

The Earth is not a regular sphere but a slightly unbalanced spheroid. Therefore when its slightly irregular and unbalanced mass rotates, and is under the attractive force of the sun, moon, and planets, a "wobble" of the axis results. This variation of the direction of the axis and also of the plane of the Equator consists of two parts—(i) a progressive variation called "Precession," and (ii) a periodic variation called "Nutation." In this book this wobble will be ignored, except where it is of practical importance.

(c) **Meridians** are semi-great circles from one pole to the other. The Equator is a Great circle whose plane is at right angles to the Earth's axis of rotation. All points on the Equator are equal distances from the poles.

Parallels of latitude are small circles whose planes are parallel to the plane of the Equator.

(d) **Measurement of Longitude.** As a datum from which longitude is measured, the meridian which passes through Greenwich is used for navigational purposes by most countries. It is called the **Prime meridian.** Then the longitude of a place is the shorter arc of the Equator between the Prime meridian and meridian which passes through the place. It is measured in degrees and minutes, or in hours, minutes, and seconds, east or west from the Prime meridian (15 degrees of arc = 1 hour; 1 degree of arc = 4 minutes; 15 minutes of arc = 1 minute of time; 1 minute of arc = 15 seconds of time). The difference of longitude between two positions is the arc of the Equator between the meridians of the two positions.

(e) **Measurement of Latitude.** The datum from which measurements of latitude are made is the Equator. The latitude of a position is then the arc of the meridian measured from the Equator to the position. Difference of latitude of two positions is the arc of a meridian between the parallels of latitude of the two positions. (**Colatitude** is 90° − latitude.)

(f) **Departure.** When longitude is changed, the actual distance moved east or west is called the Departure. Except on the Equator it is obvious that the change of longitude is not a measure of Departure. Para. 14 (*b*) of this chapter shows the relation between difference of longitude (measured as an arc of the Equator) and Departure (measured as an arc of a parallel of latitude) for a particular parallel. Dep. = d. Long. Cos Lat.

When there is a difference of latitude as well as longitude between two positions, the question arises as to which parallel of latitude will be the correct one to apply the relationship Dep.= d. Long. Cos Lat. Obviously the latitude to be used will lie between the parallels of latitude of the two positions. For practical purposes, the algebraic mean of the two latitudes is used and is called the "Mean Latitude." If the latitudes are *a* and *b*, then "Mean Latitude"

$= \dfrac{a + b}{2}$, or if *a* and *b* are of opposite names, then "Mean Latitude"

$= \dfrac{a - b}{2}$. But to be strictly accurate *for the sphere*, a latitude called

the "Middle Latitude" is used. Inman's Tables and Norie's Tables give a correction table for converting the algebraic mean latitude to the true middle latitude, resulting in an answer which is correct and accurate *for the sphere*.

(g) For both theoretical and statistical purposes it is of considerable value to appreciate a few facts concerning the dimensions of the true Earth and of arcs on its surface.

The first important point is the definition of latitude on the terrestrial spheroid. Latitude of a place (Geographical Latitude) on the spheroid is the angle between the tangent to the meridian at the place and the tangent to the same meridian at the Equator. Difference of latitude between two places, then, is simply the curvature (in a N.–S. direction) between them. Obviously, near the Equator, where the curvature is greatest, the length of one minute of latitude is much less than one minute of latitude near the pole where the earth is flatter. Thus 1′ of Lat. at Equator = 6045·7 ft., at 45′ N. or S. = 6076·7 ft., and at the Poles = 6107·9 ft.

Now on the sphere the distance between two places on the same meridian equals their difference of latitude. But on the actual spheroidal earth the distance between two places on the same meridian equals the difference between their *Reduced latitudes*. This reduction can be taken from the Figure of the Earth Table in Inman's.

Longitude and Departure, however, do not vary in the same way as latitude. Longitude on the spheroid may be defined as in the case of the sphere but the length of one minute on longitude on the spheroid is in all cases greater than on the sphere. There are two reasons for this. At and near the Equator it is due to the larger radius, and at higher latitudes it is because of the "flattened" shape of the Earth. The latter reason can best be visualized by taking the extreme case of a completely flat Earth with the North Pole in the centre and meridians radiating from it. Then obviously at a given distance from the Pole the distance between two particular meridians is greater on the flat than on the sphere. Departure is obviously proportional to the dimensions of the relative difference of longitude. It is clear therefore that sub-para. (f) above and the Middle Latitude Correction Table given in Inman's and in Norie's Tables are not correct for the terrestrial spheroid. The table, in fact, actually causes an error in relation to actual fact (on the spheroid) greater than would occur with no correction in some cases. However the difference is not large. In Burton's Tables the Middle Latitude Corrections Table includes the amplifying effect of the spheroid but the figures given and the reasoning do not appear to agree with these normally accepted for the Figure of the Earth. If Inman's or Norie's Tables are used, a good rough method of obtaining the value of Departure on the spheroid is as follows: Departure is found in the normal way for the sphere, applying the Middle Latitude correction as given. The result is then multiplied by the length in feet of one minute of longitude at the middle latitude divided by 6080 ft. by Cos Mid. Lat. Thus, if a Departure (on the sphere) at 65° N. Mid. Lat. = 400', then on the spheroid the same Departure $= 400 \times \dfrac{2579 \cdot 8}{6080 \times \text{Cos Mid. Lat.}}$ = 4016'. The lengths of minutes of longitude are included in the Figure of the Earth Table (page 497 in Inman's Tables). A table to obviate the necessity of calculating this correction factor is included in this book as Appendix V. Then the Departure is found as for the sphere, and to its log the appropriate value from Appendix V is added, the antilog of the sum being the spheroidal departure.

26. Measurement of Distance. For purposes of air navigation it is usual to measure distances over the Earth's surface in (i) nautical miles, (ii) statute miles, or (iii) kilometres. Of these the nautical mile is the only unit worthy of consideration and should be used on all aircraft.

(i) *Nautical Miles.* The theoretical nautical mile is the length of 1 minute of latitude. It can be shown that this length = 6076·8 − 31·1 Cos (2 Lat.) ft. This gives a quantity which varies with latitude from 6045·7 at the Equator, to 6077 ft. at Lat. 45°, and 6107·9 ft. at the poles (owing to the fact that the earth is not a sphere). This variable quantity is obviously inconvenient as a

measure of distance and therefore in practice the nautical mile is
taken as 6080 ft. This of course is only accurate at about 48° Lat. N.
or S. but the errors due to using this fixed value are *usually* negligible.
The following gives an idea of the magnitude of such an error in
Equatorial regions where it is the worst likely to be met with:
After flying due North from the Equator for exactly 20 nautical
miles (practical, i.e. of 6080 ft.) the actual latitude is not 00 20 N.
but 00 20·09 N. approximately. This is, the error was less than
one-tenth of a mile in 20 miles. (*Note.*—The "Geographical" mile
= 6087·1 ft.) 1 nautical mile = 1·1515 statute miles = 1·8531
kilometres. The nautical mile is the internationally accepted unit
of distance in navigation.

(ii) *The Statute Mile.* The British statute mile is purely an
arbitrary unit, and equals 5280 ft. It is unfortunately used on
many British land aircraft. 1 statute mile = 0·8684 nautical miles
= 1·6092 kilometres.

(iii) The *kilometre* equals approximately 3281 ft. (1 metre
= approximately one ten-millionth of a Quadrant of the Equator.)

1 kilometre = 0·6214 statute mile = 0·539 nautical miles.

(*Note.*—It is recommended that the conventions of abbreviating
statute miles to "ml" and nautical miles to the symbol "′" (as for
minutes) and kilometres to "km." be used. Thus 20 statute miles
= 20 ml. and 35 nautical miles = 35′. Great care must be taken
that the symbol "′" is not written so as to be mistaken for a figure 1.)

27. Measurement of Direction. (a) The direction of an aircraft's
head (i.e. the course), the direction of movement over the Earth's
surface (i.e. the track), the direction of an object in relation to an
observer (i.e. a bearing) or any other direction on the Earth's surface
is always expressed as an angle from a given datum.

(i) *True Directions* (i.e. true tracks, true courses, and true bearings)
are measured in relation to the true meridian, through 360° clockwise from North. This is obvious and straightforward. But there
are two points which must be strongly recommended here. Both
are intended to reduce the possibility of a mistake in the air. Firstly,
always express the angle in THREE figures. Secondly, *never* use
the degree sign (°) in the air; for it sometimes looks painfully like a
0. Use the block letter "T," meaning TRUE, after the group.
Thus a true bearing of 45 degrees = 045 T, or true north = 000 T,
etc.

(ii) *Magnetic Directions.* The Earth's magnetism radiates lines
of magnetic force, and the direction of horizontal component of one
of these lines of force is used as a datum for measuring direction.
Their direction with relation to the true meridians varies, of course,

in different places. The direction is measured as an angle from magnetic North through 360 degrees clockwise, and is expressed always as a three-figure group followed by the block letter "M." Thus a magnetic course of five degrees = 005 M.

(iii) *Compass Directions.* The use of Magnetic Directions as in (ii) is because the compass is the most convenient datum from which to measure direction. The compass if influenced by the Earth's field only would, of course, indicate magnetic directions. But unfortunately compass errors occur, and therefore the direction of the North-seeking end of the compass needle gives another datum from which to measure. Groups are of three figures and are followed by the block letter "C." Thus South by compass = 180 C.

(iv) *Relative Directions.* A direction may be indicated as an angle relative to an aircraft's heading (Course). It is measured to port (red) or to starboard (green) from the aircraft's head and is *not* a three-figure group. The degree sign is *not* used. Thus a bearing of 13 degrees to starboard of the aircraft's head = 13 green or 13 starboard; or a drift of 10 degrees to port indicating that track is 10 degrees to the left of the course is expressed as "Drift = 10 red" (or 10 port).

(b) As true direction is measured in relation to meridians and as any Great circle (except the Equator and the meridians themselves) cuts each meridian at a slightly different angle, it is clear that the shortest distance between two places (i.e. along the Great circle through them) is a constantly varying direction. The line which cuts meridians at the same angle (i.e. maintains a constant direction) is called a

Rhumb Line or Loxodrome. This line cannot (unless it is along the Equator or a meridian) be the shortest distance between two points, but the obvious convenience of its constant direction, etc., makes it the line used in all navigation. Even when a Great circle track is being aimed at, short Rhumb lines from point to point along the Great circle are flown. All parallels of latitude are Rhumb lines.

Convergency. Now it was stated above that a Great circle cuts each meridian at a different angle. The actual difference equals the angle of Convergency of the meridians. The Natural Convergency of two meridians is the angle between the tangents to the two meridians and = d. Long. Sin Mid. Lat. Thus Convergency at the Equator = Nil, and at the Poles = d. Long. Thus the Convergency of two meridians of 10° difference of longitude is at the N. pole 10°, and at 45° 00′ N. Lat. their Convergency is about 7° 04′ and at the Equator they are, of course, parallel (Convergency Nil).

A Rhumb line cuts each meridian at a constant angle and if a figure is drawn it can be seen that the change in direction of a Great circle from one place to another equals Convergency, and a Rhumb line being the mean of the Great circle direction differs from the initial direction of the Great circle by half the Convergency of the meridians through the two places. This is called the **Conversion Angle.** It must be remembered that a Great circle lies on the polar side of the Rhumb line, and conversion angle must be applied accordingly. Thus, for example, if the Mercatorial (Rhumb line) bearing (direction) of B from A *in the Southern Hemisphere* is 090° T then the Great circle bearing of B from A is 090° T + Conversion Angle. Similarly, the mercatorial bearing of A from B is 270° T and the Great circle bearing of A from B is 270° T — Conversion Angle. (*Note.* A Great circle is sometimes called an Orthodrome and a Rhumb line a Loxodrome.)

28. Sailings are the methods of calculating track and distance between two places or alternatively of calculating position after flying a distance on a given track from an original position.

(a) **Parallel Sailing.** If an aircraft flies due East or due West, that is, along the arc of a parallel of latitude, the distance flown equals the Departure = d. Long. Cos Lat., and d. Long. = Distance Sec Lat.; and of course the track is 090 T or 270 T.

(b) **Middle Latitude Method, or Plane Sailing.** When flying over comparatively short distances (less than 600') plane trigonometry can be employed to find tracks and distances. Thus to find the track and distance between two positions whose Lat. and Long. are known: The difference of Long. is converted into Departure (Dep. = d. Long. Cos Mid. Lat.).

Then Tan Track $= \dfrac{\text{Dep.}}{\text{d. Lat.}}$.   Distance $=$ Dep. Cosec Tr.

Dep. = Distance Sin Tr.   d. Lat.= Distance Cos Tr.

As the track obtained by the formula is less than 90 degrees it must be applied from North to East or West, or from South to East or West, depending on the obvious relative positions of the two places. Thus N. 40 W. meaning 40 degrees West of North = 360 − 40 = 320 T.

Example. Find track and distance from position 30° 20′ S. 20° 05′ W. to position 32° 55′ S. 18° 50′ W.

d. Long. = 1° 15′ East   = 75′ E.

d. Lat. = 2° 35′ South   = 155′ S.

Mean Lat. $= \dfrac{32° 55' + 30° 20'}{2} = 31° 37\tfrac{1}{2}'$

Mid. Lat. $= 31° 37\frac{1}{2}' + 1'$ $= 31° 38\frac{1}{2}'$

Dep. $= 75 \cos 31° 38\frac{1}{2}'$ Log 75 $= 1·87506$

$= 63·85$ miles   L Cos $31° 38\frac{1}{2}' = \bar{1}·93011$

          L Dep. $= 1·80517$

Tan Tr. $= \dfrac{63·85}{155}$ Log $63·86 = 1·80517$

          Log $155 = 2·19033$

$\therefore$ Track $=$ S. $22° 23\frac{1}{2}'$ E. $\overline{\bar{1}·61484}$

$=$ approx. $157\frac{1}{2}$ T

Distance $= 63·85 \csc 22° 23\frac{1}{2}'$ Log $63·85 = 1·80517$

$= 167·65$ miles (nautical)   L Cosec $22° 23\frac{1}{2}' = 0·41915$

$= 167\frac{1}{2}'$ $\overline{2·22432}$

(c) (i) Traverse Table. Nautical tables include a "ready-reckoner" for the solution of the plane right-angled triangle particularly for Plane Sailing, called the Traverse Table. Actually it is just a multiplication table of numbers by Sines and Cosines. Columns for each mile (for distance up to 600′) contain d. Lat. and Dep. printed side by side for each degree of Course. (*Note.*—This "Course" means "Track" for air navigation.) Thus to find distance and track between two positions, d. Long. is converted to Dep., then Dep. and d. Lat. are found together in one column. The head of the column gives the distance, and the track is read off the side (in the column marked Co.). Or to find change of Lat. and Long. after a given distance on a given track, reduce track to less than 90 degrees (by referring to N. or S.). Then entering the top of the page with distance and the side column with track, read off d. Lat. and Dep. Convert Dep. to d. Long.

(ii) Form of working with Traverse Table. It may be convenient, in cases such as searching, to navigate by Traverse Table entirely. The following form of working is suggested.

Time S/C A/C	Inter-val	Air Speed	Dis-tance	Course T	d. Lat.		Dep.	
					N.	S.	E.	W.
0940 − 0946	6	120	12	220 T = S. 40 W.		9·2		7·7
0946 − 0948	2	120	4	185 T = S. 5 W.		4		·3
0948 − 0952	4	120	8	322 T = N. 38 W.	6·3			4·9
0952 − 0958	6	120	12	170 T = S. 10 E.		11·8	2·1	
0958 − 1001	3	120	6	260 T = S. 80 W.		·9		4·9
1001 − 1010	9	120	18	005 T = N. 5 E.	17·9		1·6	
Wind to 1010	30	20	10	068 T = N. 68 E.	3·7		9·3	
					27·9 N.	25·9 S.	13· E.	17·8 W.
				Diff. 2′ N.			4·8 W.	

Then if the 0940 position was 5044 N. 0134 W., d.Long. $= 4.8$ Sec $50°\ 45' = 7.6$ W. Find position (i.e. at 1010) $= 5046$ N. $0141\frac{1}{2}$ W.

29. (a) Mercator's Method. Mercator's sailing is based on the same principle as Mercator's projection (see next chapter). In the projection the Earth's surface is represented on a plane by making the meridians parallel straight lines and expanding the parallels of latitude in proportion. This proportion of expanding at a particular latitude $=$ Sec Lat., or $\dfrac{\text{d. Long}}{\text{Dep.}}$. Nautical Tables give a table of "Meridional Parts" which gives the sum of the expanded latitudes from the Equator to any required Lat.

Then in Mercator's sailing, two sides, namely d. Long. and difference of Meridional Parts (d. MP) of a right-angled plane triangle are known. The scales of d.Long. and d.MP are in proportion. From this triangle track is found. Tan Tr. $= \dfrac{\text{d. Long}}{\text{d. MP}}$. Then in another plane right-angled triangle, an angle (track) is known and one side d.Lat. in minutes is known. Then Distance $=$ d.Lat.Sec Tr.

Example. Find the track and distance from position 30° 18′ S. 118° 50′ E. to position 27° 20′ S. 153° 19′ E.

	Lat.	M. Parts	Long.
From $=$	30° 18′ S.	1909	118° 50′ E.
To $=$	27° 20′ S.	1706	153° 10′ E.
Diff. $=$	2° 58′ N.	203	34° 20′ E.
$=$	178′ N.		2060′ E.

$$\text{Tan Tr.} = \frac{\text{d.Long.}}{\text{d.MP}}$$

Log 2060 $= 3.31387$

Log 203 $= 2.30750$

$1.00637 =$ L Tan Tr.

$\therefore$ Tr. $=$ N. 84° 22·32′ E.

$= 084\frac{1}{4}$ T

Dist. $=$ d.Lat. Sec Tr.   Log 178 $= 2.25042$

Log Sec 84° 22$\frac{1}{2}$′ $= 1.00848$

$3.25890 =$ L Dist.

$= 1815 =$ Distance.

Great care must be taken in calculating the distance in cases (such as the example given) where the d. Lat. is very small in relation to d. Long., that is, where the Track angle is less than about 8° or 10° from due East or West. In such cases it is generally advisable to use the formula, Distance = Dep. Cosec Tr.; the departure having been found as shown in para. 28 (b). Thus, it would be better, in the above example, to find distance from the formula—

Distance

= Dep. Cosec Tr.

= d. Long. Cos Mid. Lat. Cosec Tr.

= 2060′ Cos (28° 49′ + 2′) | 2060 Log = 3·3187

Cosec 84° 22·3′ | 28° 51′ L Cos = $\overline{1}$·94245

84° 22·3′ L Cosec = ·00210

3·25842

= 1813·1′.

Note. Sailings on the Spheroid. The methods of calculating track and distance given in the last two paragraphs are all that are required both for practical and examination purposes. But it is interesting to know the correct procedure if it is desired to obtain figures more nearly applicable to the terrestrial spheroid.

Briefly *d. Lat.* must be obtained from Reduced Latitudes, *meridional parts* tables (not including that given in Burton's) should be entered with Reduced Latitudes, and *d. Long. or Departure* should be increased (see Appendix V). It must be made clear that it is quite erroneous to correct one part of the triangle only. Thus the Reduction of Latitude is quite commonly applied alone. This causes a slight distortion of angle (Tr.) and gives only a slightly more correct distance.

Incidentally, Reduced Latitude is also called Geocentric Latitude. A further point on which care is necessary is that, if two places are one on each side of the Equator, the d. Lat. should be calculated from the Equator to the Reduced Latitude of each place and the two values so obtained should then be added.

(b) Distance by Percentage d. Lat. The author suggests the following simple means of measuring distances run in the air on tracks near 360° T or 180° T. Normally, of course, distances run are simply measured by dividers or the like, and a scale provided. But if the two positions are on different map sheets or a considerable distance apart it is more convenient to measure the latitude of each and multiply the d. Lat. by a Factor, using a slide rule. This Factor is derived simply from the secant of the Track and if a straight line is followed it remains constant. If the Track is 360° T or 180° T, then the Factor is 1 and distance = d. Lat. The method is inaccurate for Tracks near East or West and is really only recommended when the Track is near North or South.

As an example of the idea: suppose that from A to B has been calculated as 164 T for 436′ when the d. Lat. between them is 419′, then the Distance Factor is 1·04 of d. Lat. (1·0403 to be exact), i.e. distance is 104 per cent of d. Lat. Then if a fix is obtained at C in latitude 34° 15′ N. and another at D in latitude 33° 05′ N., both approx. on Track, the Run between them = 1·04 d. Lat. = 1·04 × 70′ = 72·8′.

30. (a) Great-circle Method. When the shortest distance between two places is required Great-circle sailing is employed, that is, the spherical triangle is solved to find the Great-circle distance, initial and final tracks, and if required the Vertex of the Great circle (i.e. the point of its highest latitude). The Natural Haversine Formula is used to find the distance, and the Cosecant

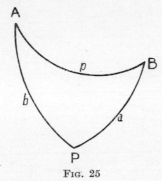

Fig. 25

(or Log Hav.) Formula to find the initial track (and/or final) required.

Example. In Fig. 25 position $A = 25° 20′$ S. 04°00′ E. and position $B = 39° 20′$ S. 116° 45′ E.; Find the Great-circle distance from A to B, and the initial track.

Now   Hav. p = Hav. $(a \sim b)$ + Sin a Sin b Hav. P
                = Hav. $(a \sim b)$ + Cos Lat. of B Cos Lat. of A
         Hav. d. Long.

d. Long. = 112° 45′	L Hav. $\bar{1}$·84096
Lat. A = 25° 20′	L Cos $\bar{1}$·95609
Lat. B = 39° 20′	L Cos $\bar{1}$·88844
	$\bar{1}$·68549 = Log
	0·48472 = antilog
$(a \sim b)$ = 14° 00′	Hav. 0·01485
	0·49957 = Nat. Hav. p.
p = 89° 57′	= 5397′ = Distance

Now   Hav. $A = [\text{Hav. } a - \text{Hav. } (b \sim p)]$ Cosec b Cosec p

$\qquad\qquad a = 50°\ 40'$ Hav. 0·18308

$\qquad\qquad b \sim p = 25°\ 17'$ Hav. 0·04790

            0·13518

         Log = $\bar{1}$·13091

$\qquad\qquad b = 64°\ 40'$ L Cosec = 0·04391

$\qquad\qquad p = 89°\ 57'$ L Cosec = 0·00000

         $\bar{1}$·17482 = L Hav. A

$\therefore$ A = Initial Track = S.45° 30$\frac{1}{3}$′ E. = 134$\frac{1}{2}$ T.

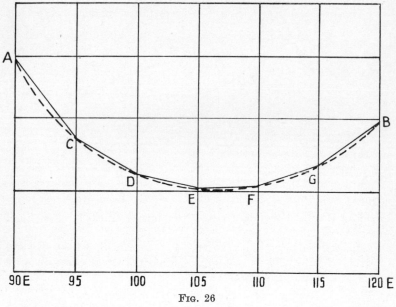

Fig. 26

Similarly, by finding B, the final track can be known. To fly a Great-circle track in practice the following is the procedure. Firstly the Great-circle distance is found as just shown. Then on a Mercator's projection (on which Rhumb lines are straight lines) the latitude at which the Great-circle track cuts the meridian of, for example, every fifth degree of longitude is marked. This is found by (a) plotting the track on a Gnomonic projection (on which Great circles are straight lines; see next chapter) and noting from it the latitude of cutting the meridians or (b) by special tables and diagrams, such as Towson's Great-circle tables, or (c) by calculation as shown in sub-para. (c). Then the points marked off on the Mercator's

projection are joined by a series of straight lines, and an approximation of the Great-circle track is made good by flying along the series
of Rhumb lines. Thus in Fig. 26 the latitude at which a Great circle
cuts each fifth meridian is marked off at C, D, E, F, and G. Then
the tracks AC, CD, DE, EF, FG, and GB are flown, the track and
distance in each case being taken from the Mercator's projection or
worked by Mercator's or Plane sailing.

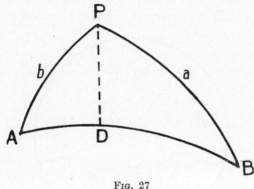

F𝚒𝚐. 27

The Great circle is shown dotted.

(b) To find the highest latitude on a Great-circle track may be
required in estimating the danger of ice formation for a particular
flight, etc. If no Gnomonic Chart or special tables are available,
it may be simply calculated, thus: It is self evident that only at the
highest point on the Great-circle track will its direction be due East
or West. Therefore a line drawn from the pole to the point of
greatest latitude will be at right angles to the track at that point:
PD in Fig. 27 forms two right angles PDA and PDB at D the point
of greatest latitude on the Great-circle track AB. Now if the
Lat. of $A = 38°\,00'$ N. then $b = $ Colatitude $= 52°\,00'$ and the
initial track A has been found to be N. $60°\,30'$ E. (i.e. $060\frac{1}{2}$ T).
Then, by Napier's Rules of circular parts in the right-angled spherical triangle ADP (the parts being as shown in Fig. 28)

$$\text{Sin } PD = \text{Cos } (90 - b) \text{ Cos } (90 - A)$$

$$90 - b = 38°\,00' \quad \text{L Cos} = \bar{1}\text{·}89653$$

$$90 - A = 29°\,30' \quad \text{L Cos} = \bar{1}\text{·}93970$$

$$\text{L Sin } PD \quad \bar{1}\text{·}83623$$

∴ $\qquad PD = 43°\,18' = $ Colatitude of Vertex.

∴ $\qquad$ Vertex $= \underline{\underline{46°\,42'\text{ N.}}}$

(c) If great accuracy is required or if no Gnomonic Chart is available, the latitude of the points at which a Great-circle track cuts the meridians can be found by the Four-part Formula, or by Napier's Rule of Circular Parts. When using the former method it is first necessary to find the Initial Track. With the other method it is first necessary to find the latitude and longitude of the Vertex of the Great-circle track.

Using the Four-part Formula, in the case shown in sub-para. (b) above (Fig. 27), it is required to find the latitude at which the

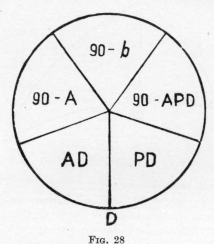

Fig. 28

Great circle, which leaves A (Lat. 38° 00′ N.) in the direction 060° 30′ T., cuts the meridians 40° 00′ E., 50° 00′ E., and 60° 00′ E., assuming that the longitude of A is 36° 50′ E.

Cos b Cos P = Cot a Sin b − Cot A Sin P.

Cos Colat. A Cos d. Long.

> = Cot Colat. of Plotting Point Sin Colat. A − Cot Init. Tr. Sin d. Long.

Sin Lat. A Cos d. Long.

> = Tan Lat. of Plotting Point Cos Lat. A − Cot. Init. Tr. Sin d. Long.

Tan Lat. of Plotting Point

$$= \frac{\text{Sin Lat. } A \text{ Cos d. Long.}}{\text{Cos Lat. } A} + \frac{\text{Cot Init. Tr. Sin d. Long.}}{\text{Cos Lat. } A}.$$

= Tan Lat. A Cos d. Long. + Cot Init. Tr. Sin d. Long. Sec Lat. A

Now the ds. Long. from A to the three meridians in question are 3° 10′, 13° 10′, and 23° 10′ respectively.

Tabulating—

For d. Long. =		3° 10′	13° 10′	23° 10′
d. Long.	L Cos =	$\bar{1}$·99934	$\bar{1}$·98843	$\bar{1}$·96349
Lat. A = 38° 00′	L Tan =	$\bar{1}$·89281	$\bar{1}$·89281	$\bar{1}$·89281
		$\bar{1}$·89215 = 0·78010	$\bar{1}$·88124 = 0·76075	$\bar{1}$·85630 = 0·71828
Init. Tr = 60° 30′	L Cot =	$\bar{1}$·75264	$\bar{1}$·75264	$\bar{1}$·75264
d. Long.	L Sin =	$\bar{2}$·74226	$\bar{1}$·35752	$\bar{1}$·59484
Lat. A = 38° 00′	L Sec =	0·10347	0·01347	0·10347
		$\bar{2}$·59837 = 0·03966	$\bar{1}$·21363 = 0·16355	$\bar{1}$·45095 = 0·28245
∴ Lat. of Plotting Point		0·81976	0·92430	1·00073
on Meridian		= 39° 20·6′ N.	= 42° 44·8′ N.	= 45° 01·3′ N.

Using the Napier's Rule method, firstly the latitude of the Vertex must be found, as shown in (b) above. Then the longitude of the Vertex is found; thus in Fig. 27 APD is the difference of longitude from the departure point of the Vertex.

And (from Figs. 27 and 28)—

$$\text{Sin } (90° - APD) = \text{Tan } PD \text{ Tan } (90° - b)$$

$$\text{Cos } APD = \text{Tan Colat. Vertex Tan Lat. of } A$$

Colat. Vertex = 43° 18′ L Tan = $\bar{1}$·97421

Lat. A = 38° 00′ L Tan = $\bar{1}$·89281

L Cos APD = $\bar{1}$·86702

$$\therefore APD = 42° 35′ = \text{d. Long.}$$

And if the longitude of A is taken as 36° 50′ E. then longitude of Vertex D = 79° 25′ E.

It is pointed out that the Vertex may not always be between the place of departure and the destination, but may lie on the continuation of the Great circle beyond one of them.

Having found the latitude and longitude of the Vertex then the plotting points are found again by Napier's Rules—

Cos d. Long. (from Vertex) = Tan Colat. of Vertex × Tan. Colat. of Plotting Point,

or

Cot Lat. of point = Sec d. Long. Cot Lat. of Vertex.

Then if it is required to find the latitude at which the Great circle cuts the meridians 40° 00′ E., 50° 00′ E., and 60° 00′ E., then the

d. Long. of these meridians from the meridian of the Vertex are 39° 25′, 29° 25′, and 19° 25′ respectively.

Tabulating the calculation	39° 25′	29° 25′	19° 25′
L Cot Lat. of Vertex 46° 42′	1̄·97421	1̄·97421	1̄·97421
L Sec d. Long.	·11207	·05995	·02543
Sum = L Cot. Lat. of point =	·08628	·03416	1̄·99964
∴ Lat. of point =	39° 20·7′ N.	42° 45′ N.	45° 01·4′N.

Similarly the latitude at which the Great-circle track passes through other meridians can be found.

A comparison of the two methods shows that for a small number of plotting points the Four-part Formula is probably very slightly shorter but when a large number of plotting points are to be calculated the Napier's Rule method is probably better. Of course, in cases where it is required to find the longitude at which a Great circle cuts a parallel of latitude, the latter method is the only one applicable.

(*Note.*—The F.A.I. method of calculating distances in a straight line is to work out the arcual Great-circle distance in a normal way. This is converted to radians and multiplied by the Earth's radius which is taken as 6,372,227 metres constant.)

(d) **A Great Circle on a Spheroid,** which the Earth really is, cannot easily be arrived at. Assuming that such a Great circle is defined as the "shortest distance" line on the surface of the spheroid, it will lie slightly to the polar side of the spherical Great circle which is normally used in practice. This results in an infinitesimally shorter distance than on the spherical distance, but in another way there is also a further definite difference between the Great circle on the Earth and the Great circle as we usually calculate it, in particular cases. It can, of course, be ignored for practical purposes, but for some purposes it may be of interest. The simplest way of finding Great-circle distances precisely on the spheroid is to calculate each Rhumb line leg, using "reduced latitudes" for northings or southings and *spheroidal* departure (see para. 25 (*g*)) for eastings or westings. The sum of the legs will, in various obvious cases, be different from the sum of the legs calculated on the sphere.

31. Composite Sailing. It may be necessary owing to meteorological conditions to limit the highest latitude to which it is safe to fly on a trip, and it may therefore be impossible to adhere to the Great-circle track. If then, it is necessary to limit the track to a latitude lower than the Vertex of the Great circle the composite sailing gives the shortest possible track within the limiting parallel of latitude.

This track consists of three parts—

(i) From the point of departure to the limiting latitude—by the arc (*AC* in Fig. 29) of the Great circle which passes through the point of departure and is tangential to the parallel of limiting latitude.

(ii) From the point where the Great circle through point of departure is tangential to the limiting parallel, to the point where the Great circle through the destination is tangential to the parallel along the parallel—(*CD* in Fig. 29).

(iii) From the point where the Great circle through the destination

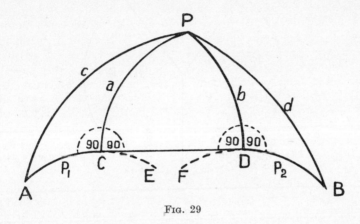

FIG. 29

is tangential to the limiting parallel, to the destination—by the arc of the said Great circle (*DB* in Fig. 29).

Thus in Fig. 29, flying from *A* to *B* with *CD* as the limiting parallel of latitude, the Composite sailing is *ACDB*. *AC* is an arc of the Great circle *AE* which is tangential to *CD* at *C*. *DB* is an arc of the Great circle *FB* which is tangential to *CD* at *D*. It must be clearly understood that *AC* and *DB* are not arcs of the Great-circle sailing from *A* to *B*.

Now as *AC* is tangential to *CD* at *C*, then *PCA* is a right angle, and similarly *PDB* is a right angle.

Then in the right-angled triangle *ACP*; $c = $ Colat. of *A*, a = Colat. of limiting parallel.

By Napier's Rules of circular parts—

(i) The angle *APC* is found = change of Long. to *C*, and from it the Long. of *C*;

(ii) The Great-circle distance p_1 is found; and if required

(iii) The initial track *A*.

Similarly in the right-angled triangle BDP, $d =$ Colat. of B, and $b =$ Colat. of limiting parallel.

Then again by Napier's Rules—

(i) The angle DPB is found—and thence the longitude of the point D;

(ii) The Great-circle distance, p_2, is found and if required

(iii) The final track B.

The Great-circle arcs AC and DB are plotted on to the map or chart to be used, by means of a Gnomonic Chart.

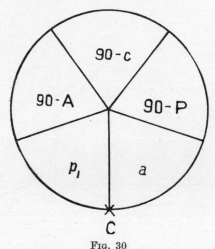

FIG. 30

Then all that remains to be done is to work out by Parallel sailing the Rhumb line distance CD (the track being 090 T).

The distance = departure = d. Long. Cos Lat. of limiting parallel.

Example. Work out the distance by composite sailing from A in position 50° 49′ N. 01° 18′ W. to B in position 51° 20′ N. 88° 22′ E. when limiting parallel is 56° 00′ N. In right angled triangle ACP (see Figs. 29 and 30)

$$\text{Sin } (90 - P) = \text{Tan } a \text{ Tan } (90 - c)$$
$$= \text{Tan } a \text{ Tan Lat. of } A$$

Colat. limiting parallel $= 34° 00′$ L Tan $= \bar{1}\cdot82899$

Lat. of $A = 50° 49′$ L Tan $= 0\cdot08879$

$\bar{1}\cdot91778 = \text{L Cos } P$

$\therefore$ $P = 34° 09\cdot2′ = 34° 09′$ approx.

and   Long. of $C = 34° 09′$ E. $- 01° 18′$ W.

$= 32° 51′$ E.

Then by Haversine Formula,

$$\text{Hav. } p = \text{Hav. } (c \sim a) + \text{Sin } c \text{ Sin } a \text{ Hav. } P$$

$$P = 34° \, 09·2' \quad \text{L Hav.} = \overline{2}·93566$$

$$90 - c = 50° \, 49' \qquad \text{L Cos} = \overline{1}·80058$$

$$90 - a = 56° \, 00' \qquad \text{L Cos} = \overline{1}·74756$$

$$\overline{2}·48380$$

$$\text{antilog} = 0·03047$$

$$a \sim c = 05° \, 11' \qquad \text{Hav.} = \underline{0·00204}$$

$$0·03251 = \text{Hav. } p$$

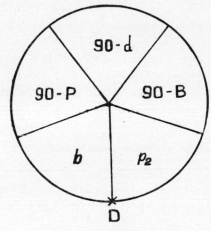

Fig. 31

$$\therefore \qquad p = 20° \, 46\tfrac{1}{2}' = 1246\tfrac{1}{2}'$$

— Great-circle distance A to C.

Then in the right-angled triangle PDB (see Figs. 29 and 31)

$$\text{Sin } (90 - P) = \text{Cos } P = \text{Tan } b \text{ Tan } (90 - d)$$

$$b = 34° \, 00' \qquad \text{L Tan } \overline{1}·82899$$

$$90 - d = 51° \, 20' \qquad \text{L Tan } \underline{0·09680}$$

$$\overline{1}·92579 = \text{L Cos } P$$

$$\therefore \qquad P = 32° \, 33'$$

and   Long. of $D = 88° \, 22'$ E. $- 32° \, 33'$

$$= 55° \, 49' \text{ E.}$$

Then by Haversine Formula

$$\text{Hav. } p_2 = \text{Hav. } (b \sim d) + \text{Sin } b \text{ Sin } d \text{ Hav. } P$$

$$90 - b = 56°00' \qquad \text{L Cos } \bar{1}\cdot74756$$
$$90 - d = 51°20' \qquad \text{L Cos } \bar{1}\cdot79573$$
$$P = 32° \, 33' \qquad \text{L Hav. } \bar{2}\cdot89509$$
$$\overline{\bar{2}\cdot43838}$$

$$\text{antilog} = 0\cdot02744$$
$$b \sim d = 4° \, 40' \qquad \text{Hav.} = \underline{0\cdot00166}$$
$$0\cdot02910 = \text{L Hav. } p_2$$

$$\therefore \qquad p_2 = 19° \, 39' = 1179'$$
$$= \text{Great-circle distance } D \text{ to } B.$$

There now remains to be found only the distance along the Rhumb line CD.

C to $D = $ d. Long. Cos Lat. $= (55°49'$ E. $- 32° \, 51'$ E.$)$ Cos 56 $= 22° \, 58'$ Cos 56 $= 1378'$ Cos 56

$$1378 \text{ Log} = 3\cdot13925$$
$$56° \, 00' \text{ L Cos} = \underline{\bar{1}\cdot74756}$$
$$2\cdot88681$$

$$\therefore \qquad \text{Distance along the parallel } CD = 771'$$

Then—

Total Distance $A - B =$ Great circle $AC +$ Rhumb line CD
$\qquad\qquad\qquad + $ Great circle DB.
$$= (1246\tfrac{1}{2} + 771 + 1179)$$
$$= 3196\tfrac{1}{2}'.$$

CHAPTER II

1. (**a**) The only way of reproducing a true undistorted picture of the Earth's surface is to do so on the surface of a figure similar to the Earth—that is, on a sphere (or to be more exact, a spheroid) or part of a sphere. To obtain the necessary detail such a figure would have to be made to dimensions far in excess of practical usable limits. Therefore for practical use the Earth's surface is represented on plane sheets in the form of maps, plans, and charts.

It must be clearly understood that no flat map can represent part of the Earth exactly in every particular. At least one characteristic will be shown inaccurately.

(**b**) A " **projection** " is a method of representing the Earth's surface on a plane. This name is in some cases misleading, for only a few methods are true geometric projections, the remainder being modifications of geometric projections or having no geometric basis at all. Therefore, the term Projection does not retain its strictly geometric meaning when used in connexion with map-making. The **scale** of a projection is the ratio of a given distance on the map to the actual distance which it represents on the Earth—expressed either as a fraction (then called Natural scale) or as the distance on the map which represents a certain actual distance on the Earth.

(**c**) The properties which a projection may or may not possess can include either (i) Equal Area or (ii) Orthomorphism (correct shape), but not both. A projection is **Equal Area** when, although its linear scale may vary, the area of *any* part of it bears a constant ratio with the area which it represents on the Earth's surface. Thus, for example, if the scale of longitude increases towards the top of the map then the scale of latitude must decrease in proportion in that part to maintain the equal area. A projection is **Orthomorphic** when the shape of a particular area on the map indicates truly the shape of the area which it represents on the Earth's surface. It is obtained by making the latitude and longitude scale the same (or varying at the same rate). Thus in an orthomorphic projection, direction is represented correctly.

(**d**) The first aim in cartography (map-making) is to construct a system of lines on a plane surface representing accurately, in as many particulars as possible, the meridians of longitude and parallel of latitude of the sphere. The method employed is, as already stated, the projection. Then the system of lines so constructed is called the

"Graticule." This Graticule must, of course, be distorted, but it can be so arranged that certain desired properties are preserved. Then details of actual ground features are plotted into the Graticule in accordance with their positions of Lat. and Long.

(e) Projections may be grouped under four main headings.

(i) Graticules constructed mathematically, etc., and not based on any geometric projection.

(ii) Projections on to a Cone—and their modifications (the cone being opened out and laid flat without distortion).

(iii) Projections on to a cylinder about the sphere—and their modifications (the cylinder being opened out and laid flat without distortion).

(iv) Projections on to the Tangential plane—and their modifications.

Under these four headings are grouped the thirteen projections dealt with in this chapter. Thus—

(i) Cassini's.

(ii) Simple Conic; Conic with two standard parallels; Conic Orthomorphic (Lambert's 2nd); Polyconic; International Modified Polyconic; Bonne's.

(iii) Mercator's; Gauss Conformal.

(iv) Gnomonic; Stereographic; Orthographic; Zenithal Equidistant.

These four groups are usually named "Constructed Graticules." "Conical projections," "Cylindrical projections," and "Azimuthal" or "Zenithal" projections respectively.

(f) The **Ellipticity** or "compression" of the Earth makes its representation on to a flat surface more complicated, due to the varying radii of curvature at different latitudes. In this chapter all projections are treated as if representing part or the whole of a true sphere. But it must be remembered that for accurate survey work the effect of ellipticity must be allowed for. Tables giving various functions of the Earth's radius, etc., and also the required formulæ for making this allowance, are available.

Of course, in maps not requiring accuracy such as small scale atlas maps, and in projections such as the gnomonic, this effect of ellipticity is neglected.

2. CASSINI'S PROJECTION.

(a) The **Principle** of Construction of this projection is based on a system of rectangular co-ordinates (see para. 12 of Chapter I). A Point of Origin O in Fig. 32 is taken on a central meridian passing through the area to be mapped. Then a given position is expressed in x and y co-ordinates (i.e. "Eastings" and "Northings" respectively) as follows—x Co-ordinate (Easting)

= the distance of the given position from the central meridian, measured along the Great circle through the position which cuts the central meridian at right angles, = distance AB in Fig. 32 where B is the given position; y Co-ordinate (Northing) = the distance along the central meridian between the Point of Origin and the point where the Great circle which is perpendicular to the central

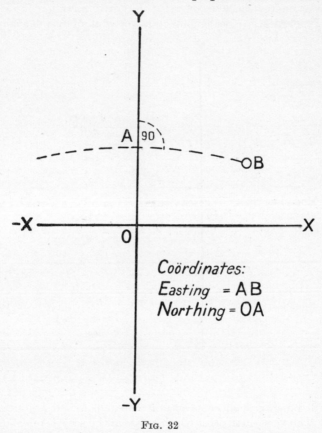

Coördinates:
Easting = AB
Northing = OA

FIG. 32

meridian and passes through the given position, cuts the central meridian = distance OA in Fig. 32.

Then these two values for x and y are plotted on the plane map sheet for the given position. Thus in Fig. 33, OC = the Great circle distance AB of Fig. 32 and $CB = OA$ of Fig. 32. It is clearly seen by studying Fig. 32 that the distance OA is not truly the difference of latitude between O and the position B. This error in "Northing" obviously becomes greater as the difference of longitude between the central meridian and the given position is increased. Because of this Cassini's projection cannot be satisfactorily used for areas of big difference of longitude.

(b) **Recognition** of the Graticule. (i) Parallels of latitude appear on a Cassini's projection as curves concave towards the Pole.

(ii) Meridians, except the central meridian which is straight, appear as curves concave towards the central meridian.

(c) **Properties.** (i) Scale is taken as *constant* all over the map and

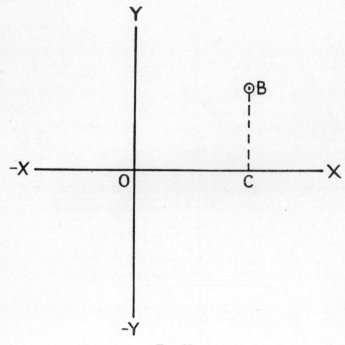

Fig. 33

when d. Long. is small, it is accurate enough for all practical purposes. The very small error which exists in the scale is only effective North and South. The scale gives correct Great-circle distances when measuring East or West.

(ii) Direction on the map is, on account of the slight scale error in one direction, slightly distorted. But this is negligible in practice and the projection may be used as if *orthomorphic*.

(iii) Straight lines on a Cassini's projection may in practice, on maps of small d. Long., be considered as Great circles; but to be strictly accurate, a straight line drawn East and West represents a Great circle but deviates from it in other directions, the maximum deviation being North and South (where, obviously, the straight line represents a curve convex towards the central meridian).

(d) Uses. The Cassini is suitable for mapping of areas of small d. Long. It is the projection used in the old Ordnance survey "$\frac{1}{4}$ inch to the mile" and "$\frac{1}{2}$ inch to the mile" and "1 inch to the mile" of England and Wales, etc.

3. THE SIMPLE CONIC PROJECTION.

(a) The **principle** of construction of this projection is as follows—A cone is tangential to the sphere around a given parallel of latitude. This is called the Standard Parallel. In Fig. 34, a cone with its Vertex over the elevated pole (i.e. on the Earth's axis produced) is tangential to the Earth at the parallel of latitude at L. Now latitude of L = $EOL = \theta$; and by simple geometry it is obvious that $QLO = \theta$, and $QVL = \theta$, Now if $EO =$ Earth's Radius $= R = LO$ then $LQ = LO$ Cos $\theta = R$ Cos θ and $VL = LO$ Cot $\theta = R$ Cot θ. Then the construction is carried out thus: (i) Draw a straight central meridian and mark the Vertex V (see Fig. 35).

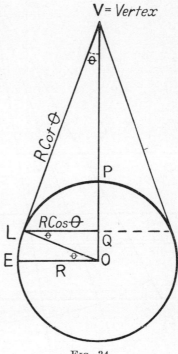

(ii) Then with radius $= R$ Cot θ × Natural scale (where $R =$ actual Earth's radius $=$ between 20,925,871 ft. and 20,855,721 ft.) describe an arc of a circle representing the Standard Parallel.

Fig. 34

(iii) Now the total length of the Standard Parallel $= 2\pi LQ$ (see Fig. 34) $= 2\pi R$ Cos θ. Reducing this to the d. Long. required and multiplying by the Natural Scale, the various d. Longs. are then marked off along the Standard Parallel (at a, b, c, e, f, and g in Fig. 35). These graduations are joined to the Vertex giving straight meridians converging to the Vertex.

(iv) Along the central meridian various d. Lats. are marked off to scale from the Standard Parallel (at h, i, j, and k in Fig. 35) and through each resulting graduation an arc with centre at Vertex is described.

(v) On to this Graticule the physical features are then plotted. The extreme simplicity of the practical construction of this projection is probably its greatest advantage.

(b) **Recognition** of the Graticule. It is obvious from the construction that—

(i) Parallels of latitude on a Simple Conic projection appear as

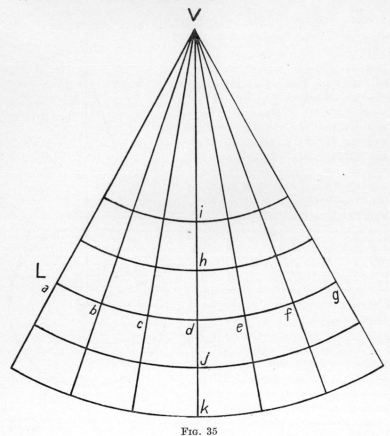

FIG. 35

arcs of concentric circles spaced evenly to scale, and concave towards the pole.

(ii) Meridians appear as straight lines converging towards the Vertex. Now the **Convergency** of the Meridians is the angle between the direction of two meridians of a given difference of longitude. In a Simple Conic projection the projected Convergency is constant for any two adjacent meridians on the map. It is obvious from inspection of Figs. 34 and 35 that Convergency (in Radians), as represented on a simple conic,

$$= \frac{\text{Length of d. Long. measured on Standard Parallel}}{R \cot \theta}.$$

(*Note.*—The symbol ε (Epsilon) = Convergency.)
(*Note.*—Natural Convergency of meridians on a sphere
$$= \text{d. Long.} \times \text{Sin Lat.)}$$

and Convergency on Conic Projection = d. Long. × Sin Standard Lat.

(c) **Properties.** (i) Scale is correct along all meridians (i.e. in directions 360 T and 180 T) and along the Standard Parallel but is incorrect otherwise. Greatest scale error is along parallels furthest from the Standard Parallel. From this it is clear that the Simple Conic projection is good for areas of small d. Lat. only.

(ii) Direction is correct North and South but it is in error otherwise—maximum error being in areas furthest from the Standard Parallel. Thus the projection is *not* Orthomorphic, but in the uses to which it is put, this is not a great disadvantage.

(iii) Straight lines on a simple Conic are very nearly Great circles—this depending on the latitude of the Standard Parallel, etc.

(d) **Uses.** The Simple Conic is often used in atlas maps. It is best suited for areas of small d. Lat., and it is unsuitable for high latitudes.

4. CONIC PROJECTION WITH TWO STANDARD PARALLELS.

(a) In this projection the **principle** of Construction is similar to the Simple Conic, but differs in that the cone is not tangential to the sphere but cuts it through two parallels of latitude (at A and B in Fig. 36). The construction is as follows: (i) Draw the straight central meridian.

(ii) Then the distance of one of the Standard Parallels from the Vertex $(= r_1)$ is deduced thus: In Fig. 37 AA_1 is parallel of latitude θ_1, and BB_1 is the parallel of the latitude θ_2.

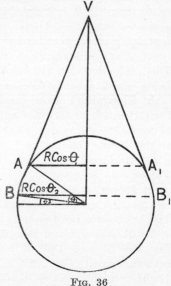

FIG. 36

Then, if $V = \text{Vertex}, VA = r_1, \text{ and } VB = r_2$

Now
$$\frac{VA}{VB} = \frac{AA_1}{BB_1} = \frac{\text{d. Long. Cos } \theta_1}{\text{d. Long. Cos } \theta_2} = \frac{\text{Cos } \theta_1}{\text{Cos } \theta_2}$$

Hence
$$\frac{VA}{VA - VB} = \frac{\text{Cos } \theta_1}{\text{Cos } \theta_1 - \text{Cos } \theta_2}$$

[This step will be clear if the algebraic axiom is remembered that

if $\dfrac{a}{b} = \dfrac{x}{y}$ then $\dfrac{a-b}{b} = \dfrac{x-y}{y}$, or $\dfrac{a}{a-b} = \dfrac{x}{x-y}$, etc.]

$$\therefore \qquad VA = r_1 = (VA - VB)\frac{\text{Cos } \theta_1}{\text{Cos } \theta_1 - \text{Cos } \theta_2}$$

Now $(VA - VB) = $ d. Lat. in arc $= $ Radius $\times$ d. Lat. in Radians.

$$\therefore \qquad VA = R(\theta_1 - \theta_2 \text{ in Radians})\frac{\text{Cos } \theta_1}{\text{Cos } \theta_1 - \text{Cos } \theta_2}.$$

Then with centre on central meridian and radius $= r_1$ to scale the arc AA_1 is drawn; and with same centre and radius $= r_1 +$ d. Lat. of A and B to scale, the arc BB_1 is drawn.

(iii) Then along AA_1 the graduations for the various meridians are marked off (at $a, b, c, d, e, f,$ and g in Fig. 37) as in the Simple Conic projection, and through these graduations straight lines representing the meridians are drawn from the Vertex.

(iv) Along the central meridian the various latitudes are marked off to scale (at $h, i, j,$ and l in Fig. 37), and with centre on Vertex arcs are drawn through the resultant graduations to represent the remaining parallels of latitude.

(v) On to this graticule the physical features are then plotted. This projection, like the Simple Conic, has the great advantage of being simple actually to construct.

(b) **Recognition** of the graticule. As in the Simple Conic

(i) Parallels of latitude appear as arcs of concentric circles, but of course the radius of the arc for a given latitude is slightly different to the Simple Conic.

(ii) Meridians appear as straight lines converging towards the Vertex.

(c) **Properties.** (i) Scale is practically correct along all meridians and along the two Standard Parallels, but is incorrect elsewhere. The scale error is, of course, less than in the Simple Conic.

(ii) Measurement of Direction on this projection is accurate only for 360 T and 180 T but is in error otherwise. It is not orthomorphic.

(iii) Straight lines on this projection are nearly Great circles.

(d) **Uses.** The Conic with two Standard Parallels has uses similar to the Simple Conic, but of course is more accurate.

5. CONICAL ORTHOMORPHIC PROJECTION WITH TWO STANDARD PARALLELS. (Lambert 2nd projection.) (a) The

principle of construction is similar to the Conic with two Standard Parallels described in the last paragraph in so far as the straight central meridian is drawn and with Vertex on it one Standard Parallel is drawn with radius of curvature, r_1, as in para. 4. Similarly also the graduations for longitude are marked off to scale

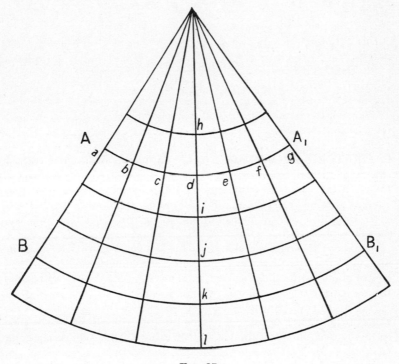

FIG. 37

along the two Standard Parallels and the meridians are drawn through these graduations as straight lines to the Vertex. But the spacing of the parallels along the central meridian are not equidistant and simply to scale as in the Simple Conic with two Standard Parallels. Instead the latitude graduation along the central meridian is modified by a factor equal to the scale error along the adjacent parallel (i.e. the longitude scale error at that latitude). Thus the scale error is in the same proportion for both latitude and longitude scales and therefore the map is orthomorphic.

(b) **Recognition** of the graticule: (i) parallels of latitude appear as arcs of concentric circles, concave towards the pole—spaced not quite evenly along the central meridian.

(ii) Meridians appear as straight lines converging towards the pole.

(c) **Properties.** (i) Scale is approximately correct along the two Standard Parallels, but in both directions it is reduced slightly between the Standard Parallels and increased slightly outside them. Scale may, however, for small distances be taken as constant and accurate enough for practical purposes.

(ii) This projection is approximately orthomorphic.

(iii) Straight lines on this projection represent Great circles very nearly.

(d) **Uses.** This projection has been used for maps of the U.S.A., Northern Canada, India, etc. In the U.S.A. where it is called Lambert's Conformal Conic it is used in various scales (sectional 1 : 500,000, Regional 1 : 1,000,000 and Distance Scaling 1 : 5,000,000) for aeronautical use.

6. POLYCONIC PROJECTION. (a) The **principle** of construction of this projection is based on the idea that a number of cones having their Vertices on the same line are tangential to the sphere at various parallels of latitude. The actual construction is as follows:

(i) Draw the central meridian and along it mark off to scale the parallels of latitude.

(ii) Then for each parallel find the radius of curvature ($r = R \operatorname{Cot} \theta$) and measure this distance along the central meridian to find the centre of curvature, i.e. the Vertex. Then describe the arc representing the parallel.

(iii) Along each parallel d. Long. to scale is marked off and graduations of the same longitude are joined to give curved meridians concave towards the straight central meridians, thus completing the Graticule. In Fig. 38 a large d. Lat. is shown to emphasize the curvature of the meridians and the difference in curvature of the parallels. The curves of the meridians make the practical construction a little difficult.

(b) **Recognition** of the Graticule. (i) Parallels appear on a polyconic projection as arcs of circles evenly spaced (to scale) along the central meridian, but they are *not* concentric.

(ii) The meridians are curves concave towards the straight central meridian. (*Note.*—In large scale maps where it is difficult to see whether the parallels are concentric arcs or not, this projection is hard to distinguish from a Bonne's projection.)

(c) **Properties.** (i) Scale is correct along all (standard) parallels and the central meridian, but not otherwise.

(ii) It is not orthomorphic, but for small areas may be taken as such.

(iii) Near the central meridian straight lines are approximately Great circles, but obviously (as meridians are curves) this is not so at any distance from the centre.

(iv) It is a close approximation to "Equal Area."

(d) **Uses.** The Polyconic is used for countries such as U.S.A. and Canada.

7. INTERNATIONAL MODIFIED POLYCONIC PROJECTION. (a)

This projection is a modification of the polyconic, arranged to distribute unavoidable errors evenly over a map. An International scheme lays down that maps of the scale 1 : 1,000,000 shall be produced for all land areas. Up to latitude 60° N. and S. each sheet covers 4 degrees of latitude and 6 degrees of longitude. In latitudes higher

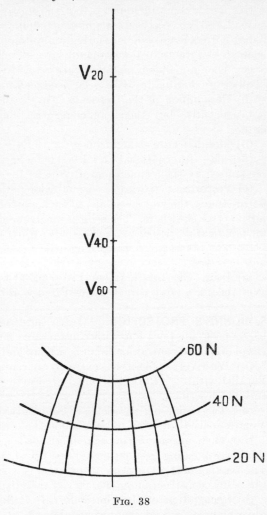

FIG. 38

than 60° each sheet covers 4° latitude by 12° longitude.

(i) The construction is based on the polyconic in that the top and bottom parallels in each map sheet are drawn as the parallels in a polyconic, each having its own vertex.

(ii) Then d. Long. to scale is marked off along the top and bottom parallel.

(iii) The first difference between this projection and the polyconic is that the meridians are straight lines drawn between the longitude graduations made on the top and bottom parallel.

(iv) The second difference is that the top and bottom parallel are spaced—not correctly to scale measuring along the central meridian —but correctly to scale measuring along the meridians 2 degrees to each side of the central meridian.

(v) The remaining parallels are constructed mathematically (Tables of co-ordinates have been produced for this purpose.)

(b) **Recognition** of the Graticule. (i) Parallels are arcs of circles not concentric but their non-concentric construction is hard to detect.

(ii) Meridians are straight lines.

(iii) The International 1 : 1,000,000 Series maps are easily recognized by their dimensions.

(c) **Properties.** (i) Scale correct along the top and bottom parallels and the two meridians 2° each side of the central meridian but in error elsewhere. The error is small enough to be neglected for all practical purposes.

(ii) For practical purposes it can be taken as orthomorphic for any one sheet.

(d) **Uses.** The International 1 : 1,000,000 Series maps, are now available for a large part of the civilized world.

8. BONNE'S PROJECTION. (a) The **principle** of construction is based on Conic lines but with considerable modification. (i) As in simple Conic, a central meridian is drawn, and

(ii) With Vertex (on it) as centre an arc representing the Standard Parallel with $r = R \cot \theta$ (where $R = $ Earth's radius and $\theta = $ latitude) is described.

(iii) The remaining parallels are concentric circles with centre at Vertex spaced correctly to scale along the central meridian.

(iv) Then on each one of them longitude is marked off to scale and the corresponding graduations joined up to give curved meridians. The making of this Graticule in practice is easy except of course for the actual construction of the curved meridians.

(b) **Recognition** of the Graticule. (i) Parallels are arcs of concentric circles spaced evenly to scale.

(ii) The meridians are curves concave towards the straight central meridian.

(c) **Properties.** (i) Scale is correct along all parallels and along central meridian, but is in error on other meridians. Scale error can be neglected when the projection is used for small countries such as Scotland, but it is very considerable in small scale maps of continents such as North America. Error is greater with increase of d. Long. from central meridian.

(ii) For practical purposes this projection can be taken as if orthomorphic for areas within a few degrees of longitude of the central meridian, but in big differences of longitude the distortion towards the eastern and western edges is *very* large. An indication of this is obvious from inspection of a Bonne's projection of a wide area. It can be seen that the meridians and parallels do not cut each other at right angles near the edges.

(iii) The projection is *Equal Area*, that is, areas are represented correctly.

(d) **Uses.** For areas of small d. Long. It is used for the Ordnance Survey maps of Scotland and Ireland, and is sometimes found in atlas maps of the narrow continents such as America.

9. MERCATOR'S PROJECTION. (a) This is associated with the **principle** of projection on to a cylinder touching the Earth tangentially around the Equator—but it differs from the geometric projection. The construction is as follows—

(i) The meridians are drawn as straight parallel lines spaced equally to a given longitude scale.

(ii) Now, as the length for a given d. Long. is the same in all parts of the projection, it is obvious that scale becomes larger with increase of distance from the Equator. Therefore, to avoid distortion (that is, to preserve orthomorphism), the parallels of latitude must be spaced according to the same increasing scale. The increase in scale at a given latitude can be deduced thus: At Equator, Departure = d. Long. At Lat. θ, Departure = d. Long. × Cos Middle Lat. But scale length of d. Long. at E = scale length of d. Long. at θ, i.e. Departure at θ has been increased to be equal to Departure at E. Therefore scale at θ = scale at E × Sec Middle Lat. Then the parallel of lowest latitude is drawn as a straight line at right angles to the meridians, and along a meridian the latitude scale is marked off, increasing as just explained. This is best done in practice by using the "Meridional Parts" given in Nautical Tables. As already explained in para. 29 of Chapter I, the Meridional Parts of a given latitude are the *summation* of the varying latitude scale from the Equator to the given latitude. Or it may be expressed thus: Meridianal Parts are the minutes of longitude scale between Equator and the given latitude. Therefore in constructing the Graticule the distance between any two parallels is the difference of their Meridianal Parts × Chart Length of 1 minute of d. Long.

(iii) The parallels are drawn through the graduations so marked off, completing the Graticule and scale marked off between the parallels on the sides of the sheet. The practical construction is extremely simple.

(iv) **Example.** Construct the Graticule to Mercator's projection for the area 51° 00′ S. to 53° 00′ S. and 57° 00′ W. to 61° 00′ W., scale length of 1 degree of longitude to equal 2 inches. Draw AB (in Fig. 39) to represent the parallel of 51° 00′ S., its length being equal to 4 degrees of longitude = 8 in. Mark off the meridians at 2 in. intervals at A, C, D, E, and B, and draw them as parallel

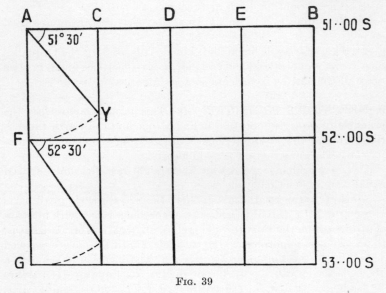

FIG. 39

straight lines at right angles to AB. Then the parallel of 52° 00′ S. is marked off at F and drawn parallel to AB. The distance AF = difference of Meridional Parts of F and A × chart length of 1 minute of longitude = $(3665 \cdot 19 - 3568 \cdot 81) \times \dfrac{2}{60} = \dfrac{96 \cdot 38 \times 2}{60} = 3 \cdot 2126$ in.

Similarly to find AG, G being the point through which the parallel of 53° 00′ S. is drawn, we have AG = d. MP of G and A × $\dfrac{2}{60}$ =

$(3763 \cdot 76 - 3568 \cdot 81)\ \dfrac{2}{60} = \dfrac{194 \cdot 95 \times 2}{60} = 6 \cdot 4983$ in.   And FG = $3 \cdot 2857$ in.

(v) Although not strictly correct, a simple graphical method gives adequate accuracy provided it is used for graduations of not more than about 2° d. Lat. It is simply based on the fact that for very small pieces of the scale d. Lat. = d. Long. scale × Sec Mid. Lat., and if d. Lat. is small enough then Mid. Lat. may be taken as Mean

Lat. The procedure is simply to draw the first parallel and to mark off the meridians to scale A, C, D, E, and B in Fig. 39, let us say at 1° intervals. Then to find the length of 1° of Lat. draw a line at an angle to the first parallel equal to the Mid. Lat. of the graduation, that is, 51° 30′ approx. in this case. This line cuts the next meridian at Y, and AY is the length of 1° of Lat. This is transferred along the meridian from A to F and the parallel is drawn through it. Similarly the next 1° of Lat. is found and so on. The method is only accurate when small values of latitude scale are found each time.

(b) **Recognition** of the Graticule. (i) Parallels are straight parallel lines, the distance between gradually increasing (as Sec. Lat.) with increase of latitude.

(ii) Meridians are straight parallel lines evenly spaced.

(c) **Properties.** (i) Scale varies but if the scale for the middle latitude of the distance required is used, then it is correct. Therefore when measuring a distance on a Mercator's projection the scale must be used of the same latitude approximately as the middle of the distance.

(ii) It is Orthomorphic. This valuable property accounts for its wide usage, together with the fact that—

(iii) A straight line represents a Rhumb line, which is of course so much used in navigation.

(iv) Area is amplified enormously towards the Poles.

(d) **Uses.** Sea charts (all Admiralty Charts except a few Gnomonic projections, and very large scale plans), navigational maps, maps of the world, etc., up to about 75° of latitude.

10. GAUSS CONFORMAL PROJECTION. This is the same method of projection as the "Transverse Mercator." It appears that it was formulated by Lambert, but that Gauss first made practical use of it in a survey of Hanover.

(a) The construction is of cylindrical type, being exactly the same in **principle** as a Mercator's but with the cylinder of projection tangential to the sphere around a meridian (and its opposite meridian) called the Central meridian. The construction is not easy to visualize, but it will be found easier if the fact is remembered that the *principle* is the same as in Mercator's.

In Fig. 40 the line AO represents the central meridian of the projection and OB the Equator, as seen on the surface of the sphere. Let Fig. 41 be the Gauss Conformal projection of the area. As the cylinder of projection is tangential along AO, it will be a straight line (ao in Fig. 41), and obviously the Equator OB will be represented by a straight line ob (remembering that the Equator in a Gauss Conformal corresponds to a meridian in a Mercator). Now the rectangular co-ordinates of x (in relation to o in Fig. 41), which represents position X on the surface of a sphere in Fig. 40 are found as follows—

(i) The "Easting" $= ax =$ the Great circle distance AX expanded (as the Lat. scale along the meridians in a Mercator) to its

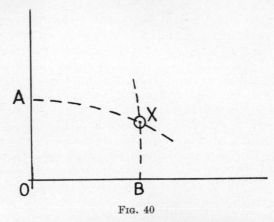

Fig. 40

"Meridional Parts," multiplied by the scale. Thus, if $AX = 600'$ $= 10°$; of which Meridional Parts $= 603·7$. Then if natural scale of projection is $\dfrac{1}{1,000,000}$, $ax = \dfrac{(603·7 \times 6080 \times 12)}{1,000,000}$ in.

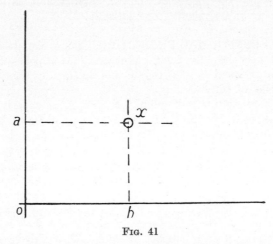

Fig. 41

(ii) The "Northing" $= bx =$ the Great circle distance XB, that is—the Lat. of X, expanded in the same proportion as was AX (i.e. to its "Meridional Parts" and multiplied by the scale used). Similarly, any other position can be plotted.

In actual use this projection is restricted to areas not more than $2\frac{1}{2}$ degrees (Great circle distance) on each side of the central meridian. The scale is then taken as constant.

(b) **Recognition** of the Graticule. (i) Parallels are represented by curves convex towards the Equator, their convexity increasing with distance from the Equator, and diverging from each other with distance from the central meridian.

(ii) Meridians are curves, cutting the parallels at right angles, and therefore concave towards the central meridian.

(c) **Properties.** (i) Scale increases with distance from the central meridian in the same way as the latitude scale in a Mercator. But if a belt of only about $2\frac{1}{2}$ degrees on each side of the central meridian is mapped, then the scale may be taken as constant for practical purposes. The maximum scale error in this case (at East and West edges) would be about 1 in 3000. ($2\frac{1}{2}° = 150'$, Meridianal Parts of $2\frac{1}{2}° = 150\cdot05$; difference $= 0\cdot05$ in $150' = 0\cdot033$ per cent $= 1$ in 3000).

(ii) It is, by construction, orthomorphic. But it must be remembered that the bearing of one place from another must be measured at the mean meridian between them, that is, at a point half-way between them.

(iii) A straight line on this projection nearly represents a Great circle when drawn East and West, but represents a curve (convex towards central meridian) when drawn North and South.

(iv) Not equal area. Area amplification becomes very large at any great distance from the central meridian.

(d) **Uses.** It is suitable for narrow countries, usually not more than $300'$ wide, in latitudes of less than 60 degrees. It has been used for maps of the China coast, Egypt, and the new Ordnance Survey maps of Great Britain.

11. GNOMONIC PROJECTION. This is an "Azimuthal" projection, i.e. on a plane tangential to the globe at one point.

(a) There are three actual constructions of this projection although the **principle** is the same in each case. The three constructions are—

(i) The "Polar gnomonic," when the point of tangency is at a pole of the Earth; and

(ii) "Equatorial gnomonic," when the point of tangency is on the Equator and

(iii) When the point of tangency is elsewhere. It must be realized at the start that the gnomonic is a true geometric projection, and as the point from which it is projected is the centre of the Earth it is truely "Zenithal." The actual construction is as follows—

(i) Case One—Polar gnomonic. A plane surface is tangential to

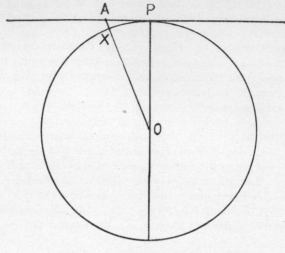

Fig. 42

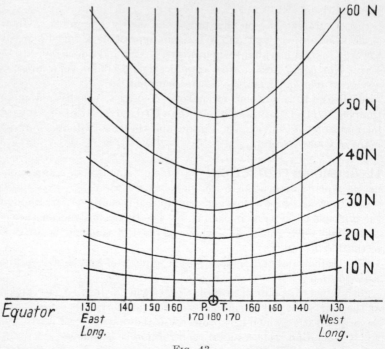

Fig. 43

the sphere at a pole. Any point on the sphere is projected on to the plane by a line passing from the centre of the sphere, through it to the plane. In Fig. 42 the point X of the sphere is represented by A on the plane. It is obvious that meridians are straight lines radiating from the pole at angles (convergency) equal to their d. Long. The parallels of latitude are drawn as concentric circles with centre Point of Tangency, P, and radius $= r = R$ Tan Colat. to scale. Thus in Fig. 42 the parallel of latitude of X is represented by a circle of

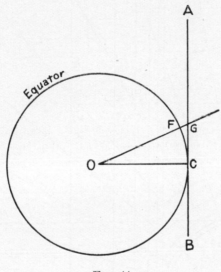

Fig. 44

radius $AP = PO$ Tan AOP to scale $= R$ Tan Colat. $\times$ natural scale.

(ii) Case Two—"Equatorial" gnomonic. The point of tangency of the plane surface is on the Equator at a given central meridian. Draw the Equator as a straight line. At right angles to it draw the straight central meridian. In Fig. 43 the Point of Tangency is on Equator at 180° E. or W. Long. Along Equator, longitude scale is marked off at distances from P.T. equal to R Tan d. Long. to scale. Through the resultant graduations straight meridians are drawn parallel to the central meridian.

On the central meridian the latitude scale is marked off at distances from Equator equal to R Tan Lat. But on the other meridians latitude scale must be marked off differently. In Fig. 44 the sphere is shown with the plane of the Equator coincident with the plane of the page. Now meridians through C and F are represented on the plane AB by straight lines at right angles to the plane of the page through the points C and G respectively. Now, in the case of the central meridian through C, the latitude scale on it = OC Tan Lat. × scale i.e. R Tan Lat. × scale. But along meridian through G the latitude scale on it = OG Tan Lat. × scale = OC Sec d. Long.

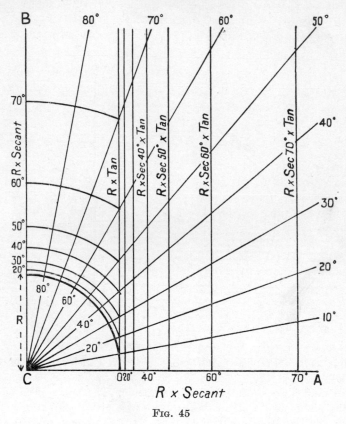

Fig. 45

× Tan Lat. × natural scale. By this formula latitude scales along all meridians are marked off and the corresponding graduations joined by curves to represent the parallels (see Fig. 43). Now in practical construction it saves time to do the whole graphically rather than by working out values using Maths. tables (for the quantities R Tan Lat., and R Sec d. Long. Tan Lat.). The procedure is as follows: From CA, in Fig. 45, BC is drawn perpendicular, and a quadrant arc of a circle is described in BCA of a radius = CO = R × natural scale (where R = earth's radius). Then around this quadrant a degree scale is marked off. From O a line NO is drawn at right angles to CA. Now lines from C through various degree graduations (say, for example, at every 10 degrees) will cut NO at distances from O equal to $R \times$ Tangent of the angle $\times$ natural scale. Then if the distances from C of the points, where the radiating lines cut NO are transferred to CA (or CB), a scale $= R$ Secant of the angles will result. Through this scale straight lines at right angles to OA are drawn (representing meridians) and along each the radiating lines cut, making a scale $= R$ Sec Tan. Now from this figure, drawn to scale, the quantities R Tan Lat., and R.Sec d. Long. Tan Lat. are taken off, and the Gnomonic projection constructed quickly and accurately.

(iii) Case Three—with point of tangency at some intermediate latitude a straight central meridian is drawn through the Point of Tangency. It is obvious from the strictly geometrical nature of the Gnomonic that direction from the Point of Tangency (only) is accurately represented. From this it can be seen that an intersection of a meridian and parallel can be plotted by measuring its Great circle bearing and its distance ($= R$ Tan Great-circle distance from P.T.) from the Point of Tangency (using Natural Haversine and Cosec formulæ). This is the general case of the Gnomonic.

(b) **Recognition** of the Graticule. Case One—"Polar" gnomonic. (i) Parallels are concentric circles about the pole, of $r = R$ Tan Colat., and (ii) Meridians are straight lines radiating from the pole, with convergency equal to their d. Long.

Case Two—"Equatorial" gnomonic. (i) Parallels are curves concave towards pole, the concavity and spacing increasing with increase of Lat. (ii) Meridians are straight parallel lines (at right angles to Equator) spaced as R Tan d. Long. (from P.T.) to scale.

Case Three—with P.T. at intermediate latitude. (i) Parallels are curves concave towards pole. (ii) Meridians are straight lines converging towards the pole. Their convergency does *not* equal their d. Long. but equals d. Long. Sin Lat. of P.T.

(c) **Properties.** (i) Scale error is very large with increase of distance from Point of Tangency. As Tan $90° =$ infinity, it is obvious that positions 90 degrees from the Point of Tangency cannot be projected, the scale error at such a distance being infinity. (*Important Note.*—Practical limit of projection of a gnomonic is about 75 degrees in all directions from the Point of Tangency.)

(ii) A gnomonic projection is *not* orthomorphic, distortion being very large except near P.T. But direction of any position measured from the Point of Tangency is truly the Great-circle bearing. It must be remembered that this is the only case of correct direction representation on a gnomonic.

(iii) *Not* Equal area.

(iv) Its only advantage is the valuable property of having Great circles represented by straight lines on it, making it invaluable for Great-circle sailings calculation. Proof of this property is fairly simple from the geometric peoperties of the projection. Obviously as the plane of a Great circle has the centre of the sphere on it and cuts any tangential plane in a straight line, a Great circle projected by lines from the centre of the sphere will appear as a straight line on the tangential plane of projection.

(d) **Uses.** For charts used to facilitate Great-circle sailings.

12. THE STEREOGRAPHIC PROJECTION. (a) This is a true geometric projection and is therefore easy to visualize. Points on the surface of the sphere are projected on to a tangential plane from

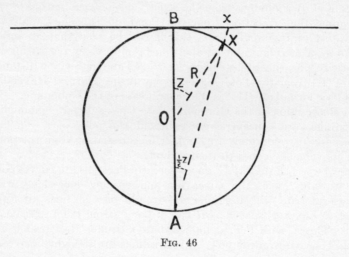

Fig. 46

a point diametrically opposite the point of tangency. As in the Gnomonic there are three cases to be considered, namely, the "Polar," with the Point of Tangency (P.T.) at a Pole, the "Equatorial" with P.T. at the Equator, and the third case (which is really the general case) with the P.T. anywhere.

In Fig. 46, B is the P.T. and A is the diametrically opposite point. X is a position on the surface of the sphere. Now, it is a geometric fact that the angle $BAX = \frac{1}{2} BOX$. Let $BOX = Z$, and $BAX = \frac{1}{2} Z$. Then, in the Polar Stereographic $Z = $ Colat., and in the general case $Z = $ Great circle distance of the position X from P.T. B.

Now

$$\frac{Bx}{BA} = \operatorname{Tan}\tfrac{1}{2} Z$$

or $$\frac{r}{2\,R} = \mathrm{Tan}\tfrac{1}{2}\,Z$$

and $$r = 2\,R\,\mathrm{Tan}\tfrac{1}{2}\,Z.$$

(i) Case One. In the Polar Stereographic, with P.T. at Pole, the meridians are first drawn as straight lines of convergency equal to their d. Long. Then with centre on pole and to radii equal to $2\,R\,\mathrm{Tan}\tfrac{1}{2}\,Z$ to scale — $2\,R\,\mathrm{Tan}\tfrac{1}{2}$ Colat. to scale, circles representing the parallels of latitudes are drawn, completing the graticule.

(ii) Case Two. In the Equatorial Stereographic, with P.T. on the Equator, the construction is more 'complicated than that described for the Equatorial Gnomonic in the last paragraph. The Equator is a straight line with the meridian through the P.T. at right angles to it. And, along the Equator and the straight central meridian longitude and latitude scales respectively are marked off at distances equal to $2\,R\,\mathrm{Tan}\tfrac{1}{2}\,Z$, where $Z =$ d. Long. and d. Lat. respectively. But the other meridians and the parallels are complex curves, and the principle of their construction is to plot positions where required meridians and parallels intersect. This is done by finding the distance and direction from the P.T. on the projection which, of course, equals $2\,R\,\mathrm{Tan}\tfrac{1}{2}\,Z$ to scale, where Z is the actual Great circle distance on the sphere of the position to be plotted from the P.T.

(iii) Case Three. In the general case the method is as just described. All positions are plotted in relation to the P.T., the direction being the Great-circle bearing, and the distance (r) from the P.T. being $2\,R\,\mathrm{Tan}\tfrac{1}{2}$ Great-circle Distance. Having the P.T. at a position not at a pole or on the Equator is most unusual in practice.

(b) **Recognition** of the Graticule. Case One—In Polar Stereographic, (i) Parallels are circles concentric about the pole, spaced as $2\,R\,\mathrm{Tan}\tfrac{1}{2}$ Colat., and (ii) Meridians are straight lines diverging from the pole at angles equal to their d. Long.

Case Two—In Equatorial Stereographic, (i) Parallels are arcs of circles, concave towards poles, of increasing curvature with increase of distance from P.T., and (ii) Meridians are curves concave towards the straight central meridian at right angles to the parallels.

Case Three—In the case of the Stereographic with its P.T. elsewhere than on a pole or the Equator: (i) Parallels are curves, and (ii) Meridians are at right angles to the parallels—concave towards the straight central meridian.

(c) **Properties.** (i) Scale is not constant, but increases with distance from the centre. For practical purposes a scale within about 6° (360′) or 8° (480′) of the P.T. may be taken as constant. (For example: 6° on the Earth = 360 nautical miles; 6° projected to scale of $= 2\ R\operatorname{Tan}\frac{1}{2}$ (6) $= 2 \times 3436\ \operatorname{Tan}3 = 360\cdot4$. The error is $0\cdot4$ in 360 miles, or measuring from one side to the other of such a map over $720'$ the error is $0\cdot8$, or about 1 in 900.)

(ii) This projection is orthomorphic (as scales increase equally). The direction of any straight line must be measured against the meridian nearest its middle point.

(iii) Not Equal area.

(d) **Uses.** For polar areas and for circular areas such as groups of islands. Also it is sometimes used to depict the world in two hemispheres. The I.C.A.N. have laid down that the Basic Aeronautical Map shall be on the Stereographic projection above 72° Lat.

13. THE ORTHOGRAPHIC PROJECTION. (a) This is another projection which is truly geometric and is on to the tangential

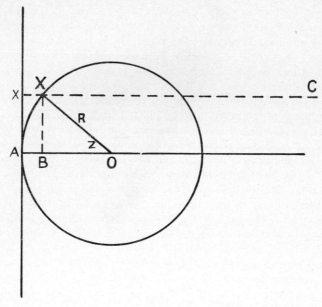

Fig. 47

plane. The point from which the projection is made is at an infinite distance in a direction at right angles to the tangential plane. Then the projecting "rays" are parallel lines. Now, in Fig. 47 CX is a line of projection, at right angles to the tangential plane, projecting X on to the plane at x. Then the distance of x from the Point of Tangency, $A = xA = r = XB = XO\operatorname{Sin}XOB = R\operatorname{Sin}Z$. In the case where the P.T. is at the pole $Z =$ Colat., and when P.T. is elsewhere Z = Great circle distance from P.T. The construction is then obvious, using $r = R \sin Z$ to scale.

(b) **Recognition** of the Graticule. In the Polar Orthographic (i) Parallels are circles concentric about the pole, spaced as R Sin Colat. or R Cos Lat.; and

(ii) Meridians are straight lines radiating from the pole at angles equal to their d. Long.

In other cases (P.T. not at pole), the graticule is similar to the Stereographic but with greater curvature, and meridians and parallels do not cut at right angles.

(c) **Properties.** (i) Scale decreases with distance from P.T., very rapidly in the extreme case of a hemisphere.

(ii) Not orthomorphic.

(iii) Not Equal area.

(d) **Uses.** The main use of the Orthographic projection is for astronomical maps. It is occasionally used for maps of polar areas.

14. THE ZENITHAL EQUIDISTANT PROJECTION. This is an "Azimuthal" projection on a plane tangential to the globe at one point. The name "Zenithal" is, however, not correct in the geometrical sense of the word. The term "Equidistant" means that distance of objects from the Point of Tangency on the map bear a constant relationship to the actual distances on the Earth. Thus in the Polar Case the parallels of latitude are equally spaced.

(a) The **principle** of construction is, of course, similar for any position of the Point of Tangency. The Polar Case is as follows: The meridians are drawn as straight lines radiating from P.T. with Convergency equal to their d. Long. Then with the P.T. as centre of curvature the parallels of latitude are drawn as concentric circles spaced evenly to scale. Thus the radius of any parallel $r = R$ (Arcual Distance in Radians from P.T.) × scale = R (Co-Lat. in radians) × scale, where R = Earth's radius.

When the P.T. is not at a pole the position of any point is plotted on the map by calculating its Great-circle distance and bearing, and plotting this distance × scale in the calculated direction from the P.T.

(b) **Recognition** of the Graticule. In the *Polar* case (i) parallels are evenly spaced concentric circles around the P.T.; (ii) meridians are straight lines radiating at angles equal to their d. Long. from the P.T.

In *other* cases (i) parallels are curves concave towards the pole; and (ii) meridians are curves concave towards the straight central meridian.

(c) **Properties.** (i) Latitude scale, i.e. along the meridians, is constant and correct to scale, but increases along the parallels with increase of distance from the Point of Tangency.

(ii) Not orthomorphic.

(iii) Not equal area.

(d) **Uses.** Occasionally used for polar maps.

15. THE I.C.A.N. MAPS. The International Committee of Air Navigation has provided that a series of "international aeronautical maps" shall comprise : a Basic map, Route maps, Local maps, and a General map. These are given in Annex F of the Convention —which should be studied.

(i) The **Basic map** is of general aeronautical interest, and is made up of twenty-four sheets. Mercator's projection, in sixteen sheets, is used up to 72° N. and S. latitude. Its scale is 1 : 10,000,000 at the Equator. Above 72° Lat. the Stereographic projection is used—of a scale such that it makes a rolling fit with the Mercators at 72° Lat. There are eight sheets of the Stereographic—four of the North polar regions, and four of the South polar regions. This makes the circumference of the 72° parallel four metres in length which is the same as the Equator's length in the Mercator.

(ii) The **Route map** intended for use in navigation over very long journeys is of very small scale, namely, 1 : 10,000,000, on a projection which might be called an Oblique True Cylindrical projection. The cylinder is tangential to the sphere along the Great circle track required. As it is a true geometric projection, distance (Great circle) at right angles to the tangential Great circle will equal R Tan actual distance × scale. Scale along the centre of the sheet is, of course, constant.

(iii) **Local maps** for general air use are the 1 : 1,000,000 International Maps of the World with slight additions (see para. 7 of this chapter).

(iv) The **General map** is on Mercator's projection of a scale of 1° Long. = 3 centimetres at the Equator. It extends up to 68° Lat. N. and S.—in 220 sheets. Up to 60 degrees of latitude each sheet covers 18° longitude by 12° latitude ; and from 60 degrees to 68 degrees each sheet covers 18° longitude by 8° latitude. In all sheets there is an overlap of 1° latitude and 2° longitude.

CHAPTER III

MAGNETISM, COMPASSES, AND AIRCRAFT INSTRUMENTS

SECTION 1

THEORY OF MAGNETISM

1. GENERAL MAGNETISM. (a) Certain materials, called **Magnetic substances** (e.g. iron, nickel and cobalt), are acted on by a force when placed near a magnet, and also by a suitable arrangement of their internal structure they themselves become magnets. Iron (steel and alloys), being by far the strongest, interests us most.

(b) The **Molecular Theory of Magnetism** states that in magnetic materials each molecule is a magnet. When the substance is not magnetized these molecules lie in a jumbled arrangement so that their magnetisms cancel out. But when the material is magnetized, the molecules are lined up in one direction (or partially so) so that their magnetisms are additive and the piece of material as a whole becomes a magnet.

There are various methods of lining-up the molecules of a piece of magnetic material and so making a magnet—the degree of success depending not only on the method but also on the nature of the material. A bar of iron becomes magnetized (or tends to be magnetized) by—

(i) Stroking it from one end to the other with one pole of a magnet;

(ii) Placing it in a magnetic field of a magnet (such as the Earth's field), the effect being made greater and more permanent by tapping it sharply (this method is of great practical importance);

(iii) Placing it in a coil of wire through which a current is passed causing a magnetic field, being assisted possibly by tapping. (*Note.*— Direction of magnetic field around a conductor with a current flowing in it is clockwise when facing the direction to which current flows; i.e. a "right-hand tractor"!)

A magnet tends to be demagnetized (by disarranging the molecules) by heating, hammering, or placing in a strong opposing magnetic field.

(c) Magnetic materials are classified under three headings—

(i) **Hard Iron**—which is hard to magnetize but is also hard to demagnetize, and therefore is the material of "Permanent" magnetism (often called Hard Iron magnetism).

(ii) **Soft Iron**—which is easy to magnetize, but which loses its

89

magnetism almost entirely as soon as the magnetizing force is with-drawn, and therefore is the material of "Temporary" or "Induced" magnetism (called Soft Iron magnetism).

(iii) **Semi-soft Iron**—which is of a medium hardness so that it is moderately difficult to magnetize but retains a considerable portion after the magnetizing force is withdrawn, and then only loses this magnetism gradually under disturbing influences. It is the worst form of magnetism affecting compasses, and is called "Sub-per-manent" magnetism.

(d) The **properties** of a magnet are: It has two different kinds ("polarities") of magnetism—one called "North," or "North-seeking" pole, and the other " South " or " South-seeking " pole. The North-seeking pole is often, in order to avoid confusion, called "Red," and the South-seeking pole "Blue." Either pole of a magnet will attract iron, nickel, or cobalt when placed near it. Two "unlike" poles (a Red and a Blue) attract each other, but two "like " poles (two Reds or two Blues) will repel one another. In a thin straight magnet, magnetized lengthwise, called a Bar-magnet, the greatest magnetic intensity is at the ends, and they may be taken as the effective positions of the poles.

(e) (i) **Unit Pole Strength** is such that if a pole is placed one centi-metre from a pole of equal strength, they will attract or repel one another with a force of one dyne (a dyne is a force which will accelerate one gramme through one centimetre per second per second).   The strength of a pole (m) is measured in Unit Poles.

The force acting between any two poles is directly proportional to the strengths of the poles and inversely proportional to the square of the distance (in cm.) between them, i.e. Force in dynes $= \dfrac{m_1\,m_2}{d^2}$.

(ii) **Intensity of Magnetization** (I) is the pole strength of a magnet per unit area of face, the face being taken at right angles to the direc-tion of magnetization. It must not be confused with Magnetic Intensity (H) (see next sub-para.).

The Intensity of magnetization will reach a maximum when all its molecules are exactly lined up giving their greatest combined magnetic effect. Nothing can then make the Intensity any greater. Such a state is called **Magnetic Saturation.**

(f) Around a magnet is a field of magnetic strain. The unit of magnetic **Field Strength** (H) or Magnetic Intensity is the field which exerts a force of one dyne on a unit pole placed in it. It is called a Gauss. It is customary to represent a magnetic field by lines (called Lines of Strength). Their direction indicates the direc-tion at any point in which a free isolated North-seeking pole would move if placed at that point, and the number of lines per sq. cm. of cross-section indicates the field strength. Obviously, field strength varies inversely as the square of the distance from the pole producing it. That is, $H = \dfrac{m}{d^2}$, where m = pole strength of the magnet producing the field and d = distance from it in cms. Actually it also varies, due to the medium in which it lies; but this will be dealt with in sub-para (i) of this para.

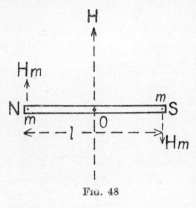

Fig. 48

(g) If a bar magnet (such as a compass needle) is placed in a magnetic field, at right angles to it, as in Fig. 48, then a turning moment will act on it tending to make it lie in the same direction as the lines of force of the field. Now if H is the magnetic field and each pole of the bar magnet is of strength m, then the turning moment of any one pole about the centre of rotation O, is $Hm\frac{1}{2}l$, and the total turning moment of the two poles = $\frac{1}{2}Hml + \frac{1}{2}Hml$ = Hml. This turning moment consists of two parts—H the field strength, and ml which is called the **Magnetic Moment** of the magnet. This Magnetic Moment (M) may therefore be defined as the moment required to hold a magnet at right angles to a field of unit strength. $M = ml$.

If the magnet is not at 90° to the direction of the field but at some other angle (see Fig. 49) then the force on each pole remains the same, but the effective length is reduced to $l\ \mathrm{Sin}\ \theta$.

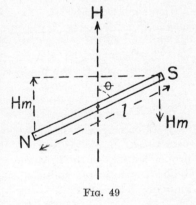

Fig. 49

Then the Magnetic Moment = $ml\ \mathrm{Sin}\ \theta$ and the turning moment = $Hml\ \mathrm{Sin}\ \theta = HM\ \mathrm{Sin}\ \theta$.

(h) If a bar magnet (such as a compass needle) is suspended by its middle point so that it is free to rotate (on a frictionless pivot, or by an untwisted silk thread), and placed in a magnetic field, it will tend to take up the direction of the lines of force. If it starts in or is deflected to a direction not coincident with the field, then it will swing to that direction and past it, and continue to oscillate to and fro. For oscillations of small amplitude the time taken to swing through a complete oscillation (i.e. from passing a point till passing the same point going in the same direction again), T, in seconds

$$= 2\ \pi\sqrt{\frac{K}{MH}},$$ assuming that there is no damping or friction.

$K =$ Moment of Inertia. $\Big($ For a square bar magnet $K =$ mass in grammes $\times \dfrac{(l^2 + b^2)}{12}$ where l is length and b is the breadth in cms. And for a circular bar magnet $K =$ mass $\times \dfrac{(l^2 + \pi r^2)}{12}\Big)$ $M =$ magnetic moment $= ml$, and $H =$ field strength.

(i) Magnetic force and intensity are not independent of the medium through which they pass. Strictly speaking the formulæ— force between two poles $= \dfrac{m_1 m_2}{d^2}$, and $H = \dfrac{m}{d^2}$ are only true in a vacuum. The effect of the medium is called the **Magnetic Permeability** (μ) of the medium. Then force $= \dfrac{m_1 m_2}{\mu d^2}$ dynes and $H = \dfrac{m}{\mu d^2}$ Gauss.

Permeability is not a constant for any given medium but varies with field strength, etc.

The magnetic materials, iron, nickel, and cobalt, are called "Ferro-magnetic" substances. μ for iron may be as high as 2000, nickel up to 300, and cobalt up to 250. A second group, called "Para-magnetic" substances, have permeabilities of just over unity, and a third group, called "Dia-magnetic" substances, have permeabilities of just under unity. Thus, for example, platinum, a para-magnetic substance, has $\mu = 1 \cdot 000017$, and bismuth, a dia-magnetic subject, has $\mu = 0 \cdot 99996$.

(j) It can be seen that when μ is large, as in ferro-magnetic substances, H is very small. But while H has been reduced in proportion to μ of the medium, something else has also taken place. Magnetism has been induced in the medium itself. The power of inducing magnetism in a medium placed in the field is called

Magnetic Induction (B), and $B = \mu H = \dfrac{\mu m}{\mu d^2} = \dfrac{m}{d^2}.$ That is, Induction is independent of the permeability but depends only on pole strength, and inversely on the square of the distance from the pole. Thus in a Ferromagnetic medium, the field H is greatly reduced but the inducing force B still remains very large, being independent of μ. Fig. 50 shows magnetic induction B in a medium plotted against various values of H, the field in which it lies. B and H are to the same scale. B rises slowly at first, then very rapidly, and then flattens out to rise very slowly. The values of μ plotted against H explain the flattening out of the $B - H$ curve.

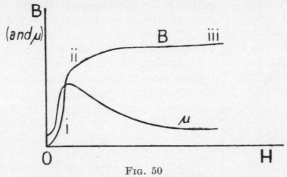

Fig. 50

Now it must be clearly understood that magnetic induction (B) is not the same as intensity of magnetization (I), but merely the

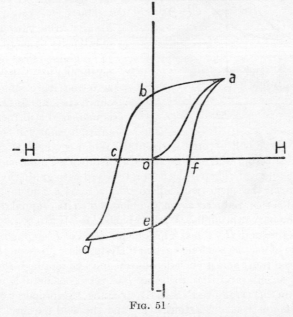

Fig. 51

power causing the magnetization. For example: Let a bar of 1 sq. cm. cross-section be placed in a field which causes it to be magnetized to 1 unit pole per sq. cm. Find B. Now 1 unit pole per sq. cm. for 1 sq. cm = 1 unit pole strength. And, at 1 cm. from unit pole, field strength is unity and there is one line of force per sq. cm. Therefore there must be 4π lines of force coming out of a unit pole (area of sphere of 1 cm. radius $= 4\pi$ sq. cm.). (*Note.*—This is Gauss's Law.) So in the bar there must have been 4π lines of force; but also there was also existing in the bar a magnetic field H. Therefore the total number of lines of force in the bar $= B = H + 4\pi$. And in the general case $B = H + 4\pi I$.

(**k**) The property by which a magnetic substance acquires magnetism when placed in a magnetic field is called its **Susceptibility** (k). The susceptibility (k) is the ratio of intensity of magnetization (I) produced to field strength (H) producing it. That is,

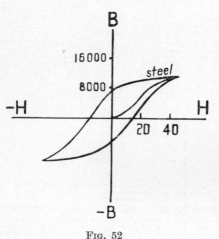

FIG. 52

$k = \dfrac{I}{H}$. Like permeability, it is not a constant, but varies in a complicated manner with the variation of field strength, etc.

The curve given in Fig. 51 gives the various values of intensity of magnetization (I) against the field (H) producing it. Starting from zero and increasing H, the curve rises along Oa. If H is increased still further saturation point will be reached and the curve will become horizontal. When the field is gradually reduced to zero, I will still be at b, the distance Ob indicating "residual" magnetism. Then if the field is reversed with gradually increasing strength the curve will fall to $I =$ zero at c, and finally to d. The field is then reduced again and changed to its original direction, taking the curve through d, e, f, and back to a. It can be seen that I values lag behind H values. This phenomenon of I lagging behind H in a cycle of magnetization is called "**Hysteresis.**" Now in the curve it is noticed that there is considerable magnetism retained, Ob (or Oe), when H is zero, and that to bring I to zero considerable opposing field Oc (or Of) is required. Strictly speaking, this property of retaining the magnetism is "**Retentivity**" and the field required to bring I to zero is the "**Coercive Force.**" Unfortunately these terms have, in some navigation textbooks, lost their most strict meaning and both mean the same, which is: The property by which a piece of magnetic material resists magnetization and demagnetization is its Retentivity or Coercive Force.

Fig. 52 illustrates the same phenomenon of hysteresis, but in this case B, the Magnetic Induction, instead of I, is plotted against H. The curve resembles the $I - H$ curve.

Obviously a certain amount of work has been done in taking the piece of material through one cycle of magnetization. This work is dissipated as heat in the material. It is proportional to the area enclosed by the $I - H$ curve.

2. EARTH'S MAGNETISM. (a) The Earth is in a magnetic field caused mainly by a magnetized core in the centre of the Earth. The poles of this magnetic core if extended cut the surface at positions called the North magnetic pole and the South magnetic pole. The North magnetic pole is at present in Hudson Bay, and the South magnetic pole is near South Victoria Land. Obviously, as the Red end (North-seeking pole) of a freely suspended magnet turns towards the North, then the Earth's core must have its Blue end towards the North. The Earth's field is strong enough to give directional properties to a free suspended magnet,

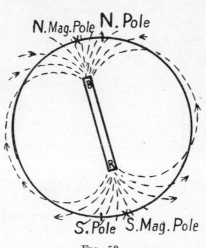

FIG. 53

but is not strong enough actually to move a magnetized body (or magnetic material) bodily.

Fig. 53 shows diagrammatically the Earth's field. The direction of the field is from South to North, but generally this direction does not coincide with the true meridians. As can be seen in Fig. 53 the direction of the lines of force are not generally parallel with the surface of the Earth. A line drawn through points on the Earth where the field is horizontal is the Magnetic Equator. To the North of this line the Red pole of a magnet tends to be drawn down, and to the south the Blue end is so affected.

The Magnetic Meridian through a place is the line lying in the direction in which a magnetic needle freely suspended to rotate in a horizontal plane under the influence of the Earth's field would lie.

(b) The **Magnetic Elements** of the Earth's field at a place are: the dip, the total field strength (T), the horizontal component of the field (H), the vertical component of the field (Z), and the variation.

(i) The **Dip** is the angle between the direction of the Earth's field and the horizontal. In Fig. 54, θ is the Dip. It is measured by means of a Dip Needle, which is a needle, balanced accurately on an almost frictionless horizontal axis in an unmagnetized state. It is then magnetized and set up so that it is free to rotate in the plane of the direction of the Earth's field (i.e. the plane of the "Magnetic Meridian"). The depression of the needle from the horizontal is read off a suitably arranged scale. Readings are taken with the needle turned over, with the needle magnetized in the opposite direction, etc., to avoid errors.

(ii) The **Total Field** (T) acts in the direction indicated by the dip needle. Actually it may be measured by timing oscillations of a dip needle (frictionless) free to rotate in the plane of the magnetic meridian, with a needle of known magnetic moment M. Then time of oscillation (for small amplitudes), t in secs., $=$

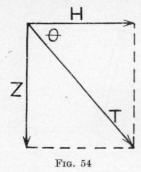

FIG. 54

$2\pi\sqrt{\dfrac{K}{MT}}$, from which T is found in Gauss.

(iii) The **Horizontal component** of the Earth's field is what its name implies and is the Directive Force of the Earth's field for compass purposes. It is marked H in Fig. 54; $H = T \cos \theta$. It is measured by timing an oscillating magnetic needle free (on a frictionless vertical pivot, or suspended by untwisted silk thread) to rotate in the horizontal plane. Then t in secs., $= 2\pi\sqrt{\dfrac{K}{MH}}$, and $H = \dfrac{4\pi^2 K}{t^2 M}$ in Gauss. On the magnetic Equator, $H = T$.

(iv) The **Vertical component** of the Earth's field is marked Z in Fig. 54; $Z = T \sin \theta$, and $\dfrac{Z}{H} = \tan \theta$. It may be measured by setting up a dip needle with its axis in the plane of the magnetic meridian. It is then free to rotate in a plane at right angles to the magnetic meridian. Of course the plane of rotation must be vertical to the Earth's surface. Then one end of the needle is drawn vertically downwards under the influence of Z only. By timing oscillations Z is found. $Z = \dfrac{4\pi^2 K}{t^2 M}$ in Gauss. $Z = T$ at the magnetic poles, and $Z = $ nil at magnetic Equator.

(v) **Variation** is the angle between the direction of the horizontal component of the Earth's field at a place and the true meridian through the place. It is named East ($+$) or West ($-$) depending on whether the North-seeking end of a compass needle, free to rotate horizontally under the influence of the Earth's field alone, lies to the East or West of the true meridian.

(c) The Earth's magnetic field undergoes considerable changes, and the magnetic elements change accordingly. These changes are: Secular, Annual, Daily, and those in Magnetic Storms. Secular change is by far the largest.

(i) **Secular change** goes through a complete cycle in about 960 years. This change is best visualized by considering the magnetic poles moving around the geographical poles in circles of about 17 degrees radius, in a clockwise or westerly direction. The circular movement of this radius causes the variation at the position of London to swing from about 24° W. to about 24° E.

(ii) **Annual change** causes the magnetic elements to vary through a small cycle once a year. It only causes a change of variation of about 2' to either side of the normal—to the eastward in summer and, to a smaller extent, to the westward in winter.

(iii) **Daily changes** are comparatively small, causing changes of variation up to a maximum of about 25' in midsummer, although usually they are less (of order of about 4' in winter). Their explanation is doubtful but they are greatest when sunspots are greatest. (*Note.*—Sunspots have an eleven years' cycle.)

(iv) **Magnetic storms** are very sudden magnetic disturbances which seem to be associated with the sudden appearance of a large sunspot, and with the auroræ. They do not cause any appreciable deflection of a compass needle.

(d) Apart from the changes described above, the Earth's field is irregular in many places. Some of these irregularities are inexplicable, but others are definitely caused by large deposits of natural magnetized material (loadstone) near the surface. There are many examples of this in various parts of the world, occurring most often in islands, and sometimes in mountains.

(e) **Maps** are specially produced to show the magnetic elements, and, of course, ordinary maps for navigational purposes always give the magnetic variation.

(i) **Isogonic** maps depict the magnetic variation, by means of Isogonals, which are lines drawn through places of equal variation. A line drawn through places of no variation (i.e. where magnetic and true meridians coincide) is called an Agonic line. There are two such lines on the Earth (see map marked Fig. 55).

(ii) **Isoclinic** maps depict magnetic dip of the Earth's field by means of Isoclinals, which are lines joining places of equal dip. The Isoclinal which runs round the Earth through places of no dip is the magnetic Equator (see map marked Fig. 56).

Chart 1.

LINES OF EQUAL MAGNETIC VARIATION 1932.

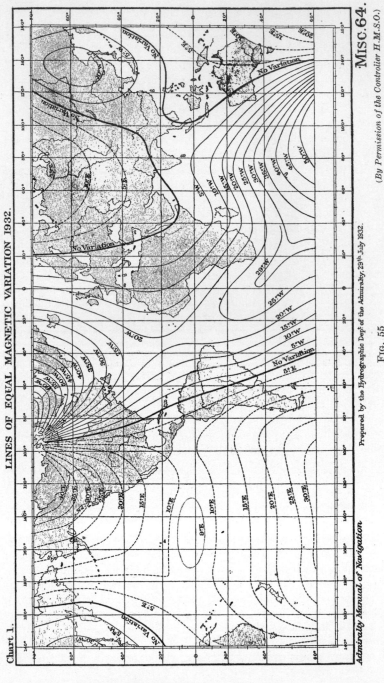

MISC. 64.

(By Permission of the Controller H.M.S.O.)

Prepared by the Hydrographic Dep.ᵗ of the Admiralty, 29ᵗʰ July 1932.

FIG. 55

Admiralty Manual of Navigation

Chart. II.

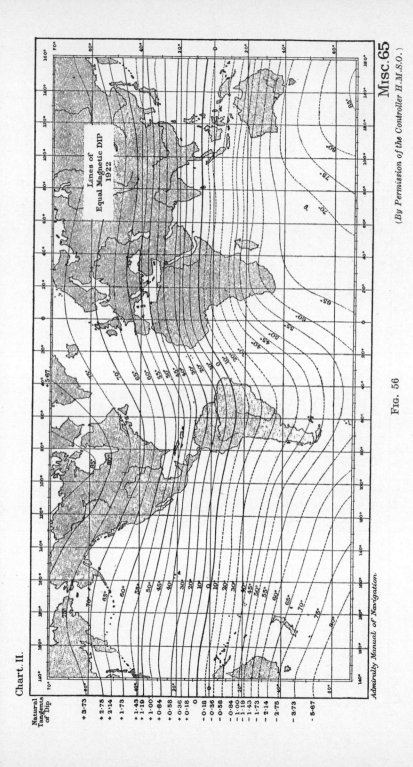

Natural Tangents
of Dip

Lines of
Equal Magnetic DIP
1922

MISC. 65

(By Permission of the Controller H.M.S.O.)

FIG. 56

Admiralty Manual of Navigation.

Chart III.

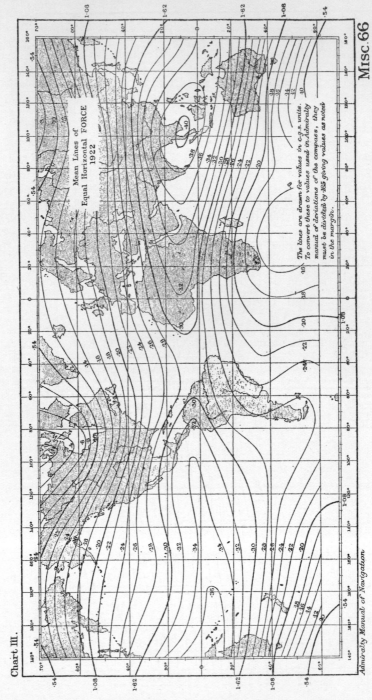

Mean Lines of
Equal Horizontal FORCE
1922

The lines are drawn for values in c.g.s. units.
To convert these to values used in Admiralty
manual or deviations of the compass, they
must be divided by 185 giving values as noted
in the margin.

MISC. 66

(By Permission of the Controller H.M.S.O.)

FIG. 57

Admiralty Manual of Navigation

(iii) **Isodynamic** maps depict the strength of the horizontal component (H) of the Earth's field (i.e. the Directive Force), by means of Isodynamic lines which run through places of equal strength of the horizontal component H. The c.g.s. units (Gauss) are usually used and they are converted to the units of the British Admiralty by dividing by 0·185 (see map marked Fig. 57).

(iv) Maps depicting the values of the vertical component (Z) of the Earth's field do so by lines running through places of equal strength of the vertical component.

(v) Similarly, maps showing the value of the total field strength (T) do so by lines running through places of equal total field strength. The points of greatest T do not correspond to the magnetic poles. There are four peaks or points of greatest field strength, two in the northern hemisphere and two in the southern hemisphere. They are called Magnetic Foci of the Earth's field.

(vi) Maps showing annual change of variation are also available.

SECTION 2

MAGNETIC COMPASSES

3. COMPASS DESIGN. Aircraft compasses operate under very adverse conditions, including vibration, cold, quick-turns, large accelerations, changes of attitude, etc.

(a) **The Magnet System and Aperiodicity.** (i) The use of a small float to reduce the effective weight of the system is impracticable in aircraft compasses, therefore the weight of the system is kept as small as possible. In modern practice this is about 3 grammes in air, ($\frac{1}{10}$ ounce), and sometimes slightly less. The effective weight is reduced by the buoyancy effect of being submerged in the compass liquid. Small weight is necessary to keep pivot friction small, and, depending on how it is disposed, to keep the moment of inertia small. Obviously if the moment of inertia (K) is large the system will be slow to start moving and slow to stop moving.

(ii) In order to make a compass which will respond quickly to the influence of a comparatively weak Directive Force a large magnetic moment (M) is necessary. This is usually of the order of 50 to 60 c.g.s. units. (*Note.*—British aircraft compasses must comply with the requirement that—

$$\frac{\text{Magnetic moment in c.g.s. units}}{\text{Wt. in grammes of system in the compass liquid}}$$

shall not be less than 10.) The magnet system is usually composed of 2, or 4 small parallel magnets.

(iii) To keep pivot friction to a minimum the system is suspended from a jewel cap, usually of sapphire, which bears on the pointed top of a pivot which is made of agate or hardened metal (e.g. iridium). (*Note*.—In British aircraft compasses the dimensions of the jewel and pivot and the position of the magnets must be such that the system is still free to revolve when the compass is tilted to an attitude 15° from level.)

(iv) To allow for the effect of the vertical component Z, the system is not weighted on one end as was the old practice, but is suspended by a point well above the centre of gravity of the system. (In British aircraft compasses the magnet system must be so suspended that the tilt will not be more than 3° between lats. 60° N. and 60° S. This means that in England the North-seeking end will be down by an angle of not more than 2°.) Old compasses may still be found which are partially weighted on one pole to counteract the effect of dip.

(v) In accordance with (i), (ii) and (iii) above, the small moment of inertia (K), the large magnetic moment (M), and the small pivot friction all tend to give a highly active and responsive magnet system, but alone it would be extremely unsteady in the air. There-fore, damping filaments are attached to the system. These are usually of very small gauge German silver wire, of unstreamlined section so as to offer resistance when rotated through the compass liquid. Usually two of these filaments (180° apart) lie parallel to the line of the magnets, and the northerly one is marked with a letter N. Sometimes in older compasses S., E., and W. are also marked on wires in their own directions. To avoid swirls in the liquid the filaments are not extended too closely to the sides of the compass bowl. The effect of these damping filaments is to retard too rapid movements and to stop the system oscillating to and fro. Of course they must not be so effective that they make the system sluggish in action. The damping factor C is large in British aircraft com-passes, but in Continental compasses it is generally very much smaller.

(vi) A fully "Aperiodic" compass is strictly one in which there is no oscillation, i.e. where the time of oscillation is infinity. Now, time

of oscillation $= 2\,\pi\sqrt{\dfrac{K}{HM - C^2}}$. To make this as large as possible C must be made big in relation to HM.

(vii) In addition to the requirements already mentioned, British aircraft compasses, when new, must comply with the following: The magnet system must not have a directional error of more than 1°. If deflected 10° and released it must return to within 1° of the former reading (light tapping allowed). If deflected 90° and released, the time to rotate through 85° must be more than 6 seconds. If deflected

30° and released the overswing past the former reading must be less than 4°. Also swirl tests are carried out, thus : The compass bowl is rotated through 180° in 30 seconds. Then the resultant deflection must not exceed 10°, and the system must return to within 5° in less than 20 seconds. When the rotation is twice as fast, the deflection must be less than 20° and time to return to within 5° less than 30 seconds.

(b) **The Compass Liquid.** (i) The requirements for liquid in a compass are : that it is of such a specific gravity that it reduces the effective weight of the magnet system considerably; that it is of a consistency giving suitable degree of damping; that it is transparent ; that it does not freeze at temperatures of − 35° C. or above ; etc. The liquid generally used which fulfils these requirements is an alcohol of Specific Gravity of about 0·81—varying slightly with different makes of compass.

(ii) The liquid completely fills the compass bowl so that there are no bubbles, and before being used in a compass has all air driven from it. The test for de-aeration is that the liquid will remain free from bubbles when subject to a reduced pressure equal to 9 in. of mercury.

(iii) Expansion of the liquid is taken up by an expansion chamber connected to the bowl. This chamber consists usually of flexible diaphragms. Expansion due to a temperature range of from − 25° C. to 50° C. is allowed for.

(c) **Vibration** is usually absorbed by sponge rubber interposed between the compass bowl and the outer container which is attached to the aircraft. The vibration test for new British compasses is that there must be no deflection of the magnet system when vibrations of amplitudes of less than 0·2 mm. and frequencies from zero to 2000 per minute are applied to the outer container.

(d) Other considerations which effect aircraft compasses are—

(i) Being an aircraft part it must be kept as light as is practicable. Most steering compasses weigh between 4 lb. and 6 lb., and bearing compasses go up to about 9 lb.

(ii) The reading of the compass must be clear and simple and the paint inside the bowl must not dissolve and so discolour the liquid, as this would make reading more difficult in poor light.

(iii) Arrangements for correcting compass errors must be provided.

4. TYPES OF MAGNETIC COMPASS. (a) Steering compasses may

usually be divided into three groups depending on the way they are read.

(i) **Parallel grid** reading compasses are the commonest in use.   In this type a rotatable grid ring is fitted on top of the bowl. A scale of 360° calibrated for every 2 degrees is marked around it, reading against a lubber-line on the bowl, which indicates the fore and aft line of the aircraft. Across the grid ring two (or four) parallel wires are set —in the direction of North and South of the scale. Then, to steer a given course, it is set on the scale against the lubber-line and locked (by a suitable arm provided) and the N. and S. wire of the magnet system is brought parallel to the grid wires by turning the aircraft.

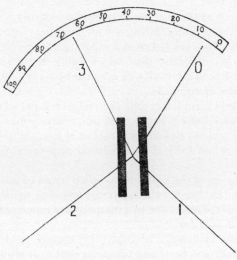

Fig. 58

(ii) **Direct reading** of a card attached to the magnet system has gone out of favour because of the disadvantages attaching to a comparatively heavy card. The well-known form of this type has a spherical glass in the rear of the bowl, with a lubber-line in its centre. Against this line is read the scale which is marked in reverse (as lubber-line is in rear of compass) on a vertical card attached (like the rim of a wheel) to the magnet system.

(iii) **Centesimal** reading compasses (incorrectly so-called) are really a form of direct-reading compass, but have the advantage of having no heavy card on the magnet system. Actually it is nowadays used mainly in bearing compasses so that they may be used for steering or checking steering, and in such compass a card for bearings is carried on the magnet system. In the centesimal system four damping filaments carry the figures 0, 1, 2, and 3. The "0" and "1" filaments are 100 degrees apart, as also are the "1" and "2," and "2" and "3," leaving the "3" and "0" 60 degrees apart. These filaments are then pointers which move near a scale of 100 degrees, in the forward part of the bowl. In Fig. 58 the "0" filament is shown against 5° on the fixed scale, giving a heading of 005° C.

(b) **Bearing compasses** (or Observer type) are of two types: the Standard type, that is, with a proper mounting, and the Hand-held type.

(i) The standard type has a rotatable verge ring which carries on it the prism and sighting device used for taking bearing. Immediately below the prism an ordinary compass card is attached to the magnet system, its centre being cut out for lightness. The card is graduated normally, but the figures on it are printed in reverse so that their reflected images in the prism are correct. The sighting device, which is adjustable, consists of open-sights. The rear sight is on the prism. It incorporates a dark mirror and two shades for taking bearings of the sun (for checking deviation). A lubber-line is provided in the forward part of the bowl, so that the prism may be locked directly over it and the sighting device used to line up the compass with the fore and aft line of the aircraft. In a prevalent type of bearing compass, a centesimal scale (as described in (a) (iii) above) is provided so that the compass can be used for steering or checking course as well. The compass is usually clamped on to its standard with a thumb screw and can be removed when not in use.

(ii) The hand-bearing compass is very small. It has a prism and sight fixed to the bowl which is rotated as required, and bearings are read off a card attached to the magnet system as in the standard type. A handle is fitted below the bowl for holding it. No vibrational device is incorporated. It is very convenient to use, but large errors will occur unless used very carefully. In any case there is no provision possible for the correction of deviation.

(c) **Night use** of compasses. (i) In steering compasses luminous paint is usually used on the N. and S. damping filaments (which are then of sealed glass tube) of the magnet system, and on the cardinal points of the scale, the lubber-line, etc., so that steering is possible in the dark. Electric light is also provided.

(ii) On standard type bearing compasses external lights are fitted to light up the scale and the open sights.

(iii) In the hand-held type a light from a battery and bulb inside the handle lights up the bowl through a ground glass bottom.

5. INSTALLATION OF COMPASSES. (a) (i) The position in which a compass is installed is very important. It must be kept away from likely causes of deviation as much as possible, particularly from variable causes such as electrical apparatus, leads, etc. In any case it must be remembered that any deviation will be doubled if the directive force (H) on the compass is halved. Therefore, the value of H in the compass position must be compared with H in that locality. This is done by setting up an oscillating needle (as described in para. 2 (b)(iii) of this chapter) in the compass position in the aircraft, and timing with a stop watch a certain number of oscillations. The oscillating needle is then removed and set up in a position well away from buildings and other magnetic influences, and the timing of the same number of oscillations repeated. Then

$$t_1 \text{ (in aircraft)} = 2\pi \sqrt{\frac{K}{MH_1}} \text{ and } t \text{ (uninfluenced)} = 2\pi \sqrt{\frac{K}{MH}}.$$

So that $\dfrac{\text{Directive force in compass position } H_1}{\text{Directive force uninfluenced } H} = \dfrac{t^2}{t^2{}_1}.$

This ratio must be found on four equidistant compass headings and the average taken. Then this ratio of directive force in the compass position to the uninfluenced directive force is the **Coefficient** λ (Lambda) of that compass position.

If the test is carried out on four equidistant magnetic headings (instead of compass headings) then each $\dfrac{H_1}{H}$ must be multiplied by Cos Deviation, and the average of the products taken as λ.

(ii) *Example.*

Magnetic Heading	Deviation in Compass	$\dfrac{H_1}{H}$	$\dfrac{H_1}{H}$ Cos Deviation
360 M	+ 12	0·75	0·73
090 M	+ 4	0·92	0·92
180 M	− 18	0·85	0·81
270 M	− 8	1·2	1·15
			3·61 ÷ 4 = 0·9 = λ

From a practical point of view it is important not only that the value of λ is high but also that the value of $\dfrac{H_1}{H}$ is never on any heading very small.

(b) It may be desirable for analytic reasons to find the value of the vertical field at a compass position (Z) in relation to the influenced Earth's vertical component (Z). The ratio is the **Coefficient** μ (Mu) of the compass position. It is found by timing an oscillating needle set up, as described in **para. 2** (b) (iv) of this chapter, in the compass position on four equidistant compass headings (then time $= t_1$) and in an uninfluenced position (then time for same number of oscillations $= t$). Then $\dfrac{Z_1}{Z} = \dfrac{t^2}{t_1^2}$. The average of the four values of $\dfrac{Z_1}{Z}$ so found is μ.

6. CAUSES OF COMPASS DEVIATION. (a) (i) **Deviation** is the angle between the direction of a particular compass needle and the magnetic meridian (that is, the direction of H), the compass being under magnetic influences in the aircraft additional to and not coincident with the Earth's field. It is named Easterly ($+$) or Westerly ($-$) according to whether the North-seeking pole lies to East or West of the magnetic meridian.

(ii) The causes of deviation in an aircraft may be classified under one of three headings: Hard Iron (permanent) magnetism, Soft Iron (temporary) magnetism, and sub-permanent magnetism.

It is customary to call each particular part of the cause of deviation, as classified hereafter, a "parameter." The parameters are indicated by capital letters for Hard Iron, and small letters for Soft Iron. The strictly mathematical meaning of the word "parameter" is: "a fixed quantity in the equation of a curve." In compass work, the curve is the deviation curve, the equation is that given for finding deviation on any course (as given hereafter in paras. 6(d) and 7(b)) and therefore the fixed quantities in the equations are the parameters.

(*Note.* Magnetic fields due to electrical circuits should not exist in a position or magnitude likely to affect a compass. Unfortunately, however, this deplorable state of affairs does sometimes occur. It is necessary therefore to check the deviation of the compass on several different headings with and without the electric circuits (particularly the compass lighting circuit) in operation. If any effect due to the electrical circuits is found, the offending circuit should be run by a different route; or, if this is not possible, two compass swings (with and without electrical circuits switched on) must be carried out, and two deviation cards displayed in the aircraft.)

(b) **Hard Iron** magnetism causing deviation in aircraft can be resolved into three components at right angles to each other, called "**P**," "**Q**," and "**R**."

(i) **P** is permanent magnetism lying in the fore and aft line of the aircraft. Obviously it will deflect the compass most when on East and West headings, and on North and South headings will not cause any deflection but will augment or diminish the directive force.

P is named + when it has its blue pole forward, that is, when it causes easterly deviation on course of 090 M and westerly on 270 M. Fig. 59 shows diagrammatically a + **P**. The **P** magnetism is shown in red and blue, the magnetic meridian by a dotted line, and the compass needle by an arrow. The curve accompanying it shows the deviations due to it on the various headings. It is a Sine curve; that is, deviation due to **P** varies as Sine of the course. Deviation such as this which reaches its peak values every 180 degrees is called "Semicircular" deviation.

(ii) **Q** is permanent magnetism lying athwartships, or across the

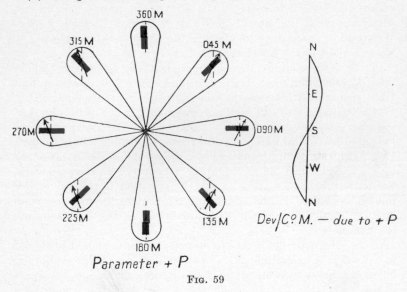

Parameter + P

Dev/C? M. — due to + P

Fig. 59

fore and aft line. It deflects the compass most on North and South magnetic headings, and on East and West courses it does not deflect the compass at all but augments or reduces the directive force. **Q** is + when its red pole is to port, i.e. when it causes easterly deviation on heading of 360 M and westerly deviation on 180 M. Fig. 60 shows a — **Q** and a graph of the deviation it causes. The graph is a Cosine curve; that is, deviation due to **Q** varies as the Cos of the course. This, like that due to **P**, is semicircular deviation.

(iii) **R** is permanent magnetism lying vertically in the aircraft. As it lies both fore and aft of the compass it causes no deviation and therefore it can be neglected. In ships where it may tilt, due to wind or ship's trim while the plane of rotation of the compass remains level, R causes deviation called "Heeling Error," which will not be discussed here.

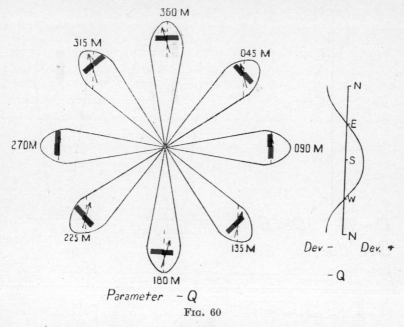

Parameter − Q

FIG. 60

(c) **Soft Iron** magnetism causing deviation in aircraft compasses is of two sorts—the Vertical magnetism "c" and "f," and the Horizontal

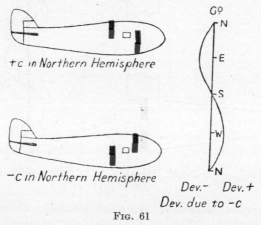

+c in Northern Hemisphere

−c in Northern Hemisphere

Dev. −   Dev. +

Dev. due to −c

FIG. 61

magnetisms "a," "e," "b," and "d." (*Note.*—Temporary magnetism has been divided into nine parameters, lettered "a" to "k, omitting the letters "i" and "j." The last three, "g," "h," and "k" give "Heeling Error" in ships, and are non-effective in aircraft.)

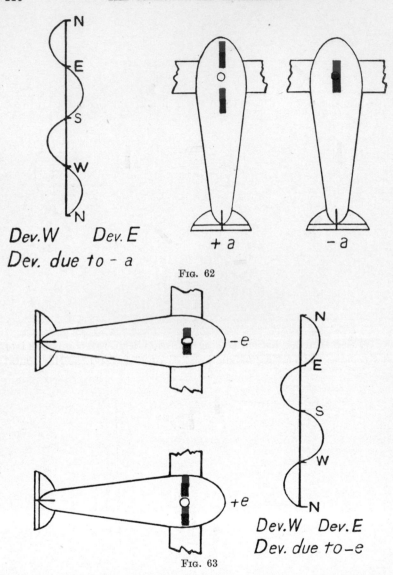

Dev.W   Dev.E
Dev. due to - a

+ a   - a

Fig. 62

-e

+e

Dev.W   Dev.E
Dev. due to -e

Fig. 63

(i) **c** is vertical soft iron which is magnetized under the influence of the Earth's vertical component Z, and is therefore proportional to Z. It is disposed fore and/or aft of the compass (see Fig. 61), and as its strength is constant on all headings a curve of the deviation which it causes will be a Sine curve. That is, deviation due to **c** varies as Sin Co. It must be remembered that this magnetism varies as Z,

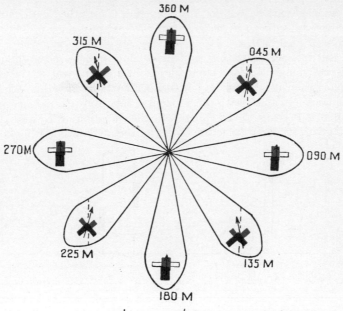

−a and −e , where −e = twice −a

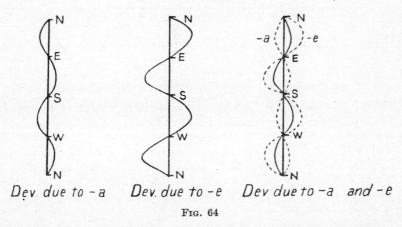

Dev. due to −a   Dev. due to −e   Dev due to −a and −e

FIG. 64

and therefore changes its polarity when it crosses the magnetic Equator.

(ii) **f** is vertical soft iron magnetized by Z. It is disposed similarly to **c** (one high and/or one low) but instead of being fore and aft, it is to port and starboard of the compass. Deviation due to **f** will obviously vary as Cos Co. f is + when it causes the North end of the compass needle to be deflected to the east on course of 360 M, and to west on 180 M.

(iii) a is horizontal soft iron disposed in the fore and aft line of the aircraft magnetized by H the horizontal component of the Earth's field, when it is coincident with it or partially so. But it must be remembered that, with all horizontal soft iron it is *not* magnetized when it is lying at right angles to the direction of H, and that its magnetization varies as the Cosine of the angle which it makes with

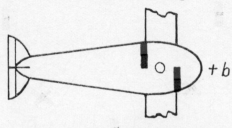

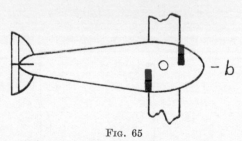

FIG. 65

the direction of H. Fig. 62 shows parameters + a and − a, and a curve of deviation due to − a. From this curve it can be seen that its effect is a maximum on the Quadrantal points (N.E., S.E., S.W., and N.W.) and is therefore called Quadrantal Deviation. It is nil on the Cardinal points. Deviation due to parameter a varies as Sin twice course. It also varies as the strength of H, but obviously does not change its polarity when it crosses the magnetic equator as does vertical soft iron.

Parameter e is horizontal soft iron disposed athwartships and magnetized by H. It is represented in Fig. 63, where the curve of deviation due to a − e shows that its effect varies like a, as Sin 2 Co.

Fig. 64 shows parameters − a and − e combined. Obviously they oppose each other, but the figure gives the case where − e is the greater. The curves due to each are shown, together with the

resultant curve. In practice this is usual, for **e** is usually nearer the
compass and is therefore more effective. In all cases, the combined

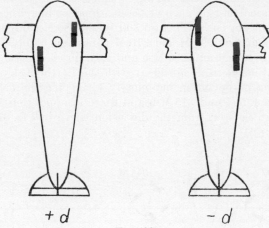

+ *d*   − *d*

FIG. 66

effect of **a** and **e** will depend on their algebraic difference. Thus two
"like" signs (− **a** and − **e**, or + **a** and + **e**) are in opposition, and the

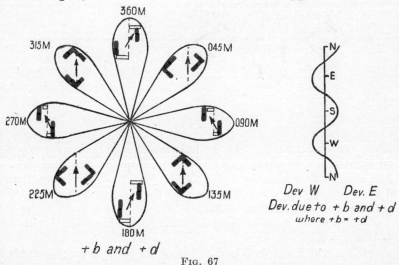

+ *b and* + *d*

FIG. 67

effects of two "unlike" signs (− **a** and + **e**, or + **a** and − **e** are
additive.

(iv) **b** is horizontal soft iron disposed as in Fig. 65. Its effect will
not be considered alone, but in conjunction with parameter **d**.

d is horizontal soft iron disposed as shown in Fig. 66. Its effect will only be considered in conjunction with parameter **b**, thus: The combined result of a **b** and a **d** of "like" signs is shown in Fig. 67. It can be seen that on each of the cardinal points either **b** or **d** is effective, but not both. Thus on 360 M and 180 M parameter **d** only is effective, and on 090 M and 270 M parameter **b** only is effective. On headings 045 M and 225 M **b** and **d** are in conjunction resulting in diagonal magnetism coincident with the Earth's field and therefore causing no deviation but merely weakening the field a little. On courses 135 M and 315 M **b** and **d** are in opposition and cancel out. It can be seen from the deviation curve in Fig. 67 that the

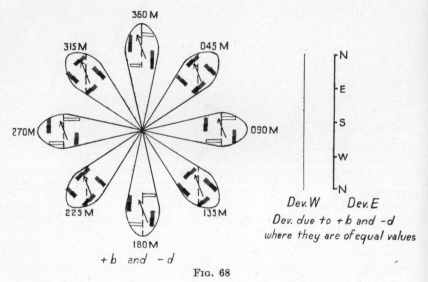

Fig. 68

effect varies as Cos 2 C°. This deviation reaches its peak value every 90 degrees (i.e. quadrant) and therefore is quadrantal deviation. But it must be remembered that, unlike the quadrantal deviation due to parameters **a** and **e**, it is *not* effective on the quadrantal points but on the cardinal points.

A similar (but opposite sign) deviation curve is obtained with a — **b** and — **d**.

(v) But with **b** and **d** of "unlike" signs the effect is very different. In Fig. 68 parameters + **b** and — **d** in combination are shown diagrammatically. The deviation is the same sign and value on all headings. A — **b** and + **d** would give a constant easterly deviation.

Such a disposal of soft iron in an aircraft is unlikely, but this type of deviation is more likely to occur when the compass is installed in a position to one side of the aircraft, thus aggravating unsymmetrical effects.

(d) Thus, deviation is caused by

    (i) Parameter **P,** its deviation varying as Sin Co.

    (ii) Parameter **c,** its deviation varying as Sin Co.

    (iii) Parameter **Q,** its deviation varying as Cos Co.

    (iv) Parameter **f,** its deviation varying as Cos Co.

    (v) Parameters **a** and **e,** their deviation varying as Sin 2 Co.

    (vi) Parameters **b** and **d** of "like" signs, their deviation varying as Cos 2 Co.

    (vii) Parameters **b** and **d** of " unlike " signs, their deviation being unchanged with change of Co.

Then deviation =

P Sin Co + **c** Sin Co + **Q** Cos Co + **f** Cos Co + (**a** and **e**) Sin 2 Co + ("like" **b** and **d**) Cos 2 Co + ("unlike" **b** and **d**).

But sub-permanent magnetism which spoils this almost perfect picture must not be forgotten.

7. THE COEFFICIENTS. (a) Deviation is classified under various coefficients for correcting purposes.

(i) Coef. A

$$= \frac{\text{Deviation on N.} + \text{N.E.} + \text{E.} + \text{S.E.} + \text{S.} + \text{S.W.} + \text{W.} + \text{N.W.}}{8}$$

having regard to the sign of each. It may be of two sorts : "Apparent A" which should not exist, being due to the lubber-line of the compass being installed in a direction not coincident with the fore and aft line of the aircraft; and "Real A," which in a well-placed compass in aircraft is usually small, being due to parameters **b** and **d** of unlike sign. It does not vary with change of course.

Note.—Another "Apparent A" may be caused by "Gaussin Error." In swinging a compass sub-permanent magnetism induced on one course remains effective for some time on the next course, and so on throughout the swing, resulting in an Apparent A. It can be avoided by turning both ways during swinging and not going on to the compass points in order of rotation. Also the aircraft should be steadied on each course for about one minute before a reading is taken. Of course, this error is impossible when aircraft are swung without engines running. In any case it is an error more likely in ships, and not a very serious one in aircraft.

    (ii) Coef. B $= \dfrac{\text{Deviation on E.} - \text{W.}}{2}$, having regard to sign.

Consists of deviation due to the parameters **P** and **c,** and therefore varies as Sin Co.

(iii) Coef. $C = \dfrac{\text{Deviation on N.} - \text{S.}}{2}$. Consists of deviation due to parameters **Q** and **f,** and therefore varies as Cos Co.

(iv) Coef. $D = \dfrac{\text{Deviation on N.E.} + \text{S.W.} - \text{S.E.} - \text{N.W.}}{4}$. It consists of deviation due to parameters **a** and **e,** and varies as Sin 2 Co.

(v) Coef. $E = \dfrac{\text{Deviation on N.} + \text{S.} - \text{E.} - \text{W.}}{4}$. Consists of deviation due to parameters **b** and **d** of "like" signs, and varies as Cos 2 Co.

Note. Strictly speaking, when ascertaining the values of co-efficients, the deviation on compass headings—and not magnetic headings—should be used. But in any case the difference of the values obtained is not appreciable in practice.

(**b**) Then Deviation on any Course

$$= A + B \text{ Sin Co} + C \text{ Cos Co} + D \text{ Sin 2 Co} + E \text{ Cos 2 Co.}$$

8. METHODS OF FINDING DEVIATION. (This paragraph does not give compass swinging procedure, or corrections, but merely the methods of finding deviation.)

(a) **By Compass Swinging Base.** The aircraft is wheeled on to the base which has lines representing the four cardinal and four quadrantal magnetic bearings accurately marked on it. Two plumb-bobs are dropped to within a few inches of the ground from the centre line of the aircraft, one forward and one aft. Then by lining up the aircraft with one of the lines of the compass base by means of the plumb-bobs, its correct magnetic course is known. Then the compass is read and the difference is the deviation. Thus, heading on base = 090 M, heading by compass = 085 C. ∴ Deviation = + 5 or 5 East.

If possible the tail of the aircraft should be raised so as to be more similar to the attitude of level flight. This method is most suitable for light aircraft which can be easily moved around.

(b) **By Landing Compass.** This method is most suitable for large land aircraft. The aeroplane is taxied on to the aerodrome clear of magnetic influences, and by moving under its own power it is headed on to any course desired. Then the landing compass, which is an accurate compass with prism and open sights, is set up on its tripod in line with the fore and aft line of the aircraft, and about 50 yds. from it or any other magnetic influences. Then the bearing of the fore and aft line of the aircraft is taken; and as the landing compass is accepted as being under the influence of H only, this is taken as the correct magnetic heading. The aircraft compass is read, and the difference is the deviation. If no landing compass is available, an ordinary aircraft bearing compass may be used.

(c) **Photographic Orientation.** This new method is carried out during flight, and constitutes an accurate check under genuine conditions. A camera is set up squarely in the aircraft and facing vertically downwards, and (either in it or externally) arrangements are made for the fore and aft line of the aircraft to be reproduced on the plate or film. Then, when on a given course the compass is read and a photo taken. After landing, the plate or film is developed and by orienting it accurately with a large scale map (or chart), the direction of the fore and aft line can be found. Variation is then applied to give the magnetic course, which is compared to the compass course to give deviation. The method can only be used over well-surveyed areas. It is most suitable for accurate checking only.

(d) All of the following methods depend on one principle. The deviation of a bearing compass on the aircraft is found and this is applied to the course by the bearing compass to give the magnetic course, from which the deviation of steering and other compasses may be found. There is one vital precaution to be taken. The deviation of the bearing compass must be the same for both prism and lubber-line (centesimal scale) readings. This is done by lining up its lubber-line with the fore and aft line of the aircraft, so eliminating any Apparent A. To do this the prism is sighted over the lubber-line in the bowl and its verge ring locked. The screws in its standard are then slackened off. By sighting along the fore and aft line of the aircraft a distant object is chosen on that line. Then, by suitably rotating the whole compass on its standard, the open sights are brought on to the object, and the standard screws tightened up. The compass is then lined-up truly. (See Note page 120.)

(e) **By Known Bearing.** This method may be employed in the air, but is more suitable on the water or aerodrome. The magnetic bearing of a distant object in relation to a given position is found from a map or chart, or by an uninfluenced landing compass. When at or over this position, the bearing of the object is taken by the aircraft bearing compass and at the same time the course is read by the bearing compass and other compasses being checked. The deviation of the bearing compass is found from the bearing taken, and applied to the course read from it to give the magnetic course. Other compass courses are then compared to this. Thus:

Correct magnetic bearing   = 147 M

Bearing by compass   = 143 C

$\therefore$ Deviation of bearing compass $= +$ 4 or 4 East.

Course by bearing compass $= 358$ C

Correct course magnetic $= 002$ M

Course by pilot's compass $= 354$ C

Deviation of pilot's compass $= +$ 8 or 8 East,

i.e., on a heading of 002 M, deviation on the pilot's compass is $+$ 8 and on the bearing compass is $+$ 4.

(f) **By Transit.** This is highly suitable for an aircraft in the air, and also for a flying boat taxying on the water. A transit is the straight line through two conspicuous objects. The direction of this line is taken from a chart or map, and, by applying variation, converted to a magnetic direction. The aircraft moves across the line and, when the two objects are exactly in line, their bearing is taken by the bearing compass, and course read on all compasses to be checked, etc., as in sub-para (e) above.

(g) **By Reciprocal** of Measured Bearing. This is most suitable for a flying boat being swung at moorings or taxying. A landing compass (or bearing compass) is set up ashore well away from any magnetic influence. Then bearings by it may be accepted as magnetic bearings. The observer ashore takes bearings of the bearing compass on the aircraft afloat, and the observer on board takes a bearing of the landing compass ashore. Then the reciprocal of the landing compass reading is the magnetic bearing of the landing compass from the aircraft. This is compared with the bearing taken by the aircraft's bearing compass to give its deviation, which is then applied to the heading by that compass to give magnetic course, etc.

Thus :   Bearing by landing compass $= 083$ C $= 083$ M

Reciprocal $= 263$ M

Bearing by bearing compass $= 268$ C

Deviation of bearing compass $= 5$ W.

Course by bearing compass $= 183$ C

Magnetic course $= 178$ M

Course by steering compass $= 180$ C

Deviation of steering compass $= 2$ W.

(h) **By Time Azimuth.** The bearing of the sun or other heavenly body (and exact time) is taken in the Azimuth mirror and sight of the bearing compass. With values regarding the heavenly body taken from the Nautical Almanac, and the known position of the aircraft, the bearing of the heavenly body is found (by working out, or from Azimuth tables as will be explained in Chapter VII). Variation is applied to this to give magnetic bearing, which is compared with the compass bearing to give the deviation of that compass. This is then applied to the course by that compass to give magnetic course against which to compare other compasses. The altitude of the heavenly body (sun) should be less than about 30 degrees.

(i) **By Bearing-Amplitude.** When the sun is rising and setting the difference between its true bearing (or azimuth) and 090 T or 270 T respectively, is its "Bearing-Amplitude." As will be explained in a later chapter, "Declination" of a heavenly body is what really constitutes the celestial latitude of the body. Thus if its declination is North then at rising its bearing will be North of 090 T and when setting it will be North of 270 T.

Knowing the latitude of the aircraft, it is entered with the declination in Amplitude tables (given in Nautical Tables) and the True bearing of the sun (expressed as an angle from 090 T or 270 T) is taken out. Actually a correction given in an adjoining table must be applied to correct for refraction, etc. Variation is applied to make the bearing magnetic.

Then the bearing of the sun is taken when its centre is on the horizon and this bearing is compared with the correct magnetic bearing, as found above to give deviation. This deviation is then applied to the course as read from the bearing compass to give the correct magnetic course. The course indicated by the steering compass at the same moment is compared with this to give its deviation.

(j) **By Equi-Course Bearings.** This method should be employed when all others are impracticable. It is quick and simple and does not require any map or chart or any work away from the aircraft. Its only disadvantage lies in the fact that it is in error to the value of coefficient A. But then, if the bearing compass is properly lined up and therefore has no Apparent A, there is the possibility that real A may not exist at all or at least be very small. If it has been found once it might thereafter be treated as if a constant index-error. This method may be used in the air, on the aerodrome, or on the water, taxying or at moorings. The aircraft is headed on eight equidistant courses. Then, *from the same position*, a bearing of the distant object is taken on each course. The course by the bearing compass is read at the same time. The eight bearings are averaged to give the accepted magnetic bearing of the object. This, applied to each bearing, gives the deviation for each course. Thus—

Bearing C	Accepted Magnetic Bearing	Deviation of Bearing Compass	Co. by Bearing Compass	Co. M	Co. by Pilot's Compass	Deviation of Pilot's Compass
127 C	135 M	+ 8	360 C	008 M	002 C	+ 6
130 C	135 M	+ 5	045 C	050 M	046 C	+ 4
136 C	135 M	− 1	135 C	134 M	134 C	
144 C	135 M	− 9	270 C	261 M	268 C	− 7
132 C	135 M	+ 3	090 C	093 M	092 C	+ 1
140 C	135 M	− 5	225 C	220 M	223 C	− 3
133 C	135 M	+ 2	315 C	317 M	314 C	+ 3
138 C	135 M	− 3	180 C	177 M	181 C	− 4

8)1080
= 135 C = 135 M

The eight bearings were averaged, giving 135, and this figure is taken as correct magnetic bearing, from which deviation is found.

It will be noticed, although observations are taken on eight equally spaced courses, the aircraft is not placed on the courses in order of rotation. This is done to avoid the possibility of an Apparent coefficient A, due to Gaussin Error (see para. 7 (a) (i)).

NOTE. In each of the methods described in subparas. (e) to (j) inclusive, the bearing compass can be replaced by a **Bearing Plate** (Pelorus). Its zero reading must of course be lined up truly with the aircraft's fore and aft line. Results with the Bearing Plate, which gives readings relative to the course, are generally at least as good as with the Bearing Compass. The Bearing Plate, moreover, is simpler. The form of working can be easily seen.

(k) By Deflector. This method, like the Equi-course Bearings, gives results in error to the value of coefficient A. It is done by an instrument called a Deflector, and relies on the assumption that if the directive force is the same on each side of the cardinal points then there is no semicircular deviation. Thus, if the directive force on North course equals directive force on South course there can be no deviation on East and West. Further, it is assumed that if the directive force is the same on four cardinal points and one quadrantal point then there is no deviation at all (except for coefficient A). The deflector is an instrument placed on top of a compass and measures the relative directive force on each heading. This is done by measuring the relative force required to deflect the magnet system through a given angle (usually 85° or 90°).

As far as is known this method has never been applied to aircraft compasses. Nor does it seem likely to be so used!

9. METHODS OF CORRECTING DEVIATION. (a) No attempt is made in aircraft to correct for deviations classified under coefficients D and E. Coefficients B and C are corrected by means of the corrector boxes described below. Coefficient A can be removed by rotating the whole compass on the compass platform. (Clockwise for a +coefficient A.)

(b) The old-type **Corrector Box** consists of a wooden block situated immediately under the centre of the compass. Holes are drilled in it lying fore and aft, and athwart ships, of a size suitable to take small corrector magnets. To correct for coefficient B which is caused by fore and aft permanent magnetism (**P**) and vertical soft iron magnetism disposed fore and aft (**c**), corrector magnets are placed fore and aft in the box, of such a size to deflect the magnet system through an angle equal to coefficient B. Red pole of corrector magnet is forward to correct a + coefficient B. In theory (see para. on change of deviation with change of magnetic lat.) correction should only be made for the deviation due to **P**, and not for **c**, as it varies. But as it is impracticable to separate **P** from **c** there is no alternative but to correct for the whole of coefficient B.

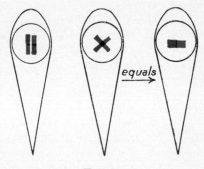

To correct coefficient C which is caused by athwartships permanent magnetism (**Q**) and vertical soft iron magnetism disposed athwartships (**f**), corrector magnets of the required strength are placed athwartships in the holes of the corrector box, a + coefficient C being corrected by placing red poles to starboard. **Q** and **f** being practically inseparable full correction for coefficient C is made.

Fig. 69

(c) The New Type Corrector Box, or **Micro-adjuster.** In this the principle of correction is the same as just described but instead of putting in corrector magnets to make corrections, magnets already in the adjuster are disposed (by turning a key which rotates the magnets) so that they become effective. In Fig. 69 the diagram on the left shows one pair only of the corrector magnets. They are in the neutral (non-effective) position, being parallel and side by side they cancel out. In the box another pair of magnets lie athwartships. The centre and right hand diagrams of Fig. 69 show how, when the fore and aft magnets are turned so that they are not parallel to each other, they have an effect similar to a magnet placed athwartships. That is, the fore and aft magnets are rotated out of parallel to correct for coefficient C, and the athwartship magnets are rotated out of parallel to correct for coefficient B. But the athwartships key hole is used to correct for Coef. C. (Clockwise removes W. Dev.)

10. COMPASS SWINGING.   (a) Preliminaries and Precautions.
(i) The compass's serviceability should be checked. Scale should
be clear and readable; there should be no discoloration of the
liquid; and luminous paint and/or lights should be in good condition. Moving parts (verge ring and locking device, etc.) should
work freely. The bowl should be completely filled with liquid (of
Sp. Gr. of 0·81) with no bubbles.

Pivot friction must be reasonably small, being tested by deflecting
magnet system through 10° and releasing. In a new compass it
should return to within 1° of original reading. (Light tapping
allowed). Anti-vibrational device should be checked. The bowl
should be suspended wholly on it, and should not touch the metal
container.

(ii) A check should be made to see that no ferrous bolts have been
put into use near the compass; nor any electric leads carried near it.
In any case, electric wires in the vicinity of the compass should
always be duplicated so that the effect of one wire is counteracted
by its return.

(iii) The corrector box should be checked to see that it is central
under the compass, and that it is secure.

(iv) The stowage of all articles containing any iron must be as in
flight. No tools nor corrector magnets should be lying about the
aircraft or on the person who is carrying out the swinging.

(v) The swinging should always be done with the aircraft in
normal flying attitude. If this is not so, the results may not be quite
accurate, but the biggest error likely to occur through this is a read-
ing-error on quadrantal points in parallel grid compass, which is
avoidable. On quadrantal points the eye of the observer must be
directly over the centre of the compass or in the line of the parallel
grid wires. If it is to one side of the grid wires, a big error will occur
(as the grid wires and the magnet system are not lying in parallel
planes.)

(vi) Readings should be only taken after any possible swirl
of the liquid has subsided, and after light tapping of the bowl
if the aircraft is stationary without engines running. Care
should be taken to avoid parallax error between the lubber-line and
scale.

(b) The **Methods and Procedure.**   (i) In para. 8 of this chapter,
nine different methods of finding deviation are given. Of these it is
obvious that those in the air, if carried out accurately, give a more
genuine result. But as it is impossible to make corrections in the air
the procedure is usually as follows: If it is an "initial" swing or an
"analytical" swing the corrector box, if of the old type, must be
empty, or if micro-adjuster, set at zero (or better still removed).

Then, in the air deviation is found by one of the methods described in para. 8 on the four cardinal points for an ordinary corrective swing, or on eight (or sixteen) points for an analytical swing. If the readings are not taken on courses within about 5° of the cardinal points (and similarly for quadrantal points) they should be plotted graphically and a curve drawn to find the deviation on the required cardinal points. The aircraft lands, coefficients C and B are calculated and, with the aircraft stationary on N. (or S.) magnetic course and E. (or W.) magnetic course respectively, are corrected for by corrector magnets or micro-adjuster. Then the aircraft is taken into the air again and deviation found on the cardinal and quadrantal points, completing the swing.

A similar procedure is used when a flying boat is swung during taxying on the water.

(ii) When one of the stationary methods are employed, such as by compass base, or by any method on the aerodrome or at moorings, corrections are made during the swing.

With the old type corrector box the well-known procedure is as follows: Aircraft is headed North and deviation taken. Aircraft headed East and deviation taken. Aircraft headed South, deviation taken, coefficient C calculated and corrected. Aircraft headed West, deviation taken, coefficient B calculated and corrected. Aircraft then headed on each of the eight cardinal and quadrantal points, coefficient A calculated, and if necessary corrected by rotating the compass.

If a large deviation is found on the cardinal points, say over 12°, it must be corrected, partially at least immediately. For obviously magnetism which causes a big deviation of one course will either weaken or strengthen the directive force on a course 90 degrees from it, and effect the deviation on that course. Then, for example, if a deviation + 15 is found on East, it should be removed immediately, and deviations then taken on North and South before calculating coefficient C.

With the new type corrector, a better procedure is as follows: Aircraft headed on North, and deviation removed completely by the micro-adjuster. Aircraft headed on East, and deviation removed. Aircraft headed on South, and half the deviation removed. Aircraft headed on West, and half the deviation removed. Then deviation is found on the eight cardinal and quadrantal points, coefficient A calculated and removed. The procedure gives the same results as the old procedure but avoids the actual calculation of coefficient B and C, and of course is much quicker.

(c) **Results.** When compass swinging is completed the final readings of deviation must be recorded in the aircraft log-book, and in addition must be recorded on a card which is fixed in a prominent position near the compass to which it refers. It may take one of the following forms—

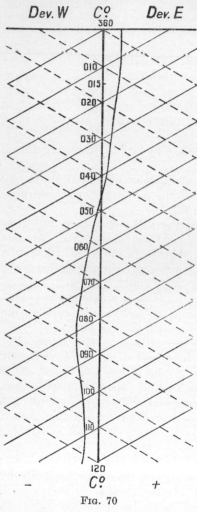

FIG. 70

(i) A Deviation Card which shows the compass course to be steered for any of eight magnetic courses (the cardinal and quadrantal points).

(ii) A Graphical Deviation Card on which is plotted a curve of deviation (+ to right, and − to left of centre line) against magnetic course. This is the best method.

(iii) Napier Diagram which is not · used in practice on account of the larger size required. It consists of a straight centre line along which course is marked off. Then across this line plain lines are drawn at 60 degrees to it, and at 60 degrees to these lines and to the centre line dotted lines are drawn. Now graph paper is usually "squared paper" but the Napier diagram is a graph which might be called "Equi-laterally-triangled paper." To plot a deviation against a magnetic heading, a distance (to same scale as the course on the centre line) is marked off along the plain line through the magnetic course. Then by returning from this mark along the dotted line to the centre line, the compass course is read off. Fig. 70 shows part of a Napier diagram (for courses up to 120 M or C) and a deviation curve is drawn on it. An example shows its use: Required compass course for 020 M. Move out along plain line to deviation curve (which in this case gives deviation = + 5) and back along (or parallel to) dotted line to read off compass course on centre line of 015 C. To find compass course for a given magnetic course

TABLE I

Co. M	Co. C	Deviation	Deviation multiplied by Sin Co. =			Deviation multiplied by Cos. Co. =			Deviation multiplied by Sin 2 Co. =			Deviation multiplied by Cos 2 Co. =		
M	C			+	−		+	−		+	−		+	−
360	007½	− 7½	+ Sin 0 =	Nil		+ Cos 0 =		7° 30′	+ Sin 0 =	Nil		+ Cos 0 =		7° 30′
022½	032	− 9½	+ Sin 22½ =		3° 38′	+ Cos 22½ =		8° 47′	+ Sin 45 =		6° 43′	+ Cos 45 =		6° 43′
045	056½	− 11½	+ Sin 45 =		8° 08′	+ Cos 45 =		8° 08′	+ Sin 90 =		11° 30′	+ Cos 90 =	Nil	
067½	080½	− 13	+ Sin 67½ =		12° 01′	+ Cos 67 =		4° 58′	+ Sin 45 =		9° 12′	− Cos 45 =	9° 12′	
090	103½	− 13½	+ Sin 90 =		13° 30′	+ Cos 90 =	Nil		+ Sin 0 =	Nil		− Cos 0 =	13° 30′	
112½	123½	− 11	+ Sin 67½ =		10° 10′	− Cos 67½ =	4° 13′		− Sin 45 =	7° 46′		− Cos 45 =	7° 46′	
135	141½	− 6½	+ Sin 45 =		4° 36′	− Cos 45 =	4° 36′		− Sin 90 =	6° 30′		− Cos 90 =	Nil	
157½	157½	Nil	+ Sin 22½ =	Nil		− Cos 22½ =	Nil		− Sin 45 =	Nil		+ Cos 45 =	Nil	
180	270½	+ 9½	+ Sin 0 =	Nil		− Cos 0 =		9° 30′	− Sin 0 =	Nil		+ Cos 0 =	9° 30′	
202½	188	+ 14½	− Sin 22½ =		5° 33′	− Cos 22½ =		13° 24′	+ Sin 45 =	10° 15′		+ Cos 45 =	10° 15′	
225	208½	+ 16½	− Sin 45 =		11° 40′	− Cos 45 =		11° 40′	+ Sin 90 =	16° 30′		+ Cos 90 =	Nil	
247½	232½	+ 15	− Sin 67½ =		13° 51′	− Cos 67½ =		5° 44′	+ Sin 45 =	10° 36′		− Cos 45 =		10° 36′
270	259½	+ 10½	− Sin 90 =		10° 30′	− Cos 90 =	Nil		+ Sin 0 =	Nil		− Cos 0 =		10° 30′
292½	287½	+ 5	− Sin 67½ =		4° 37′	+ Cos 67½ =	1° 55′		− Sin 45 =		3° 32′	− Cos 45 =		3° 32′
315	315½	− ½	− Sin 45 =	0° 21′		+ Cos 45 =		0° 21′	− Sin 90 =	0° 30′		− Cos 90 =	Nil	
337½	342	− 4½	− Sin 22½ =	1° 43′		+ Cos 22½ =		4° 10′	− Sin 45 =	3° 11′		+ Cos 45 =		3° 11′
16A = − 6½			8 B = + 2° 04′ − 98° 14′			8 C = + 10° 44′ − 74° 12′			8 D = + 55° 18′ − 30° 57′			8 E = + 50° 13′ − 42° 02′		
			= − 96° 10′			= − 63° 28′			= + 24° 21′			= + 8° 11′		
A = − 0° 25′			∴ B = − 12° 01′			∴ C = − 7° 56′			∴ D = + 3° 03′			∴ E = + 1° 01′		

the rule is to move out along plain and back along dotted lines and to find magnetic course equal to a given compass course move out along dotted and back along plain lines.

(d) **The Sixteen-Point Swing.** For particularly close investigation

TABLE II

Deviation	Deviation multiplied by			Deviation	Deviation multiplied by		
	Sin 22½ or Cos 67½	Sin 45 or Cos45	Sin 67½ or Cos 22½		Sin 22½ or Cos 67½	Sin 45 or Cos 45	Sin 67½ or Cos 22½
°	° ′	° ′	° ′	°	° ′	° ′	° ′
½	0 11	0 21	0 28	15½	5 56	10 58	14 19
1	0 23	0 42	0 55	16	6 07	11 19	14 47
1½	0 34	1 04	1 23	16½	6 19	11 40	15 15
2	0 46	1 25	1 51	17	6 30	12 01	15 42
2½	0 57	1 46	2 19	17½	6 42	12 22	16 10
3	1 09	2 07	2 46	18	6 53	12 44	16 38
3½	1 20	2 29	3 14	18½	7 05	13 05	17 06
4	1 32	2 50	3 42	19	7 16	13 26	17 33
4½	1 43	3 11	4 10	19½	7 28	13 47	18 01
5	1 55	3 32	4 37	20	7 39	14 08	18 29
5½	2 06	3 53	5 05	20½	7 51	14 30	18 56
6	2 18	4 15	5 33	21	8 02	14 51	19 24
6½	2 29	4 36	6 00	21½	8 14	15 12	19 52
7	2 41	4 57	6 28	22	8 25	15 33	20 20
7½	2 52	5 18	6 56	22½	8 37	15 55	20 47
8	3 04	5 39	7 24	23	8 48	16 16	21 15
8½	3 15	6 01	7 51	23½	9 00	16 37	21 43
9	3 27	6 22	8 19	24	9 11	16 58	22 10
9½	3 38	6 43	8 47	24½	9 22	17 20	22 38
10	3 50	7 04	9 14	25	9 34	17 40	23 06
10½	4 01	7 25	9 42	25½	9 44	17 58	23 29
11	4 13	7 47	10 10	26	9 56	18 24	24 02
11½	4 24	8 08	10 37	26½	10 08	18 44	24 28
12	4 36	8 29	11 05	27	10 20	19 06	24 56
12½	4 47	8 50	11 33	27½	10 32	19 26	25 24
13	4 58	9 12	12 01	28	10 42	19 48	25 52
13½	5 10	9 33	12 28	28½	10 54	20 10	26 20
14	5 21	9 54	12 56	29	11 06	20 30	26 48
14½	5 33	10 15	13 24	29½	11 18	20 52	27 14
15	5 44	10 36	13 51	30	11 28	21 12	27 42

of deviation the ordinary eight-point swing (i.e. on four cardinal and four quadrantal points) may not give a sufficiently complete and accurate record. Therefore the aircraft may be swung on sixteen equally-spaced points. An example in Table I shows how the coefficients are found. Note that the sign of the Sin or Cos depends on the quadrant (remember—"All Sin Tan Cos" Rule). Table II gives a ready-reckoner to assist the calculations, but even when using this the sixteen-point swing is very laborious.

11. CHANGES OF DEVIATION WITH CHANGES OF MAGNETIC LATITUDE. These changes will be considered in three parts, viz.

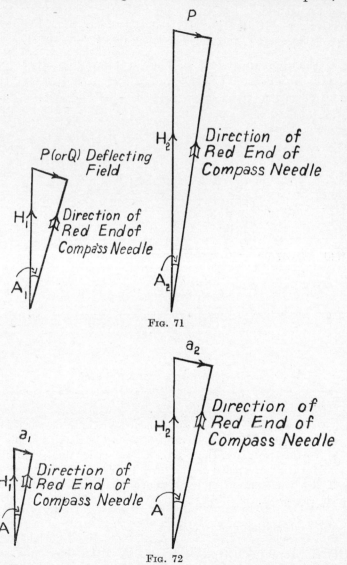

FIG. 71

FIG. 72

deviations due to hard iron magnetism, deviation due to vertical soft iron magnetism, and deviation due to horizontal soft iron magnetism.

(a) "Hard Iron" Deviation. The deviation due to parameters **P** and **Q** is proportional to them and they remain constant in all magnetic latitudes, but it is also inversely proportional to the directive force H affecting the magnet system. Fig. 71 shows H_2 twice as large as H_1 and the deflecting cause **P** constant. The angle A_2 is then approximately $\frac{1}{2} A_1$. For Sin of deviation $A_1 = \dfrac{P}{H_1}$ and Sin of deviation $A_2 = \dfrac{P}{H_2} = \dfrac{P}{2H_1}$. That is Sin $A_2 = \frac{1}{2}$ Sin A_1

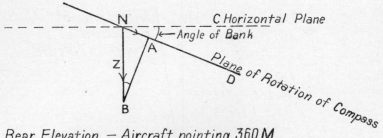

Rear Elevation — Aircraft pointing 360 M

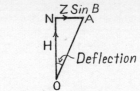

Section through Plane of Rotation

FIG. 73

and if A_1 is small, $A_2 = \frac{1}{2} A_1$. Then deviation due to hard iron varies inversely as the directive force H of the Earth's field.

(b) Vertical Soft Iron Deviation. The deviation due to parameters **c** and **f** varies inversely as the directive force H. But the cause itself also varies in direct proportion to the vertical component Z which causes it. Z changes with change of magnetic latitude.

Therefore deviation due to **c** and **f** varies as $\dfrac{Z}{H}$.

(c) Horizontal Soft Iron Deviation. Deviation due to parameters **a, e, b,** and **d** would vary inversely as H but for the fact that the causes themselves vary as H (which is the field which gives them their magnetism). Therefore this deviation remains unchanged with change of magnetic latitude. Fig. 72 shows that when H is doubled the deflecting cause a is also doubled, and the angle of deviation remains the same.

12. SEPARATION OF PARAMETERS. (a) The separation of P from c, or Q from f, is of considerable theoretical interest. This can be done when the deviation is known in two different parts of the world where the magnetic elements are different. But first, it is necessary fully to understand the relationship between (1) a parameter, (2) its resultant deflecting magnetic field, and (3) the deviation resulting from such a field. A *Parameter* is a constant Factor, and is not, in itself, a measure of magnetism or magnetic field. A Parameter does not vary with change of magnetic latitude. The *magnetic field* acts at right angles to the compass needle and the relationship between a field and its parameter is as follows—

Deflecting magnetic field due to parameter $P =$ Parameter P

,,	,,	,,	,,	,,	$Q =$	,,	Q
,,	,,	,,	,,	,,	$a =$	,,	$a \times H$
,,	,,	,,	,,	,,	$b =$	,,	$b \times H$
,,	,,	,,	,,	,,	$d =$	,,	$d \times H$
,,	,,	,,	,,	,,	$e =$	,,	$e \times H$
,,	,,	,,	,,	,,	$c =$	,,	$c \times Z$
,,	,,	,,	,,	,,	$f =$	,,	$f \times Z$

Thus it can be seen that all the deflecting fields are variables (with H and Z) except those due to P and Q magnetism. Now *deviation* is the angle between the compass needle and the directive force H of the Earth's field, and the deflecting field is at right angles to the compass needle. Therefore—

$$\text{Sin Deviation} = \frac{\text{Deflecting Field}}{\text{Directive Field}} = \frac{\text{Deflecting Field}}{\lambda H}$$

$\therefore$ λH Sin Deviation $=$ Deflecting Field.

Thus

λH Sin Coef. $A =$ Deflecting Field $\pm bH \mp dH$ (i.e. of "unlike" signs)

λH Sin Coef. $B =$ Deflecting Field $P + cZ$

λH Sin Coef. $C =$ Deflecting Field $Q + fZ$

λH Sin Coef. $D =$ Deflecting Field $aH + eH$

λH Sin Coef. $E =$ Deflecting Field $\pm bH \pm dH$ (i.e. of "like" signs)

As Coefficients A, D and E do not change with variation of the magnetic elements, it follows that two simultaneous equations cannot be used to separate b from d, or a from e. But this can be done in the case of the separation of P from c, or Q from f.

(b) Example. In Position One an aircraft's steering compass is found to have a Coef. B of 10° E. and in Position Two its Coef. B is $3\frac{1}{3}$° E. In position One $H = \cdot2$ gauss and $Z = \cdot4$ gauss (northerly dip) and in Position Two $H = \cdot15$ gauss and $Z = \cdot33$ gauss (southerly dip). Coefficient λ in each case is $\cdot8$. Find the numerical values of Parameters P and c, and the percentage of the deviation in Position One due to each parameter.

Let the index figure 1 refer to Position One and the index figure 2 to Position Two.

Then—

Deflecting Field
$$P + cZ_1 = \lambda H_1 \text{ Sin Coef. } B_1$$
$$P + cZ_1 = \cdot8 \times \cdot2 \text{ Sin } 10°$$
$$P + \cdot4c = \cdot0278 \text{ gauss} \quad . \quad . \quad . \quad . \quad (1)$$

Deflecting Field
$$P + cZ_2 = H_2 \text{ Sin Coef. } B_2$$
$$P + cZ_2 = \cdot8 \times \cdot15 \text{ Sin } 3\frac{1}{3}°$$
$$P - \cdot33c = \cdot00697 \text{ gauss} \quad . \quad . \quad . \quad . \quad (2)$$

Subtracting 2 from 1 we get

$$\cdot73c = \cdot02083$$

And $c = \cdot02855$ (which is the factor which when multiplied by Z gives the field strength due to c).

And $P = \cdot0278 - \cdot4 \times \cdot02855$

$P = \cdot0278 - \cdot01142$

$P = \cdot01638$ (which is the factor P, and also incidentally the actual field strength due to P magnetism).

Now to find the percentage of deviation due to each parameter in Position One—

$\lambda H_1 \text{ Sin } 10° = P + cZ_1$

$\cdot0278$ gauss $= \cdot01638 + \cdot02855 Z_1 = (\cdot01638 + \cdot01142)$ gauss

$\therefore$ Percentage deviation due to $P = \dfrac{\cdot01638}{\cdot0278} \times 100 = 58\cdot9$ per cent

and percentage deviation due to $c = \dfrac{\cdot01142}{\cdot0278} \times 100 = 41\cdot1$ per cent

for obviously deviation is proportional to the deflecting field forces.

13. (a) TURNING ERROR. When an aircraft on a northerly course banks to turn off that course the plane of rotation of the magnet system in the compass banks with the aircraft. Then part of the vertical component Z of the Earth's field can be resolved in the plane of rotation of the magnet system causing a deflection.

In the top figure in Fig. 73, $NB = Z$ the vertical component of the Earth's field (in the N. mag. hemisphere), and NA is that part

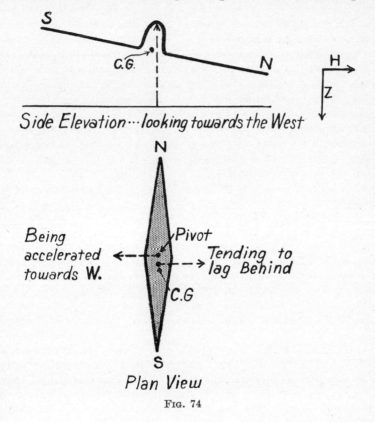

FIG. 74

of it which is resolved along a line in the plane of rotation of the compass in an aircraft pointing magnetic North and banked to an angle CNA. Now the angle $NBA = B = CNA$, the angle of bank, and the resolved part of Z along $ND = NA = NB \sin B = Z \sin B$. Now if N is the Red pole of the magnet system of the compass it will be drawn by the deflecting force NA ($= Z \sin B$) towards D, giving a large momentary easterly deviation. The lower figure of Fig. 73 shows $Z \sin B$ at right angles to the directive force H already effecting the compass, resulting in a deflection of NOA.

Then $\text{Tan } NOA = \dfrac{NA}{NO} = \dfrac{Z \sin \text{Bank}}{H}$.

An example of the magnitude of this deflection illustrates its serious nature. In England, $H =$ about 0·18, and $Z =$ about 0·43. Then deflection due to a bank of 30 degrees when facing magnetic North is found from :—Tan deflection $= \dfrac{Z \; \text{Sin Bank}}{H} = \dfrac{0·43 \; \text{Sin } 30}{0·18}$ $=$ Tan about 50°, i.e. direction of force due to bank of 30° on N. course $= 50$ degrees from 360 M. This will tend to cause the compass to show a false turn opposite to the real turn, depending on the rate of turn of the aircraft for a given angle of bank and on the damping, etc., of the compass. The effect is strong only on courses within about 35 degrees of magnetic North; and depending on the value of H and Z, and rate of turn for a given bank, will result in the compass showing an opposite turn, no turn, or a reduced turn. On courses near South it shows the turn in the correct direction but falsely large. In the southern magnetic hemisphere the effect is on opposite courses, that is, an opposite turn (or no turn, or reduced turn) is shown on courses near South, and an augmented indication of turn is shown on northerly courses.

(b) **Acceleration Error.** On courses East or West (or near East, or near West) a deflection of the compass in an aircraft will be caused by acceleration or deceleration. Fig. 74 shows that, owing to the effect of Z, the centre of gravity of the magnet system is not in the same vertical line as the pivot. Hence, as seen in the plan view, when the pivot is accelerated, the C.G. tends to lag, giving a moment which tends to deflect the system. (A single needle is shown for clarity of illustration.) The effect is small.

14. OTHER FORMS of Compass. There are two other kinds of compass reliant on the Earth magnetic field, and also there is the Sun Compass designed mainly for very high latitude work which uses the bearing of the sun as the datum for direction. The first-mentioned are the Earth Inductor Compass and the Cathode-ray Compass. The gyro compass is not yet satisfactory for air use.

The *Earth Inductor Compass* is of a type which has been used successfully but appears to offer more disadvantages than advantages. It consists virtually of an electric generator armature which rotates in the Earth's magnetic field. The brushes of this generator are then arranged East and West, and are rotatable in relation to the Course so that the pilot can set course.

Cathode-ray Compass. This compass uses the horizontal component of the Earth's magnetic field for its directional properties, but has an advantage in that it has no moving parts. There are, however, many difficulties in its development which have not yet been entirely overcome. The cathode-ray tube is fixed vertically so that the electrons are projected straight upwards to the centre of the fluorescent screen. But if a magnetic field crosses the path of the electrons they are deflected at right angles to the field—that is, to the East in the case of the Earth's field. Therefore the spot of light is moved away from the centre of the fluorescent screen to a point to the east of centre. This east point can then be used as a datum of direction.

An improvement to the fundamental idea is to arrange electrodes on each side of the East point which act as "pick-offs" and actuate relays to small electric motors. These motors then rotate the whole tube so as to keep it orientated continually. The idea of the cathode-ray compass has some possibilities but its obvious difficulties and shortcomings make its adoption somewhat doubtful.

TABLE III

SUMMARY OF DEVIATION

Coef. = Deviation on	CAUSED BY— and CHANGE due to change of Course—	Corrected by—	Change due to change of Mag. Latitude—
$A =$ $\dfrac{N.+N.E.+E.+S.E.+}{8}$ $\quad S.+S.W.+W.+N.W.$	(i) Apparent "A." By lubber-line being not truly fore and aft—causing incorrect reading on scale. Same on all courses.	Rotating lubber-line (clockwise for $+$ Coef. A).	Constant.
	(ii) Real "A." Parameters **b** and **d** of "unlike" signs, which are fore and aft, and athwart (respectively) horizontal unsymmetrical (to one side) soft iron magnetisms. Same on all courses.	Rotating lubber-line (clockwise for $+$ Coef. A).	Constant.
$B =$ $\dfrac{E. - W.}{2}$	(i) Parameter **P**—hard iron fore and aft. $+$ when blue pole is forward. Varies as Sin C°.	Corrector magnets fore and aft. (Red effect forward for $+$ Coef. B.)	If uncorrected, varies as $\dfrac{1}{H}$.
	(ii) Parameter **c**—vertical soft iron fore and aft of compass. Varies as Sin Co.	No correction.	Varies as $\dfrac{Z}{H}$ $=$ Tan Dip.
$C =$ $\dfrac{N. - S.}{2}$	(i) Parameter **Q**—hard iron athwartships. $+$ when blue pole is to starboard. Varies as Cos Co.	Corrector magnets athwartships. (Red effect to starboard for $+$ Coef. C.)	If uncorrected, varies as $\dfrac{1}{H}$.
	(ii) Parameter **f**—vertical soft iron disposed to port and starboard of compass. Varies as Cos Co.	No correction.	Varies as $\dfrac{Z}{H}$ $=$ Tan Dip.
$D =$ $\dfrac{N.E.+S.W.-S.E.-N.W.}{4}$	(i) Parameter **a**—horizontal soft iron fore and aft. Varies as Sin 2 Co.	No correction.	Constant.
	(ii) Parameter **e**—horizontal soft iron athwartships. Varies as Sin 2 Co.	No correction.	Constant.
$E =$ $\dfrac{N. + S. - E. - W.}{4}$	Parameters **b** and **d** when of "like" signs—being fore and aft, and athwart (resp.) horizontal soft iron. Varies as Cos 2 Co.	No correction.	Constant.

SECTION 3

AIRCRAFT INSTRUMENTS

15. The **AIR SPEED INDICATOR.** (a) The Pitot-Static type of tube anemometer connected to a sensitive metal aneroid cell or to each side of a diaphragm dividing the interior of the box is the commonest form of Air Speed Indicator (A.S.I.) in British aircraft. Facing straight into the airflow are two tubes: the pitot head (or pressure head) which is open-ended and is therefore subject to a pressure due to the airflow into it; and the static head which has a closed conically pointed nose and about twenty-four holes around

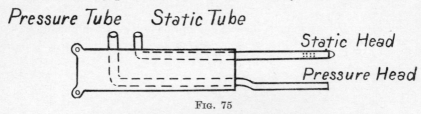

FIG. 75

its sides as shown in Fig. 75. A similar arrangement is the "trapped" type. A small tube running into the pressure head conveys the pressure through small holes in the top side of it but prevents water and, to a certain extent, insects, etc., from getting in. In modern electrically-heated types the static and pressure heads are combined. The pressure-difference in the tubes $= \frac{1}{2}\rho v^2$ where $\rho =$ air density, and v is speed. The formula is slightly modified to allow for the compressibility of air to give the practical formula—

$$P = 0{\cdot}012504 \; V^2(1 + {\cdot}43 \; V^2 \times 10^{-6})$$

where $P =$ pressure in mm. of water at 15 C.

and $V =$ Speed in m.p.h.

Or $P = 0{\cdot}01658 \; V^2(1 + {\cdot}57 \; V^2 \times 10^{-6})$

when V is in knots. These give values as shown in Tables IV and V.

This pressure difference is led by tubes to the A.S.I., the static tube generally to the metal container and the pressure tube to the inside of the aneroid cell.

Expansion of the aneroid cell is relayed by suitable levers, etc., to move an indicator over a dial.

(b) **Errors** in this type of A.S.I. are—

(i) *Position error* is due to the pressure-static head being in a position where the airflow is disturbed by some other part of the aircraft. The head must therefore be kept as clear from interference as possible.

For calibration purposes, a static head may be trailed well clear of the aircraft, with vanes, etc., to keep its head to airflow. It is

TABLE IV

Air Speed m.p.h.	Pressure Difference mm. of Water	Air Speed m.p.h.	Pressure Difference mm. of Water
40	20·0	140	247·1
50	31·3	150	284·0
60	45·1	160	323·6
70	61·4	170	365·8
80	80·2	180	410·7
90	101·6	190	458·3
100	125·6	200	508·7
110	152·1	210	561·8
120	181·2	220	617·6
130	212·8	230	676·3

TABLE V

Air Speed knots	Pressure Difference mm. of Water	Air Speed knots	Pressure Difference mm. of Water
35	20·3	120	240·7
40	26·55	130	282·9
50	41·5	140	328·6
60	59·8	150	377·8
70	81·5	160	430·6
80	106·5	170	487·0
90	134·9	180	547·1
100	166·7	190	610·9
110	202·0	200	678·5

connected by tube to the static side of the A.S.I. A more complete arrangement is to compare the A.S.I. with a vane-driven electrical Air Log trailed well clear of the aircraft. This unfortunately can only be done at fairly low speeds.

(ii) *Attitude error* is due to the pitot-static head being directed not exactly into the relative airflow. Small differences cause a very small error but a bad direction relative to airflow will cause a reduction of pressure on the pressure head and a suction on the static head.

(iii) *Instrument error*. Small constructional variations cause errors in A.S.I.s. In new instruments this must not exceed $\pm$ 2 m.p.h., and in old instruments $\pm$ 5 m.p.h. over the whole range of speeds. The instrument must be calibrated as explained in sub-para. (*c*) below, and the results entered in the aircraft log-book and displayed near the instrument.

(iv) *Height error*. The instrument is made to be correct at ground level. As the air density becomes less with increase of height the readings of the A.S.I. become less for a given speed. This error must be allowed for. In instruments based on $p = \frac{1}{2}\rho v^2$, the approximate correction is: add 1·75 per 1000 ft. Computers are available to find this correction accurately.

(v) *Lag error* is unlikely in a good instrument subject to the ordinary vibration of an aircraft. Most instruments are slightly "damped" so that when released from a given position (110 m.p.h. or 150 m.p.h.) the pointer takes over $\frac{1}{2}$ second but less than 1 second to return to zero.

(vi) *Leaks* in the pipes between the pitot-static head and the instrument will cause an error; as also will water or dirt in the pipes, or insects, etc., in the pressure head.

(c) **Calibration** of an A.S.I. This is done by a calibrator or from an A.S.I. of known accuracy. The calibrator may consist of a U tube in which the difference of height of water is measured, or a container with a single tube up which the water rises and is measured when pressure is applied. The calibrator is connected to the pressure side of the A.S.I. (or if it is installed in an aircraft to the pressure head). Pressure applied then affects both the A.S.I. and the calibrator. The water moves up the scale which is graduated in accordance with Table II or III. Readings of the A.S.I. are taken after light tapping—and recorded against the correct speeds shown by the calibrator. (Similarly an A.S.I. may be compared to another A.S.I. of known accuracy.)

(d) Other forms of A.S.I. are the Pressure Plate type where airflow forces a plate back against the action of a spring, and Venturi Anemometer Heads connected to aneroid cell indicators. In this latter type the difference of pressure $= k\rho v^2$, where k is a constant depending on the type of venturi, etc.

16. ALTIMETERS. (a) The usual form is an aneroid cell held between a C spring and connected by levers and a chain so that its movement under varying pressures is transferred to a pointer moving over a graduated dial. Compensation for temperature changes of from $-5°$ C. to $+35°$ C. is made. The whole is subject to the pressure of the atmosphere at all times. There are two methods of graduating altimeters—

(i) In isothermally calibrated instruments it is assumed that temperature is constant at all heights (assumed $10°$ C. $= 50°$ F.). This law is simple but absurd, and will probably not survive. The resulting required correction

$$= h \frac{\text{change of temperature Absolute}}{\text{calibrated temperature } 283° \text{ A}} = \text{approx.} \frac{h}{500}$$

for every 1 degree Fahrenheit, to be subtracted from indicated height when below 50° F. and added if mean temperature is above 50° F.

(ii) In instruments calibrated by the I.C.A.N. law it is assumed that air temperature falls at 6·5° C. per kilometre from a ground level temperature of 15° C.

The pressures assumed for various heights by both the isothermal law and the I.C.A.N. law are given in Table VI.

TABLE VI

PRESSURES FOR ALTIMETERS CALIBRATED BY ISOTHERMAL AND I.C.A.N. LAWS

Height in Feet	Isothermal Law Pressure in Millibars and Inches	I.C.A.N. Law Pressure in Millibars and Inches
0	1013·2 = 29·99	1013·2 = 29·99
2000	941·4 = 27·87	942·1 = 27·89
4000	874·7 = 25·89	875·1 = 25·91
6000	812·5 = 24·05	812·1 = 24·04
8000	754·8 = 22·35	752·8 = 22·28
10000	701·3 = 20·76	696·9 = 20·63
12000	651·4 = 19·29	644·4 = 19·08
14000	605·6 = 17·92	595·4 = 17·62
16000	562·5 = 16·65	549·3 = 16·26
18000	522·4 = 15·47	506·0 = 14·98
20000	485·6 = 14·37	465·7 = 13·78

(b) **Errors** in Altimeters are—

(i) Temperature error is due to the average temperature of the atmosphere up to the height measured being different to that assumed in the calibration of the instrument. It must be allowed for, in the isothermally calibrated instrument at $-\dfrac{h}{500}$ for every 1° F. as explained in (a) (i). Computers are available to find this correction accurately for both isothermal and I.C.A.N. altimeter.

(ii) Instrument error is due to irregularities and inaccuracies of the instrument and are found by calibration as explained in sub-para. (c), and recorded.

(iii) Frictional lag is due to stickiness in the mechanism and is very small in good instruments subject to ordinary aircraft vibration.

(iv) Cockpit error is due to the cockpit in which the altimeter is installed being subject to an abnormal pressure on account of its position in the aircraft and the aircraft's speed. It is best found by setting the instrument at zero and then taking a reading while flying across the aerodrome at ground level. This error decreases slightly with height and increases with speed. It is usually avoided by connecting the case of the altimeter to the static tube of the A.S.I.

(c) **Calibration** of Altimeters is usually done in a portable calibrating chamber. This consists of an airtight chamber to which is connected a suction pump by which the pressure in the chamber can be reduced. Two windows are provided for reading. In the chamber are placed the altimeter to be calibrated and an accurate aneroid barometer or altimeter of known accuracy. The pressure is reduced and, after tapping, comparative readings taken. Table VI gives values of height for given pressures for altimeters of either isothermal or I.C.A.N. calibration.

(d) The effect of change of ground-level pressure on the reading of an altimeter is about 27 ft. for one millibar. If pressure is less than when and/or where the altimeter was set this correction must be subtracted from the indicated height to give true height. Or, if pressure is greater, this correction must be added to indicated height to give correct height.

(e) **Types of Height.** The word "height" is used at present for four different meanings; two actual heights, one pressure, and one density.

(i) *Height Above Sea Level.* This is the actual linear vertical distance between sea level and the aircraft and is obtained by setting the zero of the altimeter to the prevailing ground pressure reduced to sea level and by correcting the resultant altimeter reading for temperature variation from standard (best done on a Computer). Height Above Sea Level is the best for all-round navigational use.

(ii) *Height Above Ground Level.* This is the actual linear vertical distance between the ground below the aircraft and the aircraft. It can be obtained by setting zero of the altimeter to the actual pressure on the ground in the locality and correcting for temperature, but more usually it is found by subtracting the mapped height of the ground from the Height Above Sea Level. It is sometimes called Ground Clearance, or Surface or Terrain Clearance.

(iii) *Pressure Height.* This value indicates the pressure at the aircraft instead of its linear distance from the surface. "Standard Height" used in aircraft performance testing is a pressure height and is actually the height in the International Standard Atmosphere at which the prevailing pressure would occur. It is obtained by setting the zero of the altimeter to 1013·2 millibars. Both boost pressure available and exhaust back-pressure of aircraft engines are in proportion to Pressure Height.

(iv) *Density Height* or *Equivalent Density Height* is the Standard (pressure) Height at which the prevailing density occurs. Obviously then if the prevailing temperature is the same as the Standard Atmosphere, the Density Height equals Pressure Height. Otherwise Equivalent Density Height is about 118·8 feet greater for each degree centigrade above the Standard temperature for the height. The aerodynamics of an aircraft vary with density, and so also does the I.A.S./T.A.S. conversion. This latter is a matter usually dealt with on an Air-speed Computer.

17. GROUND CLEARANCE INDICATORS. The susceptibility of the ordinary pressure altimeter to changes of temperature and of pressure makes it unsatisfactory and not entirely safe when clearing mountains, etc., in blind conditions. Moreover the heights of the ground are not always accurately known or mapped. The Ground Clearance Indicator overcomes these difficulties by providing a direct indication of the difference of height between the aircraft and the ground. The principle is similar to that of the marine echo sounder.

18. DRIFT INDICATORS. (a) Open Type. This well-known instrument provides drift wires which are rotated until coincident with the direction of the ground's movement below an aircraft, and a suitable scale by which this direction is measured in relation to the course of the aircraft. It also provides, in some cases, a height bar and timing beads for measuring by stop watch the time to cover a given distance over the ground and so finding ground speed.

Drift indications are generally more difficult to take accurately with increase of height. Drifts may be taken over water, even when practically flat-calm, by an experienced observer. If it is impossible to watch particular spots on the waves moving beneath the sight, then a practiced observer can align the drift wires with the direction of the general impression of movement of the water without focusing the eyes on any particular spot. This is only possible at moderately low altitudes.

(b) Optical Types. Various telescopic and periscopic types of drift sight are in common use. Their greatest advantage is convenience, the eye piece protruding into the cockpit or cabin. The periscopic types are particularly applicable to flying boats, where, of course, it is not possible to have a hole in the bottom of the hull for sighting purposes. The greatest disadvantage of this type of drift sight is that it is frequently impossible to make observations when over calm water. Some makes are better than others in this respect.

An optical type drift sight incorporating a moving screen by which ground speed can be found is a further development. The speed of the screen can be varied so that the objects below appear to be stationary on it. Then for the height above ground level, the ground speed can be read off. It is simply a mechanical application of the timing bead principle and suffers the same disadvantage in that it relies on the accuracy of the height above ground level which is still a poorly measured quantity.

(c) **Gyro-erected Types.** This is undoubtedly the most revolutionary development of the drift sight. A telescopic drift sight with a high magnification to give a high rate of movement of the objects below has an erecting prism interposed in the optical system. This prism is rotatable around an axis lying horizontally fore and aft, and is controlled by a gyroscope working in the same way as the Gyro Artificial Horizon. Thus all rolling movements are counteracted exactly by this prism. Even in the bumpiest weather no lateral movement can be noticed and accurate drift sights can be obtained even at great heights. This is one of the most valuable contributions made to air navigation.

(d) **Tail Drift Sights** consist of a lens system with a centre sighting line and a rotatable mirror. The whole can be turned and the angle of turn from the fore and aft line measured against a suitable scale. Objects which pass directly below the aircraft are kept on the centre line in the instrument (which is turned as required) until the object is well astern. Then the direction of the sight as indicated on the scale is the "back bearing" or "tail bearing" of the object relative to the aircraft, and this equals the drift. Objects can be watched until very far astern (by rotating the mirror), giving greater accuracy than the ordinary vertical drift indicator.

19. THE CATHODE-RAY DIP INDICATOR provides a new means of obtaining a Position Line. If the Magnetic Dip at the aircraft can be measured then that aircraft must lie on the Isoclinic Line having the value of the Dip found. Development is in hand by which a cathode-ray tube is mounted and orientated so as to rotate in the plane of the magnetic meridian. Then by bringing the cathode-ray spot to the exact centre of the screen the direction of the total field is ascertained and the angle of Dip is measured in relation to a bubble. This, of course, is a simplified description of the arrangement but demonstrates the principle.

Unfortunately there are many difficulties. Sensitivity and accuracy are, so far, insufficient. The aircraft's ferrous parts cause deviation to the direction of the Total Force, which necessitates careful calibration and application of corrections. Moreover, the available isoclinic charts, which are of course necessary, cannot be considered as sufficiently complete or sufficiently accurate.

CHAPTER IV

DIRECTION FINDING WIRELESS, AND SIGNALS

(*Note*.—Being a matter of pilotage rather than navigation the V.H.F. Blind Approach systems are not included in this chapter.)

SECTION 1

DIRECTION FINDING WIRELESS

1. THE LOOP AERIAL. (a) Directional Properties. The best means of obtaining a clear conception of the directive properties of a loop aerial is the analogy of a stick floating on water. In Fig. 76 stick A is lying at right angles to the directive of movement (or

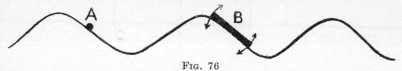

FIG. 76

propagation) of the wave motion of the water. It rises and falls with the waves, but both ends of it rise and fall in time and therefore there is no oscillation of the stick. But with stick B, end-on to the wave propagation, each end rises and falls at a different time causing the

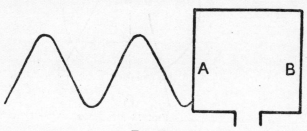

FIG. 77

stick to oscillate. Similarly with a frame or loop aerial if it is at right angles to the direction of the wireless wave motion it will not oscillate, and if in line with the direction of the waves it will oscillate at its maximum. Thus, in Fig. 77, A and B are the two upright sides of a frame aerial. The electrical potential of each one moves up and down under the influence of the wireless waves in whose path it lies. If the frame is at right angles to the wave motion the changes of potential of both A and B will be in time, and therefore there will at

no time be any difference of potential between them and therefore
no current flow. But if they are in line with the wave propagation
the variations of potential will be out of time and the greatest
difference of potential will be reached which will cause a current to
flow between them. This current will be in time with the wireless
wave. Obviously with a larger frame the difference of potential will
be greater and therefore the current will be greater.

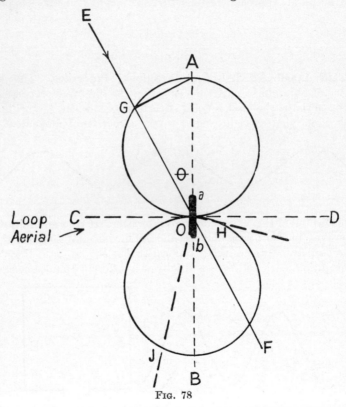

Fig. 78

Now if the powers of reception or transmission in all directions of
a frame aerial be represented by polar co-ordinates, a "figure of 8"
polar diagram as shown in Fig. 78 will result. From this several
important points can be seen—

(i) The optimum point for the frame aerial is along the line *AB*
which is coincident with it; and its strength of reception (or transmission) along this line = *OA* or *OB*.

(ii) The minimum direction is along the line *CD* at right angles
to the frame and equals nil.

(iii) The strength of reception (or transmission) along the line EF is equal to that of a smaller frame equal to ab Cos θ where θ is the angle of the frame ab to the direction of the waves EF. This can be seen from the polar diagram where the strength in direction EF $= OG = OA$ Cos θ.

(iv) Further it can be seen that the change of strength for a given change of direction is much larger near the minimum than it is near the maximum. Thus the angle DOH = angle BOJ; but, whereas near the maximum the change of strength has only been from length OB to length OJ, near the minimum the strength has changed from nil to the length OH. From this it is obvious that the minimum is the most sensitive to changes of direction.

(b) The **Errors** in Direction Finding by loop aerial(s). It is not necessary that a navigator should fully understand the errors of D/F but it is of value to know that they exist.

(i) *Vertical Error* (Antenna effect) is due to each side of the loop having a difference capacity to earth. The remedies for this fault include: screening the loop; "earthing" the centre point; by differential condenser; by feeding to the grids of two "push-pull" valves; or by coupling through a shielded transformer.

(ii) *Direct Pick-up* in D/F receivers is due to the set itself picking up signals. It is cut out by screening the whole set.

(iii) *Quadrantal Error* is due to the waves being absorbed or distorted by conductors near the frame aerial. In aircraft it is usually large. It is found for all directions and allowed for. In aircraft this is done in a manner similar to compass swinging. Knowing the bearing of a given wireless station, D/F bearings of it are taken with the aircraft on about sixteen different equally spaced headings, and a curve of error (plotted against direction in relation to the aircraft's head) is made out.

(iv) *Night Effect* in D/F reception is due to the wave front not being truly vertical and at the same time being abnormally polarized, thus affecting the top and bottom parts of the frame aerial and giving a signal strength even when the uprights of the frame are at right angles to the direction of the station. This obliterates the well-defined minimum and causes other complications. The remedy is to screen the horizontal portions of the aerial.

(v) *Coast Refraction.* Just as a ray of light is bent towards the "normal" when passing from one optical medium to a denser optical medium, so also is a wireless wave bent if it crosses a coastline at an angle. If this angle is near 90° to the coastline the refraction will be negligible but if the wave crosses the coast at a shallow angle the effect will be considerable. If a line is drawn "normal" (i.e. at 90°) through the coastline then the wireless wave will bend away from the "normal" when crossing to seawards and will bend towards the "normal" when crossing towards the land.

(vi) *Aeroplane Error*. This is similar in principle to Night Effect and does not occur when the horizontal parts of the D/F aerial are screened as in Adcock installations. It is due to the distortional effect of the height of the aircraft and the trail angle of its trailing aerial, and is greatest when the aircraft is flying on a course at right angles to the direction of the receiving D/F station. It results in a bearing lying behind the aircraft instead of through it.

(c) **The Uses** of the Loop Aerial in air navigation are many. It may be used to determine a line on which the aircraft lies (a position line), or two such lines to give its position. It may provide a means of keeping an aircraft on a given track, or of keeping it headed for a given wireless station (called "Homing.") Details of D/F stations and stations making directional Transmissions are given in the "Berne List of Stations performing Special Services."

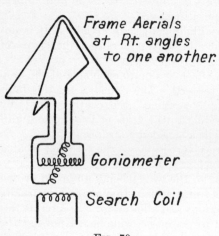

FIG. 79

The various systems may be classified thus—

(i) Ground D/F stations may be of two types—firstly, those which find the direction of incoming waves from aircraft and transmit the result back to the aircraft, and, secondly, those which make transmissions of a directional nature such as beam or beacon.

(ii) Aircraft D/F stations are of the receiving type only. In some cases rotatable means are provided so that the direction of any incoming wave may be found, but in other cases the aircraft must be headed in the direction of the waves (suitable for "Homing").

Details of the various systems follow, together with their advantages and disadvantages. D/F reception will be treated first, then transmission, and finally comparison.

2. D/F RECEPTION. (a) **A Rotating Loop** Aerial is one of the simplest forms of D/F and is very suitable for large aircraft. A loop aerial is connected to a wireless receiver. The loop is rotatable and a scale indicates the direction at right angles to it. Of course it indicates direction only and not "sense." Therefore a bearing taken by it may be in error by 180°. The loop is screened by a tubular sheathing, and owing to its appearance is sometimes called a "bicycle tyre" loop. A sense-finding circuit can be included (Fig. 82).

(b) (i) **Fixed Loop** Direction Finders have two fixed loops at right angles to one another and, when on the ground, facing N. and S., and E. and W. respectively. Each aerial is connected to a coil in a "goniometer," the coils being at right angles to one another. The signal strength in each of these coils corresponds to the receptive power of its aerial, and a "search" coil rotatable in the two fixed

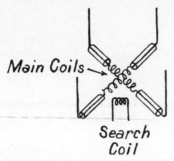

Main Coils→

Aerials with
screening on
horizontal parts

Search
Coil

FIG. 80

coil finds the "minimum" position of incoming signals, which is read off on a scale provided. The aerials, of course, must be accurately matched. Being fixed they can be made very large giving good signal strength, but they cannot be tuned as this might spoil their matching. This system is called the Bellini-Tosi, and is shown diagrammatically in Fig. 79.

(ii) A modified application of this principle is the Adcock, in which provision is made to cut out night effect. The aerials are not complete frames, the only horizontal part being along the bottom and this is screened (and screening earthed). It is shown diagrammatically in Fig. 80.

(c) **Sense Finding** D/F Receivers. If a loop aerial is suitably coupled with an ordinary open aerial, the sense as well as direction of an incoming signal may be found. A switch arrangement allows the receiving set to be connected to the loop aerial alone or to both the open aerial and the loop aerial in either of two different ways—one with open aerial and loop in conjunction, and one with them in opposition. The procedure is as follows: Firstly the switch is put to loop aerial only and direction (by minimum note) found. Then the coil is rotated through 90 degrees (to maximum strength) and the switch put over to each of the other two positions in turn. In one position the strength will be greatly increased and in the other greatly diminished, giving the "sense" of the bearing. Fig. 81 shows the circular polar diagram of an open aerial with the figure-of-eight polar diagram of a loop aerial imposed upon it, giving the heart-shaped diagram of their combined results. If the switch is put over to the other position the heart-shaped diagram will be to the left instead of right. A sense-finding arrangement is usually incorporated in Fixed Loop Direction Finders. The switch

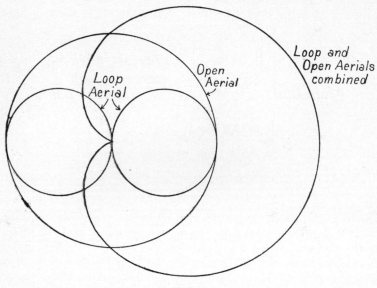

FIG. 81

arrangement for reversing the loop effect is not necessary, the search coil being rotated through 180° instead.

(d) Marconi-Robinson **Homing Device** is a particular application of the sensefinding circuit in modern use in aircraft, particularly where the pilot is also the navigator. This applies the principle just described and employs the three-way switch, but instead of a rotatable loop it has the loop-aerial wound round the aircraft itself in a vertical plane at right angles to the fore and aft axis. Fig. 82 shows the polar diagram. Then if a signal from direction of C is received, the ratio of signal strength with switch at Position 1 and Position 3 respectively will be as OB is to OA. By turning the aircraft till direction of flight is towards C, the signals will be equal $(= OD)$ with switch at 1 or 3.

(e) **Cathode-ray Indicators** are a valuable modern development to

overcome the human errors which may occur in finding the
"minimum" aurally. The two carefully matched Adcock aerials are
coupled through carefully matched circuits to two deflecting elements, at right angles to each other, of a cathode-ray tube. The
ray is projected inside the tube from its base on to its flattened
top, which is called the "screen," where it appears as a spot of
light. A small electrical potential applied to a deflecting plate close
to the ray will deflect it to one side. Incoming signals are applied
proportionately to the two elements provided and the spot of light

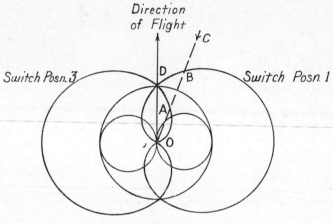

Fɪɢ. 82

is deflected sharply in the direction of the incoming signal which
is read on a graduated circle around the screen.

The main advantages of this means of detecting direction are that
the human element is reduced and that no long dashes are required.
A dot is sufficient to give direction accurately. Moreover D/F on
this principle can be used to fix the position of thunder storm areas
(see chapter on Meteorology).

3. DIRECTIONAL TRANSMISSION. (a) A **Rotating Beacon** transmits a continuous note through a rotating loop aerial. The speed of
rotation is in British stations at present 360° per minute. The continuous note is stopped only to allow two signals to be made. One
(the "North" signal) is to indicate when the plane of the aerial is
lying East and West and therefore its minimum is North and South.
The second (the "East" signal) indicates when the loop has travelled
through 90° and therefore has its minimum lying East and West.
This is for the benefit of an aircraft lying due North or South of the

beacon and therefore was unable being in the minimum, to hear the "North" signal.

The procedure is to time with a stop watch from the North signal to the centre of the first (or second) minimum. Then as 60 seconds = 360°, 1 second = 6°. From this, time is converted into direction which gives the bearing (or reciprocal) of the aircraft from the beacon.

(b) (i) Aural **Equi-signal Beacons** as extensively employed in the airways radio range stations of the U.S.A. have in the older types two frame aerials at right angles to each other, and each at 45° to the track which it is desired to indicate. Each aerial transmits at equal intensity a distinctive signal and the two are interlocked to give a continuous note. The letters used are usually A (·−) and N (−·). All modern installations, however, use vertical type aerials.

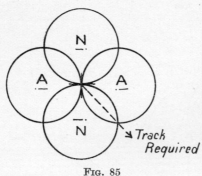

FIG. 85

Fig. 85 gives the polar diagram of the two-loop aerials. Obviously if on the correct track the A and N will interlock to give a continuous note. If off the correct track either A or N will predominate.

(*Note.*—All recent types transmit through goniometer coupling and by this means it is possible to orient the transmission to any desired direction.)

(ii) Visual Equi-signal beacons have two aerials as in the Aural Equi-signal stations, but instead of transmitting interlocking signals, each aerial transmits a continuous signal by "spark" waves at a given frequency. The frequencies chosen are usually about 76 and 85 cycles per second. In the aircraft two reeds side by side, which have natural frequencies of 76 and 85, vibrate under the influence of the two incoming waves. If off the correct track one signal will be stronger then the other and its reed will vibrate through a greater amplitude. This system is not in favour in practice, mainly because the aural system is better.

(c) **Reflected Beams,** particularly on short wavelengths, seem to have big possibilities and of course have been applied in Blind Approach systems.

4. Advantages and Disadvantages of the various systems. (a)
Rotating coil Aerial (i) Advantages: Simple electrically; can be

tuned to frequency of incoming wave; accurate, comparatively; small rotating coils can be used in aircraft; can D/F any station working; can be used with ordinary receiver.

(ii) Disadvantages: Its small size means small signal strength; suffers from night effect; is extra weight in an aircraft.

(b) Bellini-Tosi Fixed Loop D/F. (i) Advantages: Large aerials giving big signal strength picked up; accuracy—any errors can be accurately found and allowed for; requires only the normal transmission and receiving equipment to be in the aircraft; when two or three such stations are working together their results can be quickly plotted at the control station and an actual position sent to the aircraft.

(ii) Disadvantages: Losses in the goniometer; matched aerials cannot be tuned; fairly expensive to install and operate; serves only one aircraft at a time; suffers from night effect.

(c) Adcock. As for (b) above but does not suffer from night effect.

(d) Marconi-Robinson Homing Device. (i) Advantages: Convenient for pilot-navigator; can be used to "home" on any station transmitting or broadcasting.

(ii) Disadvantages: To take ordinary bearing the aircraft may have to be turned off its course; constitutes added weight in the aircraft.

(e) Rotating Beacon. (i) Advantages: Any number of aircraft can take bearings simultaneously and in any direction from it; requires only a receiver in the aircraft.

(ii) Disadvantages: Expensive to maintain in operation; not as accurate as Fixed Loops D/F; slower to take, but no waiting.

(f) Equi-signal Beacon. (i) Advantages: Requires receiver only on aircraft to keep it on its correct track; easily (and best) worked by pilot, therefore no operator required; suitable for regular route; number of aircraft on track can use it simultaneously.

(ii) Disadvantages: Indicates fixed directions only; expensive to maintain in operation; increases risk of collision on much used routes; suffers bending, "multiple courses," local fading, etc.

5. PLOTTING D/F BEARINGS. (a) As a wireless wave travels along the shortes distance between two points it passes along the Great circle between them. Thus D/F bearings are Great circle bearings, and in the case of a bearing *from* a ground station the derived Position Line on which the aircraft must be is part of the Great circle. On some maps a straight line nearly represents a Great circle and therefore for moderate distances D/F bearings may be plotted as found. But on projections where a straight line represents a Rhumb Line a Conversion Angle must be applied to find the

Mercatorial (Rhumb Line) bearing (see para. 27 of Chapter I). The correct procedure on an Admiralty Chart (Mercator's projection) is shown by the following example: a D/F bearing from Hattie's Camp in Posn. 48° 58′ N. 54° 38′ W. is 070° T. The D.R. Posn. is 49° 56′ N. 49° 18′ W. Plot the Position Line derived from this bearing.

Hattie's Camp	48° 58′ N.	54° 38′ W.
D.R. Posn.	49° 56′ N.	49° 18′ W.
Sum and Diff.	98° 54′	5° 20′ = 320′

Conversion Angle = ½d. Long. Sin Mid. Lat. = ½d. Long. Sin Mean Lat. approx.

$$= 160 \, \text{Sin} \, \frac{98° 54'}{2} = 160 \, \text{Sin} \, 49° 27'$$

$$= 121' = 2° 01' = 2° \text{ approx.}$$

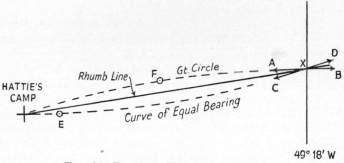

FIG. 84   PLOTTING D/F POSITION LINES

Then if Great-circle bearing is 070° T the Rhumb Line (Mercatorial) bearing = (070 + 2) T = 072° T.

(The Great circle lies on the polar side of the Rhumb Line.)

This Rhumb Line is then plotted from Hattie's Camp in the direction 072° T. But it is not the correct Position Line. To be exact the correct Position Line is part of the Great-circle bearing. To plot it the Mercatorial bearing is first continued to meet the D.R. longitude and through the point where they meet (X in Fig. 84) a small piece of the Great circle (which can be taken as a straight line) is drawn. The direction of this Position Line is obtained by applying Convergency to the original direction of the D/F bearing at the station or by again applying Conversion Angle to the Mercatorial bearing. Thus the direction of the Great circle through the point where the Mercatorial bearing cuts the D.R. Long. is—

$$\text{D/F Bearing Convergency} = 070° \text{ T} + 4° = 074° \text{ T,}$$

or

$$\text{Mercatorial Bearing} + \text{Conversion Angle} = 072° \text{ T} + 2° = 074° \text{ T.}$$

This is the Position Line to be plotted (*AB* in Fig. 84).

(b) The above is fairly obvious, but an entirely different situation occurs if the aircraft takes a D/F bearing of the ground station. The Position Line then obtained is not part of the Great circle path of the wireless wave but instead is part of a **Curve of equal Bearing** which lies on that side of the Mercatorial bearing opposite to the Great-circle bearing. Its direction differs from the Great-circle D/F bearing taken by the value of Convergency.

Now, for example, if at the same moment as Hattie's Camp took the bearing of the aircraft of 070° T, the aircraft took a bearing of 254° T (corrected) to Hattie's Camp, then the line of bearing is the Great circle *AB*, but the Position Line on which the aircraft must be is the Curve of Equal Bearing *CD*. This is clearer if it is noted that at *E* or any other position on the Curve of Equal Bearing the bearing is also 254° T, whereas the bearings of Hattie's Camp from various positions on the Great circle are different in each case. Thus at *F* the bearing to Hattie's Camp would be about 252° T.

To plot the Position Line when the bearing is taken from the aircraft the Conversion Angle is found and the Mercatorial bearing is plotted as in sub-para. (*a*) above. Then through the point where the Mercatorial bearing cuts the D.R. Long. a small part of the Curve of Equal Bearing is drawn.

The Curve of Equal Bearing differs from the Rhumb line by the value of Conversion Angle and lies on the equatorial side of the Rhumb line.

(c) Distance Off a D/F Datum. The author employed the following method in the first instance in conditions where plotting was carried out in difficult circumstances, but its simplicity and reasonable accuracy make it useful for all cases of long distance D/F. All the calculations can be done with a pocket slide rule, but tables can be used if desired.

The principle is best demonstrated by a simple though somewhat unlikely case. Suppose that a D/F station is situated on the North Pole. An aircraft leaves it and flies due South down the Great circle which is the meridian of 70° 00′ W. Now suppose after the aircraft travelled 900′ the D/F station takes a bearing which runs down the meridian 69° 00′ W. Then the aircraft is 1° to port of his intended track. If a diagram is drawn, it can be obviously seen that the Distance to port of his Track = Departure

$$= 1° \text{ Cos Lat.}$$
$$= 1° \text{ Sin Co-Lat.}$$
$$= 1° \text{ Sin Distance from station}$$
$$= 60' \text{ Sin } 900'$$
$$= 60' \text{ Sin } 15° = 15·5' \text{ to port of the meridian } 70° \ 00' \text{ W.,}$$

which has, in this case, been taken as the Datum.

To take a more real case, suppose an aircraft was flying from Foynes, Ireland, to Botwood, Newfoundland, both of which have short wave D/F stations, then the Great circle between them would be carefully plotted on to the chart before flight as a datum. The direction of this Great circle through Foynes is 281° 50' T, and 065° 13' T through Botwood. If after running a distance of 1100' from Foynes that station gives a bearing of 283° T, then the aircraft is to starboard of the datum, and the Distance Off the Datum

$$= \text{Bearing Diff. } \times \text{ Sin Arcual Dist. from station}$$
$$= (283° - 281° \ 50') \text{ Sin } 1100'$$
$$= 1° \ 10' \text{ Sin } 18° \ 20'$$
$$= 70' \text{ Sin } 18° \ 20'$$
$$= 22' \text{ off datum to the northward.}$$

This distance is therefore marked off at right angles to the Great-circle datum and through the mark the Position Line, if desired, is plotted. The direction of this Position Line is the direction of the datum nearest the D.R. Posn. + or − the Bearing Difference × Cos Arcual Distance from station. Thus in this case if the datum is, for example, running in the direction 260 T then the Position Line direction is $(260° + 70' \text{ Cos } 18° \ 20') = (260° + 66') = 261° \ 06'$ T $= 261°$ T approx.

A somewhat different case is shown by the following example.

Example. Horta in the Azores bears 231° 34' T by Great circle from Foynes, Ireland, at a distance of 1171'. The track of an aircraft from Botwood in Newfoundland to Horta approaches this track at right angles to it approx. During the flight a bearing of the aircraft of $239\frac{1}{2}°$ T is obtained by Foynes. At what distance from Horta is the aircraft according to this bearing?

The datum used is the Great circle through Foynes and Horta. Then—

$$\text{Distance off} = \text{Bearing Diff. Sin Arcual Distance}$$
$$= (239° \ 30' - 231° \ 34') \text{ Sin } 1171'$$
$$= 476' \text{ Sin } 19° \ 31' = 158·7' \text{ from Horta.}$$

An approximate method of calculation can, if desired, be used for bearings when the aircraft is not more than about 900′ from the station. Above this distance the method would not be sufficiently accurate. It is as follows: Instead of the formula,

Distance Off = Bearing Diff. Sin Arcual Distance,

which is strictly accurate, the following approximation may be used.

Distance Off = Bearing Diff. in Radians × Distance

$$= \frac{\text{Bearing Diff. in Degrees}}{57 \cdot 3} \times \text{Distance}$$

This formula is only correct in a plane triangle and therefore its use must be limited to small distances to avoid inaccuracies in spherical triangles.

6. TESTING THE SENSE OF A D/F BEARING. At regular intervals during the past few years mishaps have occurred to British civil aircraft due to errors in the "sense" of D/F Bearings taken. Even although the D/F Receiver includes a means of determining the sense as well as the direction of a bearing, it is highly desirable that whenever the slightest doubt exists the sense should be tested and ascertained navigationally. This may be necessary with any bearing, but is more likely in the case of a bearing taken by the aircraft's own loop. In all cases the principle is the same. It depends on the direction of change of bearing when the aircraft flies on a course which will ensure a change of bearing. This course must ensure that the Radio station lies to port or to starboard. A series of bearings are then taken. If the bearing of the station from the aircraft is increasing, then the station is to starboard; if it is decreasing then the station is to port. This statement applies to corrected true bearings and to relative bearings read on a 0°–360° scale, but it does not apply to relative bearings on the more confusing 0°–180° to port and 0°–180° to starboard scale unless the bearings happen to fall in the starboard half of the scale. In the case of the P. and Stbd. scale it is highly advisable to reduce the readings to corrected true bearings.

Example. Captain A in G-EBXN in poor visibility is approaching station XYZ on a small island where he intends to land. When very near the station on a course of 045° T his Radio Officer takes a bearing of XYZ of 001° (scale 0°–360° to Stbd.). Q.E. Correction Nil. That is, XYZ is almost exactly dead ahead. Further bearings taken during the next ten minutes continue to indicate that the station is dead ahead. But as it does not appear, Captain A alters course 90° to port to test sense, i.e. to 315° T. The last bearing on Co 045° T was 000 Q.E. Nil. ∴ Bearing = 045° T to XYZ. After flying on the new Co 315° T for three minutes another bearing is taken and equals 055°, Q.E. Corr. = + 5°, ∴ Bearing = 015° T. The bearing is decreasing. To confirm this, Captain A flies on for a further four minutes and another bearing is taken of 015°, Q.E. Corr. + 5°, ∴ Bearing = 335° T, which is a further decrease. This indicates that the station is to port of the new course, that is, it has been overflown.

If in doubt plot the bearings, or even sketch them roughly.

The following rule of thumb is sound. If in doubt when homing on a station as to whether it is ahead or astern, alter course to port, and if the bearings then decrease the station has been overflown, or if they increase the station has not been reached.

(Loops with scales graduated from 0° to 180° to port and starboard are confusing for this purpose and should not be used in aircraft.)

SECTION 2

SIGNALS

7. DISTRESS SIGNALS are only to be made on the authority of the Captain of Aircraft, and this will only be given when the aircraft is in grave danger, or grave danger to the aircraft is imminent, and requires immediate help. The following are the methods of indicating distress—

(a) By Wireless Telegraphy (W/T). (i) SOS will be sent three times followed by "de" and the call sign of the aircraft. This will be followed if possible by the position of the aircraft, and if circumstances still permit the nature of the distress. This is sent on the aircraft wavelength 900 metres (333 Kcs.) if over or on land, but on 600 metres (500 Kcs.) if over or on the sea, at a speed of not more than sixteen words per minute.

(ii) Automatic alarm gear is carried by many ships. If over or on the sea the distress signal should, but only if time permits, be preceded by the alarm signal which consists of twelve long dashes of four seconds each with one second break, sent in one minute. Any three consecutive dashes if sent properly are sufficient to actuate auto-alarms and so attract the attention of operators to the fact that a distress signal is being sent.

(b) Radio Telephony (R/T). The word MAYDAY is spoken three times followed by the call sign of the aircraft, and if possible the position and nature of the distress.

(c) By the International Code distress signal which consists of the flags " NC." N is a blue and white chequered flag and C has blue, white, red, white, and blue horizontal stripes.

(d) By the distant signal which consists of a black ball or shape with a square flag above or below it.

(e) By the firing of a gun or other explosive signal at one minute intervals.

(f) By a continuous sound on any fog signalling apparatus.

(g) By lamp flashing or sound signalling, the signal SOS is sent as in W/T.

(h) At night, by any sort of rocket or shell fired at short intervals one at a time.

(i) At night, by flames or flares on the craft in distress.

8. URGENCY SIGNALS are only made concerning the safety of
(i) the aircraft which sends it,
(ii) some person on board the aircraft or,
(iii) some craft or person within sight of the aircraft. One of the following methods will be used—

(a) By W/T. (i) In a general case the signal XXX is sent three times before a call addressed to the nearest ground (or in exceptional circumstances to "CQ" = All stations) giving the urgent message.

(ii) Only in the case of the aircraft's being about to forced-land the signal PAN will be sent three times instead of the XXX. This indicates that the aircraft does not require immediate assistance.

(b) By R/T. In the general case and in the case of the aircraft forced-landing, the word PAN will be spoken three times and then the message, addressed to the nearest ground station, will be sent.

(c) By lamp signalling, etc., the group XXX may be used as for W/T. If this is to be done from the air to a ship, the aircraft should first circle round and fire green lights or make green flashes before passing the message.

(d) If no visual signalling apparatus is on the aircraft and it wishes to draw the attention of a ship to some craft or person in danger, it should circle the ship, fire green lights and then fly straight from the ship towards the craft or person in danger.

9. SAFETY SIGNALS are made concerning matters affecting safety of navigation, etc., or meteorological information of a serious nature.

(a) In W/T the group TTT is sent three times followed by "de" and the call sign of the aircraft, and then the message.

(b) In R/T the word "Sécurité" is spoken three times followed by the call sign of the aircraft and the message.

10. The **PRIORITY** of Wireless Messages is as follows—

   (i) Distress messages.

  (ii) Urgency messages—XXX.

 (iii) Urgency messages—PAN.

 (iv) Safety messages.

  (v) D/F working.

 (vi) Government messages (S).

(vii) Meteorological reports and information.

(viii) Service messages (pertaining to the signals service—A).

 (ix) Routine traffic messages (positions, etc.).

  (x) Public telegrams.

11. SEMAPHORE SIGNALLING. The semaphore alphabet is given in Table I, which also shows the "Attention" sign, the "Answering"

TABLE I

and acknowledging sign (C) and the "Break" sign. Then the procedure is as follows (assuming that the identity of each is known to the other)—

   (i) Sender faces receiver and makes Attention sign.

  (ii) Receiver prepares to read and makes the Answering sign.

 (iii) Sender signals the words of the message and the receiver acknowledges each word with the letter C. If a word is not acknowledged the sender repeats it immediately.

 (iv) If a mistake in sending is made it is erased by a number of

TABLE II
INTERNATIONAL MORSE CODE ALPHABET

A · –	H · · · ·	Q – – · –	1 · – – – –
ä · – · –	I · ·	R · – ·	2 · · – – –
à · – – · –	J · – – –	S · · ·	3 · · · – –
B – · · ·	K – · –	T –	4 · · · · –
C – · – ·	L · – · ·	U · · –	5 · · · · ·
CH – – – –	M – –	ü · · – –	6 – · · · ·
D – · ·	N – ·	V · · · –	7 – – · · ·
E ·	ñ – – · – –	W · – –	8 – – – · ·
è · · – · ·	O – – –	X – · · –	9 – – – – ·
F · · – ·	ö – – – ·	Y – · – –	0 – – – – –
G – – ·	P · – – ·	Z – – · ·	

TABLE III
PUNCTUATION AND PROCEDURE SIGNS

Meaning	Sign	
Call for Unknown Ship . .	AA AA, etc.	= · – · – · – · –
From	de	= – · · · ·
Answering sign	T̄T̄T̄T̄	= ––––
Full stop or decimal . . .	I I I	= · · · · · ·
Space	I I	= · · · ·
Break	B̄T̄	= – · · · –
Oblique Bar (fraction bar) . .	X̄Ē	= – · · – ·
Repeat	ŪD̄ or ĪM̄Ī	= · · – – · ·
All after	Λ A	= · – · –
All before	A B	= · – – · · ·
Word after	W A	= · – – · –
Word before	W B	= · – – – · · ·
Repeat back	G	= – – ·
Ending sign	ĀR̄	= · – · – ·
You are correct	C	= – · – ·
Word received	T	= ––––
Message received	R	= · – ·
Light not properly trained or focused	W	= · – –
International Code groups follow .	P R B	= · – – · · – · – · · ·

E's, and the last correct word repeated before continuing the message.

(v) After the last word has been acknowledged, the sender makes the Ending sign—the letters AR.

(vi) Numbers must be spelt out, and the word "Decimal" spelt to indicate a decimal point.

(vii) The standard speed of working is eight words per minute.

12. MORSE SIGNALLING. (a) The International Morse Code alphabet is given in Table II, together with the numerals. Punctuation and procedure signs are given in Table III.

A message consists of five parts—the call, the identity of the sender, break sign, the text of the message, and the ending sign. The procedure is as follows—

(i) The sender calls up with AA's or the receiver's call sign.

(ii) The receiver answers, when all ready, with a series of long dashes.

(iii) Then, only if it is desired to exchange identities, the sender sends "de" and his call sign which is repeated back by sender, and gives "C" for the repetition. Then the receiver's identity is passed to the sender in the same manner.

(iv) Before the text of the message the break sign is sent and repeated back by the receiver.

(v) The text is sent. If in plain language each word is acknowledged with a T by the receiver. If in code each group is repeated back as soon as it is sent, and a C obtained from the sender. A number is always repeated back, like a code group, as soon as it is completed (not each figure separately, but the whole number), and a C obtained for the repetition.

(vi) The Ending sign (AR) is made by the sender at the end of the message.

(vii) If the whole message has been received the receiver sends R. If part has been missed or is doubtful the receiver sends the repeat sign followed by WA, WB, AA or AB as appropriate, and the sender repeats the required part.

If the whole is doubtful the receiver sends the repeat sign only and the whole message is repeated.

(b) (i) The "Repeat Back" sign is used when great accuracy is required. When it is used the receiver must repeat back every word of the message as soon as received and obtain a C for it from the sender.

(ii) The signal W sent from A to B may indicate that B's light is burning badly, is out of focus or that it is not trained on to A accurately. In the first case the light is adjusted or focused until A ceases

TABLE IV
INTERNATIONAL CODE OF SIGNALS

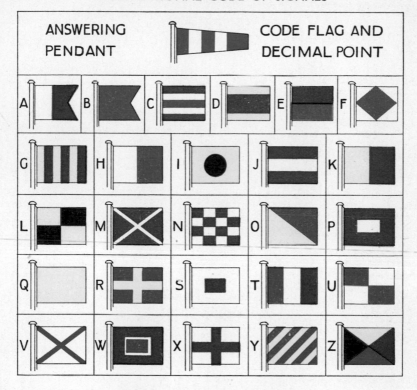

ANSWERING PENDANT

CODE FLAG AND DECIMAL POINT

NUMERAL PENDANTS

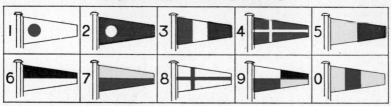

SUBSTITUTES

FIRST SUBSTITUTE

SECOND SUBSTITUTE

THIRD SUBSTITUTE

to send W's. In the latter case, B, with key pressed, sights firstly at A, and then at various points around A. As soon as the beam is directed properly at A he quickly makes a T to B, from which B ascertains the error in alignment of his lamp and in future allows for it. Of course this will not occur at night as sights are unnecessary —sighting along the beam usually being better.

13. (a) The **INTERNATIONAL CODE OF SIGNALS** provides a means of signalling when within visibility range, by means of flags (see the 1931 International Code of Signals, Vol. 1). The twenty-six alphabetical flags, the numeral pendants, the three substitute flags, and the answering pendant are given in Table IV. By means of these flags, groups to which meanings are given by the code and groups constituting call signs, etc., may be sent, and plain language spelt out. Groups are always read from the top downwards. The following must be understood—

(i) A "Hoist" is a group or groups of flags on one halyard.

(ii) "Close up" means that the flags are hoisted up to the full extent of the halyard.

(iii) "At the Dip" means that the flags are hoisted only about half-way up.

(iv) A "Tackline" is a length of line about 6 ft. long used to separate two groups.

(b) **Types of Signals.** Groups consist of one, two, three, four, or five letters. Letters and figures are never mixed except that positions, times, and bearings have a letter preceding the figures to indicate their nature. If names occur in a signal they are spelt out using the alphabetical signals given in sub-para. (e).

(i) Single-letter signals are allotted meanings of special importance and are given fully hereafter.

(ii) Two-letter signals are also allotted important meanings including distress, navigational, weather, and seamanship warnings, etc. A few examples only are given hereafter. The following two signals must be remembered:

JD means "You are standing into danger."

and NC means "I am in distress and require immediate assistance."

(iii) Three-letter signals are allotted the multitudinous meanings of the general vocabulary section and also the meanings given in the special sections such as model verb, standard time, relative bearings, and points of the compass. No attempt is made here, on account of the space required, to give three-figure signals with their meanings. Publications such as "Brown's Signalling" give a large and useful selection.

(iv) Four-letter signals are the call letters (which are the same as the W/T call sign) of ships, except for those four-letter groups which have the letter A uppermost. Such groups are geographical signals meaning the names of places, etc., all over the world.

(v) Five-letter signals are aircraft call letters (which are the same as their registration letters and W/T call signs).

(c) **Substitute Flags** are provided so that by their use it becomes unnecessary to carry a large number of each alphabetical flag and numeral pendant. A Substitute Flag indicates a repetition of a flag or pendant already in the group.

The first Substitute indicates repetition of the top flag of the group.

The second Substitute indicates repetition of the second flag of the group.

The third Substitute indicates repetition of the third flag of the group.

But it refers to the top, second or third flag respectively of the same class as that immediately preceding it (that is, alphabetical, or numerical). Thus:

AAA (meaning "1 Point on the Port Bow") is hoisted as A, 1st Sub., 2nd Sub.

AALL (meaning "Amazon River") is hoisted as A, 1st Sub., L, 3rd Sub.

T 1221 (meaning "1221 Hours") is hoisted as T, 1, 2, 2nd Sub., 1st Sub.

P 5151 (meaning 51° 51′) is hoisted as P, 5, 1, 1st Sub., 2nd Sub. If the Answering Pendant is used in a group of figures (to indicate a decimal point), it is not counted in interpreting Substitute flags in the group.

(d) The **Model Verb.** In order that verbs taken out of the general vocabulary may be read in their correct tense, mood, etc., a group indicating this is hoisted before the group meaning the verb required. The model on which the first group is based is the verb " to glean." The groups ADW to AGP inclusive are allotted various forms of the verb to glean—in the Affirmative, Negative and Interrogative, First Second and Third Persons, Singular and Plural. Then for example AGJ—HQU—AJMX, means "Have you informed Longships Light." From

AGJ   = "Have you gleaned."
HQU   = "Inform."
AJMX = "Longship Light" (from the Geographical section).

(e) **Alphabetical Signals.** When it is desired to spell out a name the following is the procedure—

Alphabetical Signal No. 1 is made to indicate that the signals which follow form a word or words, and not Code groups. This indication is effective until cancelled by Alphabetical Signal No. 3.

Alphabetical Signal No. 2 is made to indicate the end of a word or a full stop between initials.

Alphabetical Signal No. 3 is made to indicate that spelling is finished and anything which follows has its Code meaning.

(i) Alphabetical Signal No. 1 = Answering Pendant, over E.

(ii)   ,,   ,,   No. 2 =   ,,   ,,   ,, F.

(iii)   ,,   ,,   No. 3 =   ,,   ,,   ,, G.

(f) **Time.** (i) Time is expressed by the letter T followed by four figures indicating hours and minutes of the 24 hour day notation.

(ii) Groups indicating the Standard or Time Zone used are allotted, thus: ACN = Fiji time; ADC = G.M.T. or Western European time; ADR = Ship's time; ADU = Zone Time of Zone plus— (Zone number indicated).

(g) **Position.** Latitude and Longitude are signalled by a letter P followed by a four-figure group indicating degrees and minutes. Latitude is always signalled first and longitude second. It is usually not necessary to signal North or South Lat., nor East or West Long. But near Equator, or the meridian of Greenwich or of Long. 180°, it may be necessary. In this case the flags N or S, E or W, are used as appropriate, following the group to which they refer and separated from it by a tackline. Thus: P 0012 — N, P 4830 would mean 00° 12′ North Lat., 48° 30′ Long. (East or West being known.)

If the longitude is over 100° E. or W. the first figure, indicating the hundred, is omitted without causing confusion.

(h) **Bearings.** (i) Bearings are signalled by the letter X followed by three figures indicating number of degrees in the three-figure notation. True bearing is meant unless magnetic is expressly stated. Thus: JXN — X 005, means "Object bearing 005 T." And WR — X 084 — IXU, means "You should steer directly for the beacon or object bearing 084 M." The group IXU means Magnetic. Bearings are always reckoned from the ship making the signal.

(ii) Relative bearings are signalled by three-letter groups. A group is allotted for each point (11¼°) to port and starboard and for each 10° to port and starboard, of the heading. They include from AAA to ABF for bearings to port, and ABG to ACM for bearings to starboard.

(i) **Courses** are signalled by a group of three figures indicating the course in degrees by the three-figure notation, and means True unless stated to be Magnetic. This group is preceded by a group from the Code. Thus: JL — 100, means "I am about to alter course to 100 T."

(j) Distances are signalled simply as numerals expressing miles— presumably Nautical (unless otherwise signalled). Thus X 124 — 37 — AAFD means "Position bearing 124 T from Ailsa Craig distant 37 miles."

(k) Procedure. (i) To call a particular craft its call letters are hoisted first, or above the signal. If the signal is meant for all craft it is hoisted without addressing call letters.

(ii) To answer, the craft addressed hoists the Answering pendant at the Dip as soon as it is ready to read. When it has read the signal it hauls its Answering pendant close up, and the sender then can haul down the group or groups then displayed.

(iii) To end a message the sender hoists his Answering pendant singly close up—this acknowledged in the usual way (by the receiver hauling his Answering pendant close up).

(iv) Hoists, if made on a number of halyards simultaneously, are read in the following order of priority: Foremast; triatic stay (between masts); starboard yard-arm; port yard-arm. If more than one group is on one halyard they are separated by a tackline and read in order from the top.

(v) When signals are read but not understood the receiver must keep the Answering pendant at the Dip, and hoist an appropriate group such as VB meaning "Signal is not understood though flags are distinguished."

SINGLE-LETTER SIGNALS

A   I am undergoing a speed trial
B   I am taking in or discharging explosives
C   Yes (Affirmative)
D   Keep clear of me—I am manœuvring with difficulty
E   I am altering my course to starboard
F   I am disabled. Communicate with me
G   I require a pilot
H   I have a pilot on board
I   I am altering my course to port
J   I am going to send a message by semaphore
K   You should stop your vessel instantly
L   You should stop. I have something important to communicate
M   I have a doctor on board
N   No (Negative)
O   Man overboard
P   IN HARBOUR (Blue Peter)—All persons are to repair on board as the vessel is about to proceed to sea
     AT SEA—Your lights are out, or burning badly

Q   My vessel is healthy and I request free pratique
R   The way is off my ship; you may feel your way past me
S   My engines are going full speed astern
T   Do not pass ahead of me
U   You are standing into danger
V   I require assistance
W   I require medical assistance
X   Stop carrying out your intentions and watch for my signals
Y   I am carrying mails
Z   To be used to address or call shore stations

TWO-LETTER SIGNALS

Abandon

AC Aircraft indicated if necessary will have to be abandoned
AD I must abandon my vessel

Afloat and Aground

AT I am aground and require immediate assistance

Aircraft

BL Aeroplane is down in position indicated and requires immediate assistance
BM Aeroplane reported in distress is receiving assistance
BN Aircraft are engaged in taking off and landing on, or near, this vessel. You should NOT approach too near
BO Aircraft indicated if necessary left at time indicated
BP Aircraft indicated if necessary is seriously damaged. Will you take off mail and passengers
BU I am about to alight to make good defect. Will you stand by me
BV I am alighting in position indicated; am short of petrol
BX I am alighting to pick up crew of disabled aircraft in position indicated
BY I am forced to alight. Stand by to pick up crew
BZ I shall endeavour to fly to the land now
CD Sea is smooth enough for you to alight near me
CE Sea is too rough for you to alight
CG You should alight as near to me as possible
CH You should alight to leeward of me, I am stopped
CI You should alight to windward of me, I am stopped
CN Have you sighted or heard of aeroplane in distress
CP Is aeroplane in a condition to proceed
CR Is the sea smooth enough for me to alight near you

Anchoring.

DC You should anchor as convenient

Assistance.

DO I am drifting and require assistance
DT I cannot render assistance, to
EA I will stand by you, or vessel indicated
EH Can I assist you
EI Can you assist me, or vessel indicated
JD You are standing into danger
NC I am in distress and require immediate assistance

CHAPTER V

"Precision Pays"

(*Note.*—"Dead Reckoning," or D.R. as it is usually called, appears to have originated from the expression "Deduced Reckoning" which was abbreviated to "Ded. Reckoning.")

1. PRINCIPLES SUMMARIZED. Air navigation, which here includes the term "Air Pilotage" is neither an art nor a science but a very interesting and rather complex mixture of both. Very occasionally it may be a little disappointing, but it is generally of the utmost importance in both safety and economy.

Fundamentally, navigation consists of calculation aided and checked by some form of observation, terrestrial, celestial, or radio. This calculation consists of finding "how to get there"—the "how" being the direction and the distance, and how to maintain that direction and for how long, etc. All this calculation, requiring as it does a knowledge of mathematics, plotting, map projections, compasses, meteorology, etc., may be rightly included in the term Dead Reckoning. Although Dead Reckoning (D.R.) is regarded sometimes as something rather elementary, it is the backbone and foundation of all good navigation. Although simple in principle, it benefits enormously from additional knowledge, wide outlook, and versatility. It is the skeleton of calculations, mathematical and plotted, to which are attached the data derived from observations of any sort.

This chapter is based on the general principles that—

(i) Some data are usually known to start with or indicated in the aircraft (usually Original Position, Course, and Air Speed).

(ii) Some data can usually be found by observations (usually resulting in data concerning Wind Speed and Direction, Track, Ground Speed (G/S) a Position Line, or a Position).

(iii) From (i) and (ii) used in conjunction with data of the form of the Earth, or data from maps, reckoning and/or plotting may be carried out to conduct the aircraft with surety to its required destination.

So much for generalizations. To proceed with the details of ways and means, and of procedure, etc., very briefly—

2 (a) General. The following points should be remembered in taking observations—

(i) Whenever possible, such as in taking Drifts and Tail Bearings, a number of sights should be taken and the average taken as the correct sight. Thus—

Drifts = 10 Red, 12 Red, 11 Red, 8 Red, all taken within three minutes.

Therefore Average Drift = $10\frac{1}{4}°$ = 10 Red.

Tail Bearings = 320 C, 317 C, 319 C, 325 C, and 319 C—all taken within five minutes. Therefore Tail Bearing = 320 C.

(ii) It is advisable to give the pilot warning when an observation is to be made, so that he may pay very special attention to keeping the aircraft steady and on its course, and so helping to obtain accurate observations.

(b) **A Position Line** is a line on which it is known that the aircraft is, or was at a particular time. Position Lines may be obtained by one of the following methods—

(i) *Relative Bearings* of objects within sight are measured by sighting a Bearing Plate on to the object and reading the angle indicated on the Plate, relative to the Course of the aircraft. This, when applied to the Co. T, gives the True Bearing which may be plotted on a map or chart.

Care must be taken that the aircraft is exactly on its Course, when the sight is taken.

(ii) *Compass Bearings* of objects within sight are taken by bringing the sights on to the object and reading its direction through the prism on the scale below. Then Average Compass Bearing ± Deviation = Magnetic Bearing. And Magnetic Bearing ± Variation = True Bearing which is plotted.

In using a Bearing Compass much depends on the accuracy with which bearings are taken. The observer should first watch the aircraft's movements and when he sees that it is straight and level he should immediately take his bearing of the object.

(iii) *Visual Transits* of terrestrial objects give most accurate position lines. A transit is the passing of an aircraft over or along a straight line through two terrestrial objects. The time of a transit is observed, the two objects recognized on the map or chart and a straight line drawn through them giving a Position line. This is the simplest and most accurate Position Line obtainable in air navigation. The ratio of distance between objects to distance of aircraft from nearest object should be large if possible.

(iv) *D/F Wireless Bearings* are taken and modified if necessary by Conversion Angle, as described in the last chapter.

(v) *Astronomical Position Lines* are obtained by methods to be described in a later chapter.

(c) **Course** is the direction in which the aircraft's fore and aft line is pointing expressed in degrees (as a three-figure group) measured from the True meridian, Magnetic meridian, etc. In marine navigation the term "course steered" has the same meaning, and in American aviation "heading" is generally used.

Course may be laid off by reference to, or may be measured by: (i) the ordinary magnetic compass, (ii) the gyro compass (not at present applied satisfactorily in the air), (iii) the magnetic master gyro compass, (iv) the Earth inductor compass, (v) sun compass, (vi) the so-called radio compass (which gives a course in relation to a particular wireless station), etc.

The angular difference between the course steered and the track made good is the **Drift** measured in degrees to port or starboard of the course.

Track is the direction in which the aircraft is moving over the Earth's surface, usually expressed in degrees (as a three-figure group) measured from the True meridian, or Magnetic meridian.

The following observations give the track of an aircraft more or less directly—

(i) *Drift* may be measured by any form of drift indicator, as an angle to port or starboard of the course steered. If the drift wires are being lined up to the general impression of ground movement (particularly over the sea) the eye of the observer should be well away from the wires, giving an apparently faster movement along them. But if particular objects are moving down the drift wires for sighting purposes, then the eye should be close (depending on the height of the aircraft), so that the one object can be watched over a long distance. In either case the head of the observer should be steadied against some part of the aircraft.

If Course = 178 T, and Drift = 10 Red, or 10 to Port. Then Track = 168 T.

(ii) *Tail Bearings* (Back Bearings) may be measured in four ways —by Tail Drift Sight, by Bearing Plate, by markings on the tailplane, or by Bearing Compass—in all cases sighting on an object which has been passed over by the aircraft (or on an aluminium-dust Sea Marker or smoke bomb, dropped from the aircraft if over the sea) and measuring its direction.

In the first three methods the direction is measured in relation to the aircraft's direction and therefore care must be taken that the aircraft is steady on its exact course when a sight is being taken. In the last method the care necessary for all compass bearings must be exercised. In all cases the object should be observed for as long as it is in sight, or until an alteration of Course. An average of a number of sights should be accepted.

(iii) *Map-reading* may give track—by recognition of two objects passed over, and measuring on the map the direction of the second in relation to the first.

(d) Air Speed. The *True Air Speed* (TAS) is what it says and is best expressed in Knots. It is generally measured by an air-speed indicator to which a number of corrections must be applied. Firstly there are the two atmospheric corrections, Height correction and Temperature correction, which are usually applied together (under the name of the former) by means of a computer, but may be applied separately. When no computer is available, the correction factor can be found accurately as follows: if the temperature differs from the standard for the height (see Appendix IV (4)) then the "pressure height" (corrected altimeter with index reading from 1013·2 mbs.) must be converted to "density height" by subtracting about 118·8 ft. for each degree Centigrade above Standard temperature, and vice versa. This "density height" is then entered in the list of Relative Densities (σ). The factor by which Indicated Air Speed

(I.A.S.) must be multiplied to obtain the T.A.S. is $\dfrac{1}{\sqrt{\sigma}}$. Inversely,

I.A.S. $= \sqrt{\sigma} \times$ T.A.S. (See Appendix IV for values of $\dfrac{1}{\sqrt{\sigma}}$.)

The other two corrections to be applied to the air-speed indicator reading (A.S.I.) are the Position Error correction and Instrument correction. The latter, which must be small, is found by calibration against the pressure in a U-tube or against another air-speed indicator (see Chapter III). The former error is, however, most involved (more so than is generally realized). It is due to the interference effect on the pressure and/or static head of the air-speed indicator due to other parts of the aircraft and varies with speed and attitude (and therefore load and/or height). It is found by comparison with (i) electric air-log trailled well clear, (ii) trailing static head A.S.I., (iii) double ground runs flying fairly low, etc. Then, A.S.I. $\pm$ P.E. $\pm$ I.E. $=$ I.A.S.

I.A.S. $\times$ Height Corr. (and Temp.) factor $=$ T.A.S.

i.e. I.A.S. $\times \dfrac{1}{\sqrt{\sigma}} =$ T.A.S.

Instead of multiplying by $\dfrac{1}{\sqrt{\sigma}}$, a simple approximation of adding 1·6 per cent of the I.A.S. for every 1000 ft., or about 1·7 per cent for each 1000 ft. if flying higher than 10,000 ft., may be used.

Ground Speed which is the actual speed of the aircraft in relation to the ground, may be found more or less directly by the following observations—

(i) Timing Bead method of measuring ground speed (G/S) can best be used over land but is also practical over the sea in many cases. The height of the aircraft as read by altimeter and accurately corrected by computer (and corrected for the height of the ground) is set on the rear-sight slider on the height bar of a drift indicator and the time is taken by stop watch for an object to move along the drift wires from one bead to another. The distance between these beads is so arranged in relation to the scale of the height, that they subtend a given distance on the ground. The principle is obvious if a figure is drawn. Error is likely to occur owing to inaccuracies in height.

(ii) Map-reading and timing the aircraft's movement over a given distance is the simplest means of measuring G/S.

(iii) A Cross Bearing cutting the track of an aircraft at right angles or thereabouts gives a fairly accurate indication of distance covered since last known position, and therefore G/S. This method is particularly useful in flying boats when leaving a coast.

3. WIND FINDING. (a) General. The wind, being so variable, constitutes the most awkward problem in practical air navigation. It varies from day to day and season to season, is subject to squalls, gusts, and lulls, and varies with topographical irregularities. Therefore Wind Speed and Direction (W.S.D., or W.S. and D.) must be found accurately and often for good D.R. Hereafter are given a few methods of finding wind. Naturally those methods which can be carried out without requiring the aircraft to turn off its course are the more valuable, and are given first. (*Note.*—The bombsight being a Service instrument only, none of the bombsight methods are given here. But they are the same in principle as three of the methods described.

It is recommended that on long flights the wind should be marked on the map or chart where and when it is found. These wind-plottings together with a previous knowledge of the meteorological map of pressure distribution, etc., may often form a valuable guide as to future probable wind changes.

Wind may be found by—

(b) The **Constant Course method** is that in which the aircraft flies at a constant known course and Air Speed (A/S) from a known original position. After a short while (preferably about 10–15 minutes, to get a good average) the position of the aircraft over some object recognizable on the map, and the time are noted. Of course, this second position may have been found by some method other than map-reading (e.g. two cross bearings, etc.), or the Tr. and G/S may be found by drift, and timing bead. Then one of two methods can be used—

(i) The Co. may be plotted and the air-distance (i.e. distance which would have been travelled in still air) is marked off on it at a point. A line drawn from this point to the second position is the direction of the wind, and its length according to the scale multiplied by $\dfrac{60}{\text{Time in Minutes}}$, is the wind speed in knots.

(ii) The track may be measured, and the distance flown over the ground in the given time converted to G/S. Then Tr. and G/S, and Co. and A/S are plotted to find wind as in Fig. 85. This may be

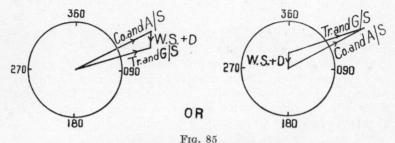

FIG. 85

done on any form of Course and Distance Calculator (C.D.C.) if preferred.

(c) The **Double Drift method** necessitates flying on at least two courses about 30 degrees apart, at the very least. But if it is arranged that these courses are flown to each side of the required course and

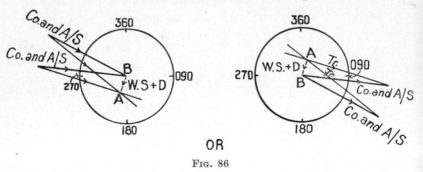

FIG. 86

for a few minutes only each, this method will not take the aircraft off its correct track to any appreciable extent.

The procedure is: Aircraft flies on one course and the drift is measured by drift indicator or tail bearing. It then flies on another course (at a fairly wide angular distance—to give a good "cut") and the drift is again measured. The two courses and A/S's are plotted from one point and the track of each plotted as shown in Fig. 86. AB = wind speed to scale. A third course may be steered and drift taken, as a check. It will probably be found that the three tracks do not cut in one point but make a small triangle, or "cocked-hat." The centre of this triangle is then taken in measuring the wind speed and direction.

The courses suggested are: the course required, course required + 25 degrees, and course required − 25 degrees. It should only be necessary to be on the two last mentioned for about two or three minutes each.

(d) **Partial " Guess-timation."** ("Guess-timation" is an art in navigation which should not generally be encouraged as it can become a dangerous practice. But it undoubtedly has its uses and therefore cannot be ruled out. The two methods that follow can only be used successfully at comparatively low altitudes.)

(i) Wind direction is estimated. This may be done by taking a bearing of smoke direction or on wind "lanes" on water giving surface wind direction, and from meteorological knowledge and experience making an allowance for height. Drift is then measured by drift indicator or tail bearing when on a known Co and A/S. Then Co, A/S, Tr. and Wind Direction are plotted—Track and Wind Direction cutting to give Wind Speed and G/S.

(ii) Wind speed is estimated. This is done on similar lines to the above. The surface wind speed is estimated and allowance made for the height at which the aircraft is flying. Then Course A/S, and Track (from drift or back bearing) are plotted, and with radius equal to wind speed to scale and centre on centre of plotting, the track line is cut. It can be seen in Fig. 87, that in this method there are two points where wind speed could cut the track line. Therefore this method cannot be used unless it is certain which is correct. In any case (i) above is the much better method.

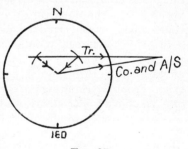

Fig. 87

(*Note.*—The following methods require the aircraft to fly specially for the purpose of wind finding.)

(e) The **Timing Bead** method is done by flying directly into wind (or down wind) so that there is no drift. This is done by setting a drift indicator at zero and, by altering the aircraft's course, eliminating drift. Then with height slider set to corrected height an object is timed from one bead to the next, giving G/S. Then the difference between A/S and G/S is the W/S, and the Course (or its reciprocal if flying down wind) is the wind direction.

(f) The **90 Degree Method** is done by finding the wind direction as in the above method, and then turning on to a course at 90° to it and measuring the drift. Wind direction, the course at right angles to it, and the track on that course are then plotted as in Fig. 88 to give W/S.

(g) The **Quick Turn** (or Reciprocal Track) method is carried out by flying away from an object on any definite course (A/S being constant)

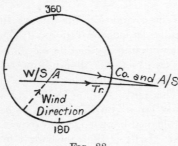

and noting the drift (usually by a back bearing). This Course is maintained for a given time (usually about five minutes) which is noted, and then the aircraft is turned about quickly on to a Course = Reciprocal of Original Course out ± twice the drift to give a Reciprocal Track. Thus, if Co. Out = 150 T and drift = 12 Red, then Co. In = (150 + 180) − 24 = 306 T. Or, if Co. Out

FIG. 88
(Angle A = about 90°)

= 150 T and drift = 11 Green then Co. In = (150 + 180) + 22 = 352 T. Then this Co. In takes the aircraft over the point of departure and the time on this course is noted. The Co. and Air Distance out and the Co. and Air Distance in are plotted, and the difference of the air position so obtained in relation to the ground position (i.e. the departure point) is the wind effect for the total time, which is converted to knots and its direction measured.

(h) The **Reciprocal Course** method is suitable for the pilot-navigator. A course is set out from an object for a given time, the aircraft is then turned quickly on to a reciprocal course for the same time. From the resulting position the aircraft is flown directly at the original object; its course is read giving wind direction, and the time is taken to return to the object. Then Wind Speed is found thus—

$$\frac{\text{Time on last Co. (i.e. towards object)} \times \text{A/S}}{60} = \text{Wind Distance.}$$

And $\dfrac{\text{Wind Distance} \times 60}{\text{Total Time}} = \text{Wind Speed,}$

where total time includes time on Co. Out, time on reciprocal Co. and time to return to object.

(i) The **Drift and Bearing** method is carried out by flying away from an object on a given course and taking a back bearing of it. After a given time (2 to 5 minutes) which is noted, the aircraft alters course (A/C) to a course at about right angles (or other wide angle) to the original course, and after another few minutes (which is noted) a bearing of the object is again taken. Then the plotting required to find the Wind Speed and Direction is as shown in Fig. 89. The first course is plotted and along it the air distance flown on it is marked at A. Also the air distance which would have been travelled if it stayed on the first course for the whole time (of first and second courses), is marked off at C. From C the back bearing which was taken is plotted. From A the second course and air distance is plotted to B, and from B the second bearing is plotted cutting the back

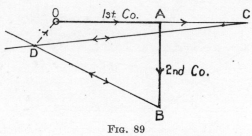

Fig. 89

bearing at D. Then DO is the wind effect in total time spent on both courses. Its length to scale is multiplied by $\dfrac{60}{\text{Total Time}}$ to give Wind Speed and its direction is measured.

(*Note.*—There are very many other methods not given here. Incidentally, any method which requires quick turning is unsuitable for use in aircraft of large turning radii.)

4. POSITION (Posn.) may be ascertained by any of the following—

(a) **By Dead Reckoning.** In this case the Posn. is reckoned from a Tr. and G/S deduced from a knowledge of the Co. and A/S and the W. S. and D. There is no proof that it is correct and therefore it must be treated as liable to error and always marked "D.R. Posn."

(b) **By a Fix,** which is the position obtained by the intersection of two or more Position Lines, of any sort. More than two Posn. lines always reduce the liability of error. If the Posn. lines are at a narrow angle to one another then obviously a slight error in one will cause a large error in the Fix. A narrow angle between Posn. lines gives a bad "cut," and a wide angle gives a good "cut."

The various combinations of Posn. lines are—

(i) A Transit and a Bearing (terrestrial) taken simultaneously. (*a*) and (*b*) respectively, in Fig. 90, giving the 1010 Fix.

(ii) Two Bearings (terrestrial), each of a different object, taken simultaneously.

(iii) Two Bearings of one object taken with a time interval between

174 THE COMPLETE AIR NAVIGATOR

them. This is called a "Running Fix." The first Posn. line, (c) in Fig. 90, is brought forward along the D.R. Tr. at the D.R. G/S for the time difference between it and the second bearing. (d) in Fig. 90 is the "Transferred Posn. line" brought forward five minutes from (c). Then the 1030 Posn. line (e) cuts it to give the 1030 Fix.

In this case the G/S would have been checked by measuring the

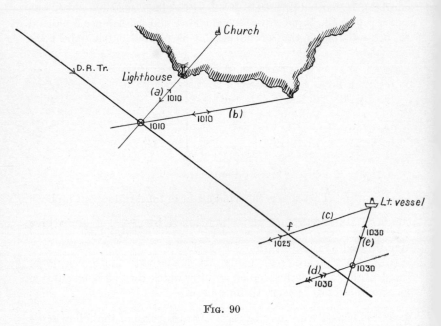

Fig. 90

distance between the 1010 Fix and the point (f) where the 1025 bearing cuts the D.R. Tr. Then $\dfrac{5}{60}$ of this G/S is the distance along the Tr. through which the Posn. line (c) must be transferred to (d). Three instead of two such bearings giving greater accuracy should be taken and used if possible.

(iv) Two D/F bearings from or of two different stations simultaneously.

(v) Two or more D/F bearings from or of one station, giving a "Running D/F Fix."

(vi) One D/F bearing and one terrestrial bearing simultaneously.

(vii) Two astronomical Posn. lines obtained simultaneously.

(viii) Two astronomical Posn. lines at different times, one being transferred to give a Running Astronomical Fix. (Used largely in ships.)

(ix) A D/F bearing and an astronomical position line.

(x) A terrestrial bearing and an astronomical position line (unlikely except when practising astronomical work).

(xi) Two angles subtended by three terrestrial objects (measured by a sextant held horizontally) and plotted by a station-pointer or by drawing three straight lines at the measured angles on a Douglas protractor or transparent paper, and placing this on the map or chart. It is moved around by trial so that the three lines pass through the three objects; then the intersection of the lines is the position. This method of fixing position is not very suitable for air work, but is possible.

(c) **By a Bearing and Distance** from an object.

(d) **By Map-reading,** which is the commonest and simplest way of fixing position, will not be dealt with in detail here. But there are a few points deserving attention.

(i) In high-altitude flying, which is becoming increasingly popular with aircraft operators in order to obtain greater efficiency, it is very difficult to decide exactly which point on the ground the aircraft is vertically over. Accurate navigation is more essential but more difficult at high altitudes, and therefore every effort should be made to obtain precision.

(ii) There are dozens and dozens of ways of recognizing physical features and ground objects. The usual practice is to study their nature and shape. This excellent method is practised so entirely that sometimes it is almost forgotten that the direction of ground features is also a very valuable means of identification. Thus, on crossing a railway or a coast line which cannot immediately be identified, its bearing should be accurately taken and compared with the direction of possible features on the map.

5. RECKONING generally consists of solving triangles or a combination of triangles. The solution is carried out by (i) plotting, (ii) by any form of Course and Distance Calculator or Aerial Ready Dead-Reckoner (generally called C.D.C's hereafter), or (iii) by mathematical calculations (the Sailings and Traverse Table).

Both speed and accuracy are essential in aerial D.R. C.D.C.'s are quicker but plotting is more accurate and is only slightly slower.

(a) Various problems solved by **Plotting.** (i) Plotting may be done from the centre point of a compass rose on the map or chart in use or on a separate paper called a Plotting Chart, or from any other point on the map or chart such as the departure point of the track to be flown. For simple problems such as the solution of the wind, course, and track triangle, plotting at the compass rose is usually quicker and more convenient, particularly when much flying is done at one A/S, so allowing a circle of radius = A/S to scale to be described around the centre point of the compass rose. For more complex problems such as Constant Bearing from and subsequent Interception of ships, etc., plotting from the point of departure is equally convenient and quick. Either method can, of course, be used exclusively and it seems advisable to take to one method and stick to it whenever practicable. Scale used in plotting problems must be a constant scale. Therefore when using a chart on Mercator's projection Lat. (distance) scale should not be used. Half Long. scale is usually convenient.

(ii) To find Wind Speed and Direction (W.S.D.) knowing Co., A/S, Tr. and G/S. (*Note.*—The navigator should when using this method of plotting, always plot either towards the centre of the compass rose or away from it. In this example the plotting is done away from the centre which then shows the wind blowing from Tr. to Co. which is really contrary to fact!) In Fig. 91 the outer circle is of a radius = A/S to scale. The course is drawn, and to the point where it cuts the A/S circle the track is drawn of a length = G/S to scale. Then the wind blows towards the centre of the rose. Its length to scale gives W/S and its direction is measured directly on the scale of the rose.

In practice the lines would not be drawn fully but only those parts necessary. Thus the course would only be drawn just where it cuts

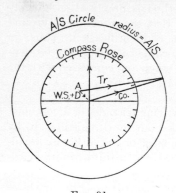

the A/S circle and the point A would be the only part of the track line actually pencilled on the chart. The wind, however, should be marked in fully as it may possibly be used in solving other problems.

(iii) To find Co. and G/S, knowing Tr., A/S and W.S.D. (*Note.*—In this example the plotting is shown towards the centre of the rose, and full lines are not drawn. Actually, in practice, the only marks made should be the W.S.D. and a small mark at

Fig. 91

B. A ruler is placed across the rose to read course.) In Fig. 92, W.S.D. are first plotted down wind. Then by parallel rule the Tr. required (in this case 082 T) is transferred to the end of the wind line at A and laid back to cut the A/S circle at B. Then Co. is from B to the centre of the rose, and G/S is the length BA to scale.

(iv) To find Radius of Action, knowing Tr., A/S, and W.S.D. (*Note.*—Here again the plotting is shown to the centre of a compass rose.) In Fig. 93 W.S. and D. are laid off down-wind and from its end the Tr. Out and the Tr. In are laid off to the A/S circle at B and C respectively. The Co. Out and Co. In are measured and also the G/S Out ($= BA$ to scale) and G/S In ($= CA$ to scale). Then

$$\text{Radius of Action} = T\left(\frac{\text{G/SO} \times \text{G/SI}}{\text{G/SO} + \text{G/SI}}\right) \text{ where } T = \text{total safe}$$

endurance in hours. But it is suggested that this formula is unnecessary if any form of slide rule (as on C.D.C's) is available. It is much

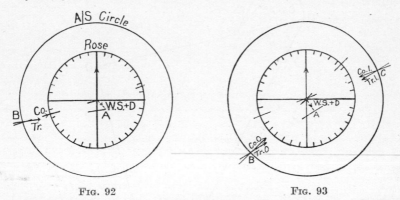

Fɪɢ. 92   Fɪɢ. 93

simpler to put G/SO on one scale against G/SI on the other scale and find two numbers opposite each other which together add up to the total time (endurance) in minutes. One of these is the time out in minutes and the other the time in.

(v) To intercept another craft, knowing its Tr. and G/S, its Posn., W.S.D. and your own A/S. From your own Posn. draw a straight line to the other craft's Posn. This gives its bearing and distance from you. See Fig. 94. The other craft's Tr. and G/S are plotted in reverse (i.e. reciprocal) from your own position O, to A. From A, W.S.D. are laid off down wind to B. From centre B and with radius=own A/S, the line of bearing is cut at C. Then $BC =$ own Co. and A/S, and $AC =$ own Tr. and G/S. The Tr. AC is laid off from O. Where it cuts the other craft's Tr. at E is the point of interception; and time to intercept

$$= \frac{OE}{\text{own G/S}}, \text{ or } \frac{OD}{\text{Speed of Closing}}$$

These should agree. (The length $OC = $ Speed of Closing.)

(vi) To leave a craft on a constant bearing from it, and return to it—knowing its track and G/S, and your own A/S.

In Fig. 95 the other craft's speed is laid back along the reciprocal of its track from O to B. From B the W.S.D. are laid off down wind to *A*. Through *O* the required line of bearing from the other craft is laid off (in Fig. 95 equal to 60 degrees on the starboard bow). Then from *A*, with radius = A/S, the bearing line is cut at *C*. Then

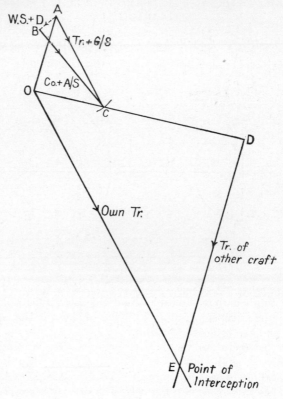

Fig. 94

to leave the craft on the required bearing the Co. and A/S = *AC*, and the Tr. and G/S = *BC*. The speed of opening = *OC*.

Now to return to the craft again is simply an interception. The reciprocal of the line of bearing *OD* is drawn. Then with centre on *A*, and radius = A/S, this line of bearing is cut at *D*. To return, then, to the craft your own Co. and A/S = *AD*, your Tr. and G/S = *BD*, and speed of closing = *OD*.

(vii) To find Radius of Action returning to a Different Base—knowing the required Tr. Out, A/S and W.S.D. The best method of dealing with this problem is to assume that an imaginary craft moves from the Base of Departure to the Base of Return in the total time of the flight (endurance). The speed of this imaginary craft is found by dividing the distance between bases by the total time. Then the problem is treated similarly to that in (vi) above. In Fig. 96 the aircraft has to leave base O and proceed on the track OB returning to the base E in three hours. From O the W.S.D. are laid off down

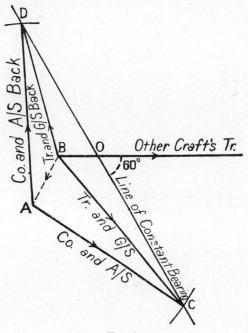

Fig. 95

wind to A and with centre on A and radius $=$ A/S the track is cut at B. Then AB $=$ Co. and A/S Out, and $OB =$ track and G/S Out.

Now speed of imaginary craft $= \dfrac{OE}{3 \text{ Hours}} = OC$. From B a line is drawn through C. This is the constant bearing from the imaginary craft, and $CB =$ Speed of Opening from it.

Now again, with centre on A and radius $=$ A/S the bearing line is cut at D. Then $AD =$ Co. and A/S In, $OD =$ Tr. and G/S In. And $CD =$ Speed of Closing. The Tr. In, OD, is transferred to E so as to cut the Tr. Out at F. Then F is the point at which the aircraft alters course for E. Time out $= \dfrac{OF}{\text{G/S Out}}$; Time In $= \dfrac{FE}{\text{G/S in}}$. Time out $+$ time in $=$ total time $=$ 3 hours in this example.

Checking may be carried out by placing speed of opening on one scale of a slide rule against speed of closing on the other scale, and

then finding two opposite numbers which add up to the total time in
minutes. One of these numbers is the time out in minutes, and the
other the time in.

(*Note.*—A plotting chart, of plain paper, is often convenient for
plotting work, particularly in astronomical work. Fig. 97 gives the
construction of a scale of d. Long. against distance (and d. Lat. and
Dep.) for a given Lat. for use with a plotting chart. The angle at O

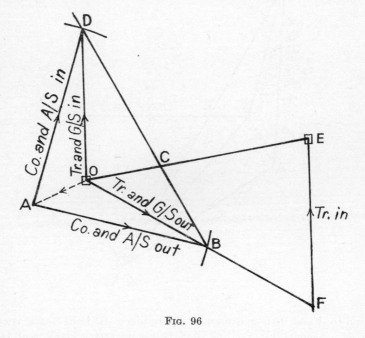

FIG. 96

equals the middle Lat. of the area of plotting. Now Dep. = d. Long.
Cos Lat., which is the basis of construction. Actually the base line
(adjacent side) is divided equally to a suitable scale, and perpendiculars from it cut the hypotenuse.)

(b) (i) **C.D.C.s** may be used almost entirely for reckoning, but in
some problems the use of a C.D.C. become so involved or the results
are so inaccurate that it is advisable to use some other method such
as plotting or mathematics.

In most cases provision is only made for solving simple triangles
but C.D.C.'s are available with provision for a fourth vector so that
interceptions, constant bearings, etc., can be reckoned. But even
when this is not provided an ordinary C.D.C. can solve any of the
problems given in sub-para. (*a*) of this para. Where there are four
vectors, the combined vectorial effect of the W.S.D. and the other

craft's Tr. and G/S is first found. It is then called the "Funny Wind" or "Relative Wind"—and used as an ordinary wind would be. Thus, in Fig. 96, Funny Wind = OB; in Fig. 95, Funny Wind = OA. In Fig. 96 the triangle OAB is first solved, and then with

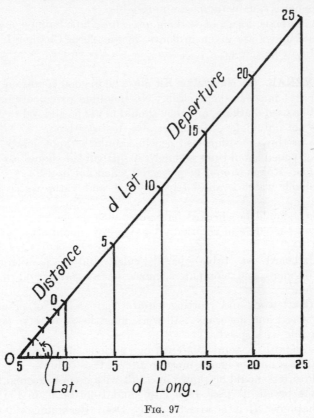

FIG. 97

known OB and OC, the triangle OCB is solved to find the speed of closing and relative bearing, CB. Obviously, the navigator must have a clear mental picture of the solution of the problem.

(ii) Most good C.D.C.'s are theoretically capable of working Plane Sailings but owing to the small size of a C.D.C. this should only be used, in practice, for comparatively short distances.

Conversion angles, departure into d. Long., etc. can also be worked out on a C.D.C. The method is obvious, depending on the type. A diagram of the triangle to be solved will help if in doubt.

No attempt to go into the details of C.D.C.'s or their actual use, will be made here owing to the large variety in use.

(c) **Mathematical Calculations** should be used to find the track and distance between two positions of which the Lat. and Long. are known

(i) when the distance is large, or

(ii) when available maps are unreliable.

The methods, forms of working, etc., for Plane Sailings and Mercator's Sailings are given in paras. 28 and 29 of Chapter I, which should now be re-read.

6. GENERAL. (a) **Navigation Kit** must be in good condition. Maps and charts must be kept clean. No indelible or coloured pencils should be used on them, and they should never be allowed to get wet as this not only defaces them but also distorts them.

Two or three medium lead pencils should be kept sharp. Short stubs of pencil should not be used. A soft rubber should always be available. Rulers should be protected when not in use.

A reliable watch is absolutely essential, and a stop watch is very useful.

C.D.C. should be checked for errors, such as slackness or eccentricity of the circle of rotation. A navigator should always use the same C.D.C.

Chart-board or table, parallel-ruler and/or parallel-motion arm, dividers and computers, must be available and in good condition.

(b) **Chart work** and plotting require a great deal of practice to attain speed and accuracy. All work must be as neat as possible, compatible with speed.

A standard system, representing various information to be plotted on a map or chart, must be adopted, as follows—

(i) Position should be shown by a dot with a circle around it, and the time beside it. (See 1010 Posn. and 1030 Posn. in Fig. 90 of this chapter.) If it is arrived at by Dead Reckoning the letters "D.R." should be printed beside the position, or if by Direction Finding then "D/F" should be printed.

(ii) A Position Line should be shown as a faint straight line with one arrow-head facing each way and the time printed beside it. (See (a), (b), and (c) in Fig. 90.) If it is obtained by astronomical means, the name of the body should be printed beside it, e.g. "Sun," "Vega," etc. If it has been obtained by D/F, then "D/F" should be printed.

(iii) A Transferred Position Line should be shown by a line with two arrow-heads each way and the time printed beside it. (See (d) in Fig. 90.)

(iv) Track should be shown by a line with a single arrow-head indicating the direction, and the letters "Tr." should be printed beside it. Course may be shown similarly, with "Co." beside it.

(v) Plotting should be done in thin lines.

(c) The **Navigator's Log** should contain a complete but very brief record of all courses steered, observations taken, winds found, results of reckoning, etc.

In order to keep the Log within reasonable limits of space it is necessary to use abbreviations. To avoid ambiguity, or difficulty when changing navigators, it is essential that all abbreviations are to an agreed form and that the method of keeping the Log is to a standard form also. Table I gives an example of a Navigator's Log sheet. It should be studied in detail. There are a few points worthy of note—

(i) Wind speed and direction should be made very obvious by heavy underlining (or even by drawing a rectangle around it).

(ii) Position as bearing and distance from an object should be written in the order—bearing, object, distance. Thus 180 VARNE 20' means 20 nautical miles south of Varne Lt. This order of expressing a position by bearing and distance is not published here without due consideration. Unfortunately there is not unanimity on the point. In wireless the order is—distance, bearing, object; and in the International Code the order is—bearing, distance, object. The order recommended (most strongly) here is widely used and seems least likely to give errors.

(iii) The degree sign (°) should never be used as it can look very like a nought when made in bad conditions. For a True, Magnetic, or Compass group there must be three figures and the letter T, M, or C. Drifts may be in one or two figure groups with Red (or to Port) or Green (or to St'b'd) following.

(iv) Names should always be printed in block letters.

(v) The following abbreviations are acceptable for use in Navigation Logs—

T	= True	G/S	= Ground Speed
M	= Magnetic	W.S.D.	= Wind Speed and Direction
C	= Compass	S/C	= Set Course
Tr	= Track	A/C	= Altered Course
Co	= Course	Posn	= Position
A/S	= Air Speed	E.T.A.	= Estimated Time of Arrival
m.p.h.	= Miles per hour	Kts.	= Knots (i.e. nautical miles
k.p.h.	= Kilometres per hour		per hour)

(d) Example. Table I is the Navigation Log of a short flight, given here as a guide. (Admiralty Chart No. 1825a—Irish Sea, Northern.)

TABLE I

From	To	A/S	Tr. T	Dist.	Co. T	Varn.	Co. M	G/S	Time	E.T.A.
Mew I. Lt.	N. Brighton Lt.	Kts 115	130½	116′	117	− 15	132	Kts 114	62	1016
128 Clay Hd. 5·7	N. Brighton	115	134	60	126½	− 14¼	141	118	30½	1013½

Time	Track Reqd.	Co. steered		Log
		True	Mag.	
0857				Airborne at Belfast.
0903	—	040	055	Belfast Dock S/C for Wind Finding. Ht. 2000 Ft.
0909	—	—	—	Posn. White Hd. Buoy. ∴ WSD = 26 Kts from 034 T
0909	—	—	—	„ „ „ „ „ S/C by sight for Mew I.
0914	130½	117	132	Mew I. Lt. S/C New Brighton Lt. (Liverpool).
0917	130½	117	132	Back Bearing = 319 C = 321 M = 306 T ⎱ Fix
0918	130½	117	132	Skulmartin Lt. V. bore 049 C = 051 M = 036 T ⎰
				∴ Tr = 126 T. G/S = 120.
				WSD = 25 Kts from 003 T @ 2000 Ft.
0922	130½	120	135	Posn. 126 Mew I. Lt. 16 A/C (for new wind).
0935	130½	120	135	Crossed coastline. ∴ G/S = 117 Kts ⎱
0941	—	120	135	Posn. Clay Hd. ∴ Tr = 128 T ⎰
				∴ WSD @ 1800 Ft. = 15 Kts. from 026 T.
0943	134	126½	141	Posn. 128 Clay Hd. 5·7. A/C N. Brighton.
0948	134	126½	141	Drift = 7 Green. ∴ Tr = 133¼ T.
0954	134	126½	141	Drift = 8 Green. ∴ Tr = 134¼ T.
1008	134	126½	141	Bar Lt. V. bore 228 C = 230 M = 215½ T @ about 2′
1014	—	—	—	Posn. N. Brighton.
1017	—	—	—	Landed in R. Mersey at Liverpool.

The aircraft, a flying boat, took off in Belfast Lough. A course was set in proceeding down the Lough in order to find wind. On fixing position at White Hd. Buoy, course was altered towards Mew Island Lt., and while flying towards it the data obtained on the constant course down the Lough are plotted to give the wind. Then course is set from Mew Island Lt. direct for Liverpool. A back-bearing shows that the Tr. made good is 4 degrees to port of the required Tr., and a cross-bearing gives the G/S. From these a new wind is found and Co. is altered to allow for it. On crossing the N.W. coast of the Isle of Man the coastline is straight and featureless for a few miles and therefore exact position cannot be determined. But the coastline, being at right angles to the Tr., affords an excellent means of finding G/S. On crossing the S.E. coast Posn. is accurately fixed over Clay Head. Immediately a new required Tr. is found, (from a D.R.Posn. of three minutes later) a new wind is found, and Co. altered accordingly. A cross-bearing and estimated distance from the Bar Lt. Vessel provides a check. A few minutes later the aircraft arrives over New Brighton and proceeds by sight to Liverpool.

(e) **Accuracy and Routine Habit.** (i) Errors in navigation may perhaps cancel each other out giving a result very nearly accurate. But, on the other hand, the effect of the errors may be additive giving a result which may be in error to a dangerous degree. Therefore the spirit which says of an error, "Oh it is near enough. There are so many other errors," must be banished. Every little counts in navigation.

(ii) Discipline in navigational habits is highly commendable. Slackness in navigation should be avoided in all large aircraft. In bad weather, navigation is essential to safety and of course it is necessary on long over-sea trips, etc. But even in good weather, on an easy route, good navigational habits will be valuable. If Log sheets are kept by all aircraft on a regular run much valuable data regarding winds at various levels, etc., could be collected.

Good airmanship in bad weather and general common sense are vital to the good navigator, but can hardly be taught by a book. Similarly it is impossible to teach the art of keeping a cool head, an active pencil etc., and an alert mind in navigating in very bad conditions.

7. Note on MAXIMUM RANGE. (a) The **Air Range,** i.e. range in still air, is dependent on three factors, namely, the aerodynamic efficiency, the engine efficiency, and the airscrew efficiency.

(i) Maximum Aerodynamic Efficiency is obtained at a given attitude or angle of incidence, which is published by the aircraft makers. The aircraft should be kept at this attitude throughout the flight. The only way of determining this angle of incidence in the air is to fly at the correct A/S for a given load. But it must be remembered that the economical cruising speed at a given height varies with loading. There are two ways of flying for maximum aerodynamic efficiency.

Firstly, the indicated A/S, which gives the incidence of maximum efficiency for the all-up load at the beginning of the flight, is flown throughout. But to allow for the gradually diminishing load (due to petrol consumption) the aircraft is allowed to climb so that in spite of the same A/S and incidence, the lift is reduced (by the smaller air density) to offset the reduced weight.

Secondly, the indicated A/S may be gradually reduced, by throttling back, as the petrol load diminishes, giving reduced lift with a constant incidence at a constant height. The amount of reduction

$$= \left(\frac{\text{Wt. of Fuel Used}}{\text{Wt. of aircraft Full}} \right)^{\frac{1}{2}} \text{ multiplied by the economic I.A.S. with}$$

full load.

(ii) Maximum Engine Efficiency is obtained by flying at the correct revolutions per minute for the required power, and using altitude control (and ignition control if required) correctly. As engine power below a certain minimum can only be taken at the expense of efficiency it may be necessary at light loads to exceed the best A.S.I. as given in (i) above.

(iii) Maximum Airscrew Efficiency occurs at a given value of $\frac{V}{nD}$ (where V is forward speed, $n = $ rev. per sec., and $D = $ diameter) for a given pitch. For fixed pitch airscrews designed for cruising conditions it generally happens that if factors (i) and (ii) above are attained, then the airscrew efficiency will be somewhere near its maximum. For constant speed airscrews, however, the situation is more complicated and a somewhat involved combination of the three factors may be necessary to fly for maximum air range.

(b) The **Ground Range,** that is the actual range over the ground including wind effect depends on three factors, namely, the aerodynamic efficiency and engine efficiency just mentioned, and on the wind effect. It is generally found advantageous with aircraft of moderately fast speeds to increase the A/S over the normal economical speed when flying into a head wind (or a wind with a component from ahead) by an amount equal to about $\frac{1}{4}$ to $\frac{1}{3}$ of the head wind effect. The resultant advantage usually consists of a very slight increase of range (not appreciable) but also a saving of time which is sometimes considerable. The advantage of being subjected to wind effect for a shorter period is usually offset to a large extent by the reduced aerodynamic and engine (petrol consumption) efficiencies, so that very little extra economy results, but the saving of time is sometimes of value.

(c) In practice the **wind effect,** particularly with slower aircraft, is usually more important to range and economy than aerodynamic and engine efficiency. Therefore every effort should, when other conditions allow, be made to fly at a height where the wind is most favourable or least adverse. But at the same time the remarks under (a) and (b) above should be remembered.

Thus, summarizing, the aircraft should be flown in a manner constituting the best possible compromise of the following—

(i) Flying at a height where wind is most advantageous.

(ii) Flying at a constant angle of incidence, giving maximum aerodynamic efficiency.

(iii) Flying at the most efficient engine revolutions per minute, with correct use of altitude control, etc.

CHAPTER VI

SECTION 1

CHRONOMETERS

1. (a) The **CHRONOMETER** is an accurate time-keeper working on the same principle as an ordinary watch, but with certain refinements—

(i) The drive from the main spring is not direct, but arranged so that the spring exerts a constant force. This is done by driving through a chain which winds round a spiral track on the drum of the main spring. This spiral is of decreasing diameter so that the variable force exerted by the spring in different degrees of tension is converted into a constant force in the chain. This arrangement is called the "Fusee" and "Fusee Chain."

(ii) The balance wheel, which is equivalent to a pendulum, is made of two metals of different coefficients of expansion so that temperature effect is accurately compensated.

(iii) Workmanship is the best. To secure accuracy, parts are very fine, and therefore a chronometer is easily damaged.

(b) The **care** of a chronometer is very important. Being a delicate instrument it must never be jolted. It should be kept in its double case with both lids closed. The outer (wooden) lid is only opened to take readings, and both lids (wooden and glass) are only opened to wind the chronometer.

The use of a chronometer in aeronautical navigation is usually as a check. It is kept at the ground station and should be in a room where the temperature is as even as possible.

2. The **CHRONOMETER WATCH** is suitable for use in the air. It is made on the same principles as the chronometer but is slightly more robust and is unfortunately less accurate. It is contained in a small padded wooden case. Although slightly more robust than a chronometer it still requires the greatest care in service.

The second hand in a chronometer watch usually beats every fifth of a second.

3. GENERAL. (a) **To wind** a chronometer its cases should be opened. It should be carefully turned over (most chronometers are mounted on gymbals), and the key provided inserted in the back, having first opened the dust-cover. Then holding the chronometer firmly the key is turned evenly in an anti-clockwise direction until it is felt to butt against the stop. The turns should be counted as a guide. Then the key should be removed and the dust-cover closed. The chronometer is turned over slowly till it is face up. Chronometers generally have an indicator to show the state of winding. This should be inspected. Then the lids are closed.

To wind a chronometer watch its lid should be opened, and being of the keyless type its milled head should be turned clockwise until it is felt to butt against the stop. The lid is then closed.

Winding should be carried out daily at the same hour (this applies to eight-day and two-day chronometers) and by the same person if possible.

(b) **To set** a watch which is stopped or run down, the side catch is engaged and the hour and minute hands are turned to the time required (to the time of a wireless time signal or to suitable time if being started from another chronometer). Particular care must be paid to synchronization of the minute and second hands. Thus, if the second hand is at 30 seconds the minute hand must be pointing half-way between two minute graduations.

(c) **To Start** a chronometer (or watch), it should be rotated briskly in the horizontal plane through about 90 degrees. This should be done at the right moment so that it shows correct time as nearly as possible.

4. CHECKING AND RATING. (a) **Checking** a chronometer (or watch) may be carried out by comparing its time with one of the following—

> Wireless time signal;
> Another chronometer;
> Astronomical observations;
> or Visual time signal.

The amount it is fast or slow is its **Error.**

(i) Wireless time signals are broadcast by a number of stations throughout the world, at various times, on various wavelengths, and by various types of signal. Usually there is a signal sent for normal checking for navigational purposes, followed in some cases by a rhythmic signal for extremely accurate checking which we may disregard here.

Rugby radio (GBR) sends out signals at 1000 hrs. and 1800 hrs. G.M.T. on 18,750 metres. Thus—

> At 0955 and 1755, a dash followed by 60 dots.
> At 0956 and 1756, ,,   ,,   ,,   ,,

> At 0957 and 1757, a dash followed by 60 dots
> At 0958 and 1758, ,,   ,,   ,,   ,,
> At 0959 and 1759, ,,   ,,   ,,   ,,
> At 1000 and 1800, a dash.

The beginning of the dash coincides with the minute.

Eiffel Tower (FLE) sends out signals at 0930 hrs. and 2230 hrs. G.M.T. on 2650 metres. Thus—

A series of X's, followed by six dots, the beginning of the last dot coinciding with 0928 or 2228.

A series of N's, followed by six dots, the beginning of the last dot coinciding with 0929 or 2229.

A series of G's, followed by six dots, the beginning of the last dot coinciding with 0930 or 2230.

Other stations using the X's, N's, and G's, in some cases send three dashes instead of 6 dots, the end of the last dash coinciding with the minute.

Then, to check, the station is tuned in, and exactly on the minute signal the chronometer is read, second hand first (and exactly) and then minute and hour hand. This should be repeated on two more minutes for additional surety.

(ii) Comparison with another chronometer is carried out as follows: Let the chronometer to which reference is to be made be called A. It has recently been checked and its rate is known. Chronometer B is to be checked by A. The navigator can only watch one at a time. Therefore he first watches A and when the second hand is on 55 he starts counting. Thus "Five," "Six," "Seven" in time with A at 55, 56, and 57 seconds respectively. By 59 his counting is nicely in time with A, and he looks away from it and as he says "Ten" he reads the second hand, and then the minute and hour hands of B.

Thus—

$$
\begin{array}{lrl}
 & \text{H.} \quad \text{M.} \quad \text{S.} & \\
\text{Time by } A = & 08 \quad 43 \quad 00 & \\
\text{Error of } A = & \quad 1 \quad 26 \cdot 6 & \text{Slow} \\
\hline
\text{G.M.T.} \quad = & 08 \quad 44 \quad 26 \cdot 6 & \\
\text{Time by } B = & 08 \quad 45 \quad 06 \cdot 6 & \\
\hline
\text{Error of } B = & \quad 40 & \text{Fast} \\
\end{array}
$$

This is repeated to confirm the result.

(iii) Astronomical Observations can be used to check the error of a chronometer, at a known position on the ground. There are various methods but as astronomical work has not at this stage been covered, no detail will be given now. In any case, in view of wireless time signals, it is of theoretical interest only.

(iv) Visual Signals indicating some exact time are made by many observatories. The signal usually takes the form of a ball dropped from the top of a short flagstaff. The moment the ball starts to fall is the time required.

(b) **Rating** a chronometer consists of determining its rate of change. The difference of error at two successive checkings gives the rate for the *Epoch*, (i.e. for the period of time between the checkings). This is converted accurately into the rate per day, or Daily Rate gaining or losing. Thus

H. M. S.

Error by W/T time signal
@ 1000 hrs. G.M.T. on 2/1/36 = 00 04 32 Slow
Error by W/T time signal
@ 1800 hrs. G.M.T. on 9/1/36 = 00 03 03 Slow

Difference for Epoch of 7·333
days = Gained   00 01 29

∴   Daily rate of gain = 12·2 secs.

The daily rate of a good chronometer is always less than six seconds, and if the conditions remain fairly constant it should not vary to any appreciable extent.

Then when a chronometer is read, its change in the time since the last checking (daily rate × days) is applied to the error found at the last checking and the result applied to the chronometer reading to give the correct G.M.T.

(c) A **Chronometer Log,** usually in the form of a small book, is kept for each chronometer. In it are entered particulars of windings (and by whom made), checking, rate, and temperature.

(*Note.*—A chronometer may be adjusted to keep Sidereal time (explained in the next chapter) instead of G.M.T. This is convenient in work with stars. Such a chronometer moves through its 24 hours of Sidereal time in 23 hrs. 56 mins. and 4·0906 secs. of mean Solar time.)

SECTION 2

SEXTANTS

5. THE MARINE SEXTANT is an accurate instrument by means of which the altitude of heavenly bodies, and horizontal angles can be measured.

(a) The **principle** of a sextant is based on several optical laws.
(i) If a ray of light strikes a plane mirror at a certain angle of

incidence it is reflected from it at an equal angle. Thus, in Fig. 98, the ray striking the mirror I is at an angle B from the vertical line through the mirror (NI) and the reflected ray is also at an angle B from the vertical (or "normal") line through I.

(ii) If a ray is reflected in one plane by two plane mirrors then the resultant deflection of the ray equals twice the angle between the direction of the mirrors. Thus, in Fig. 98, FI is the ray reflected in I and H to the final direction HE. Then the angle between FI and $HE = IDH$. The angle between the direction of I and $H = ICH$. And it is a simple geometric fact by construction that $IDH = 2 ICH$.

(iii) If H be made so that it is half mirror and half clear glass, then

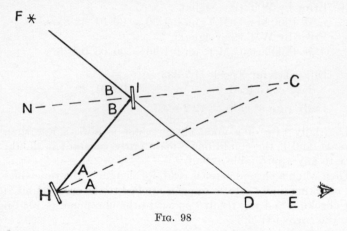

FIG. 98

the line EH may be sighted past H at some reference such as the horizon or other object. This fixes the direction of EH and so affords a datum from which the direction of FI is measured. Actually the direction of FI is given by measuring the angle of the mirror I in relation to the direction of H, and doubling it.

(b) The **construction** of the marine type of sextant is on the following lines—(see Fig. 99). (*Note*.—The Vernier reading type will not be considered.)

(i) The **Frame** of the sextant (A) may be one of a variety of patterns which are in all cases designed with a view to eliminating the possibility of distortion. The frame is upright when the sextant is in use. The left hand face of the frame (facing upwards in the figure) is called the Plane of the sextant. The lower side of the frame is the arc of a circle (B) and is called the **Arc** or Limb of the sextant. On its left face it carries a scale (C to D) (usually engraved on silver inlaid into the arc). This scale is marked off in degrees to double its

real angular values from zero (C) at the right-hand end of the scale
to 120° (or sometimes 150°) (D) at the left. This doubling of angular
values is because the sextant is an instrument of reflection (see (**a**)
(ii) above). Below the zero mark are some further graduations called
"Arc of Excess."

(ii) The **Index Bar** (E) is pivoted about a centre coincident with
the centre of curvature of the arc. Directly above its pivot is carried
a small plane mirror (I) called the **Index Glass.** This mirror is

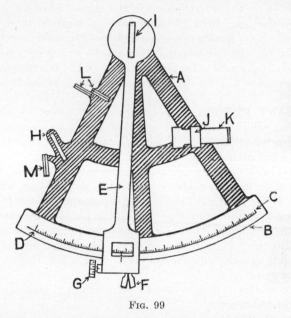

Fig. 99

perpendicular to the Plane of the sextant and rotates with the bar.
Angles through which the bar swings are measured against the scale
on the arc—to whole degrees. Minutes are read by the endless
Tangent Screw (a worm-gear) which engages in serrations in the
underside of the arc. This Tangent Screw has a **Micrometer Head**
(G) with a scale around it reading against a fixed mark. Then when
the Index Bar mark is exactly opposite a whole degree graduation
the micrometer should show zero. In addition many modern sextants have a vernier scale beside the fixed mark and adjacent to the
micrometer for reading seconds of arc. The vernier line which is
exactly opposite one of the micrometer graduations gives the seconds.
Then degrees are read from the arc scale, minutes from the micrometer scale, and seconds from the vernier scale. By pressing the
quick-release (F) together the tangent screw is disengaged and

the index bar can be moved freely by hand. On releasing (*F*), the screw engages again and the tangent screw is rotated for smaller and finer movements of the index bar.

(iii) The **Horizon Glass** (*H*) is carried on the frame, perpendicular to the plane of the sextant. Half of it is a plane silvered mirror, and the other half is clear glass

(ıv) Level with the Horizon Glass and on the other arm of the frame is a **Collar** (*J*) with an internal interrupted thread to take a **Telescope** (*K*). The interruptions in the thread allow quick engagement and disengagement. Various telescopes can be used.

(v) Two sets of **Shades** of various degrees of opaqueness are hinged from points on the frame so that they can be swung into use as suitable. One group (*M*) is for use in the line of the Horizon Glass, and the other group (*L*) is for use in the line of rays from the Index Glass.

6. SEXTANT ERRORS. The errors, their detection, and their corrections where possible, are as follows—

(a) **Perpendicularity.** (i) If the index glass is not exactly perpendicular to the plane of the sextant an error will result.

(ii) To check for perpendicularity, proceed as follows: Hold the instrument so that its plane is horizontal, with the arc away from you and to the right, and the index glass towards you. By placing the eye close to the index glass and to the plane of the instrument, and looking obliquely into the index glass an image of the arc can be seen. Also the arc itself can be seen. The image should be in a straight line exactly with the arc itself. If it is not, there is perpendicularity error.

(iii) To correct this, if necessary, adjustment is made by a screw behind the index glass.

Important: If Perpendicularity error exists it must always be corrected before other errors.

(b) **Side Error.** (i) If the horizon glass is not exactly perpendicular to the plane of the sextant, Side Error will exist.

(ii) To check for side error, either one of two methods may be employed. The sextant may be held horizontally and sighted through the telescope at the sea horizon with the index bar set at zero on the scale. The true horizon and its reflected image in the horizon glass should be in one straight line. If not, side error exists.

Another method is to set the index bar approximately at zero and holding the sextant vertically sight at a bright star through the telescope. By moving the tangent screw the star and its image can be brought together and past each other. As they pass each other the image should coincide with the star itself. If it passes to one side of the star, then side error exists.

(iii) To correct this, adjustment is made by a screw behind the horizon glass.

(c) **Collimation Error.** (i) If the axis of the telescope (called the line of collimation) is not parallel to the plane of the sextant Collimation Error will exist.

(ii) To check for collimation error an inverting telescope is necessary. With this inverting telescope screwed into the collar, two heavenly bodies which are not less than 90° angular distance apart, are brought together on one of the vertical lines (i.e. parallel to the plane of the sextant). Then, without touching the tangent screw, the sextant is turned slightly so that the heavenly bodies are seen on the other vertical wire. They should still be together. If they are not so, collimation error exists.

(iii) To correct this, adjustment is made to the telescope collar, but in most modern sextants this is a job to be done by the makers or qualified marine opticians. In any case this error is very unusual.

(d) **Index Error** (I.E.). (i) If the index glass is not parallel to the horizon glass when the scale is exactly at zero, then Index Error will exist.

(ii) To check for index error either one of two methods may be employed. The first method is to sight at the sea horizon with the plane of the sextant vertical, and to bring the reflected horizon exactly coincident with the real horizon. Then the scale is read. If there is a reading on the arc proper there is an I.E. "on" or I.E. minus. If there is a reading on the Arc of Excess, the I.E. is "off" or plus. The mean of three readings should be taken. The second method is generally more accurate. With suitable shades and using a telescope the sun's image is firstly brought into contact with the upper limb (the top edge) of the direct sun. The scale is then read and will be found to be "off" the scale proper by a certain amount which is noted. Then the upper limb of the reflected sun is brought into contact with the lower limb of the real sun, and the reading, which in this case will be "on" the scale, is taken. Half the algebraic sum of the two is the value of the index error.

Thus—

$$\begin{aligned}
\text{Reading "off"} &= + 31'\ 00'' \\
\text{Reading "on"} &= - 33'\ 48'' \\
\hline
2) &- \quad 2'\ 48'' \\
\hline
\therefore \text{Index Error} &= - \quad 1'\ 24'' \text{ or } 1\cdot4' \text{ On.}
\end{aligned}$$

As a check, the arithmetic sum of the two readings divided by 4, should equal the sun's semidiameter. Thus—

$31'\ 00'' + 33'\ 48'' = 64'\ 48''$ divided by $4 = 16'\ 12''$.

(iii) If a very large correction is necessary, adjustment is made to the horizon glass by a screw behind it. If this is done side error should be checked again. Usually I.E. is not corrected but found and applied as a first correction to all readings.

(e) **Centring Error.** (i) If the pivot of the index bar is not exactly coincident with the centre of curvature of the arc, Centring Error will exist.

(ii) To check this, sextants used to be sent to an observatory or marine optician. But there is a prism attachment available so that navigators can themselves find the centring error at any time.

(iii) No correction can be made, but the error when known can be allowed for, like the I.E.

(f) **Prismatic Error.** If the mirrors are irregular in any way errors will result, but this is extremely unlikely in a good sextant.

(g) **Shade Errors.** If shades are not ground absolutely plane and with each side parallel errors will result. But again this is unlikely in good instruments.

Note.—Errors should always be corrected in the order given. Thus, Perpendicularity is first, then Side error, followed by Collimation, and finally I.E. The undesirability of attempting to make adjustments, except when they are absolutely necessary, must be stressed.

7. THE USE of the marine type of sextant in aviation is somewhat limited, for, although it is a more accurate instrument, it is unsuitable for use in the air, compared to the air sextant.

(a) Firstly, the sea horizon is too distant to be seen clearly from any appreciable height except in very good visibility, and there is the difficulty of allowing for the aircraft's height. This may be overcome with a large degree of success by either of two methods—

(i) A small bubble clinometer may be attached to the sextant. This clinometer is watched instead of the real horizon. Or

(ii) The aircraft can fly very low so that fairly accurate allowance for the height can be made, when using the sea horizon. Results by this method compare very favourably with sights by air sextant.

(b) Secondly, there is the difficulty of keeping the sextant directed at heavenly bodies in bumpy conditions. Even with large mirrors, and with telescopes having large fields of vision, this failing in marine sextants is a serious obstacle in air work. This difficulty applies to the measuring of horizontal angles (between terrestrial objects) as well as altitudes of heavenly bodies.

8. THE ARTIFICIAL HORIZON. (a) When used in conjunction with a marine sextant on the ground, it has a number of uses, as, for example, when checking a chronometer by astronomical means, or when finding an astronomical position line with no sea horizon available. Of course it can only be used when it is stationary.

(b) The **Principle** of the Artificial Horizon in use is as follows:
The Artificial Horizon provides a plane mirror which is perfectly
horizontal (AB in Fig. 100). A ray of light from a heavenly body X
is reflected by AB up through the horizon glass (H) of a sextant to the
eye (E) of the observer. Also a ray from X is reflected by the Index
glass (I) and Horizon glass (H) to the eye of the observer. By moving
the Index bar these two images are brought exactly into coincidence.
Then the angle which the sextant has measured is that between XI
and HC. This is the same as the angle between XC and CY (for CX
is parallel to XI, and CY is the same straight line as HC), which is

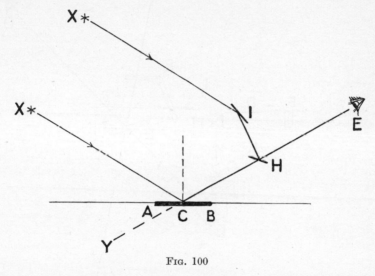

FIG. 100

XCY. But XCY is by the law of reflection $= 2\ XCA$. And XCA
obviously $=$ altitude of the heavenly body. That is, the angle
observed by the sextant is twice the altitude of the body.

(c) The **Form** of an Artificial Horizon may be—

(i) A trough containing mercury which forms a horizontal plane,
except near its edges. Other liquids such as clean refined oil, tar,
etc., may be used in cases of necessity. Usually a carefully made
glass roof covers the trough to avoid wind ripples on the liquid.
Although every effect is made to avoid distortion, etc., in the glass,
sights should be taken through the roof in alternatively opposite
directions.

(ii) A plane black glass held in a small frame which has adjustable
legs and two small spirit levels to make the glass exactly horizontal
can be used. This type has one great advantage over the liquid type
in its portability. (It is 4 in. by 6 in. approximately.) But being

dependent on the spirit levels for its correct horizontal level it is a
little more liable to error.

9. THE BUBBLE SEXTANT for air use is designed for ease of operation and reading, and it is independent of the natural horizon and

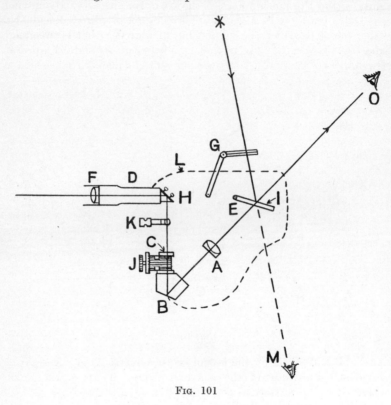

Fig. 101

therefore is suitable for use at any height. It is not as accurate as a
marine sextant.

(a) The **Construction** is based on the same principles as the marine
sextant but actually the bubble sextant is very different. The
following describes British practice (see Fig. 101)—

(i) Two metal **side plates** (*L*) are the foundation of the structure.
To the right of the right side plate is a **revolving drum** with the scale
on it, and to the left of the left side plate is a circular wooden
handle which is held in the left hand. The main parts are between
these side plates.

(ii) The **Mirror** (*I*) corresponds to the Index glass of a marine sextant. It is a piece of plate glass with accurately ground parallel faces. It is clear and can be seen through, but in addition it also reflects with appreciable intensity. This Mirror is pivoted about a point E. Its movement is controlled by the rotating of a drum (not shown in figure), through suitable gearing. On this drum, which is on the right of the instrument, is the scale from which angles of the reflected ray are read off.

(iii) Below the mirror is the **collimating lens** (A) and the **reflecting prism** (B) which has its lower face silvered so that it acts as a mirror.

(iv) Immediately above this prism is the **bubble chamber** (C) with its upper and lower lens. The upper lens is concave on its lower side, and it is against this surface that the bubble floats. The bubble chamber is filled with hexane, a spirit which vaporizes fairly easily. The bubble is formed of hexane vapour. A screw (J) moves a **flexible diaphragm** which forms part of the bubble chamber. By this means the bubble can be varied. The position and type of this screw varies. In old type instruments it is in the front and in newer types it is usually in the handle on the left of the instrument.

(v) Above the bubble chamber is the **prism** (H) of **horizon sight** (D). At the forward end of this short tube is the **lens** (F)

(vi) Scale may be of various types. The large drum type has a scale on the periphery of the drum. Two and two-thirds revolutions of the drum move the mirror from one extremity to the other. The scale reads angles from $-3°$ to $80°$. The graduations are for every $5'$ of arc and the degrees are numbered. Interpolation between the $5'$ graduations is done by sight. This type has a drum scale covering 30 degrees only. A small additional scale and pointer indicates the number of tens of degrees. Thus "2" on the small scale and "3" on the drum means $23°$. A recent type has figures appearing on small windows indicating degrees and minutes.

(vii) Two or three **shades** (G) are provided on a swinging arm so that they can be interposed between the sun and the mirror as required, or between the eye and the mirror (as for finding I.E. by the sun).

(viii) **Lights** are provided for use at night. The main light is the bubble light (K) which can be slipped into position directly above the bubble chamber, and so illuminate it. Its brightness can be varied by a rotating variable resistance operated by hand to suit. An external light can be switched on to read the scale. A small 2-volt battery with a lead and plug is the source of supply, or a small torch battery.

(ix) An **ivorine tablet** with columns for times and altitudes is provided.

10. THE ERRORS of the bubble sextant. Most of the errors of a marine sextant should not exist owing to the construction of the bubble sextant, and in any case no provision is made for their correction. The only errors considered in use are the Index Errors. There are two I.E.s—one applying to angles in relation to the level by the bubble, and the other applying to angles in relation to some external datum (such as sea horizon) viewed through the horizon sight.

(a) The **Bubble Index Error** is found as follows: The bubble is adjusted by means of the milled-headed screw, to a suitable size (about $\frac{3}{16}$ in.). Then comparison is made with the sea horizon. There are two different methods, thus—

(i) Firstly, the observer may sit very close to the water holding the sextant close to the surface. With the scale near zero the drum is rotated so that the reflected sea horizon as seen in the mirror cuts the centre of the bubble (seen through the mirror and reflecting prism), the bubble being approximately in the centre of its chamber. Then the reading " on " or " off " the scale is the I.E. when using the bubble. Obviously this method can only be used when the sea is calm. It must be remembered that even at a height of one foot the dip or angle of depression of the horizon is nearly 1′ of arc. Therefore the sextant must be held very close to the water.

(ii) The second method is not so awkward in practice. In it no attempt is made to hold the sextant near water-level, but instead sights of the sea horizon in relation to the bubble from a definite known height (about 6 ft. above sea level) are taken and due allowance is made for dip. Thus: When reflected horizon bisects bubble, observing at 6 ft. above sea-level,

Reading " on "		$= 00° \ 02′$
Dip at height 6 ft.	$=$	$2·4′$
Therefore Bubble Index Error		$- 4·4′$

Or	Reading " off "		$= 00° \ 04′$
	Dip at 6 ft.	$=$	$2·4′$
	Therefore Bubble Index Error $=$		$+ 1·6′$

In either method a mean of about six observations should be accepted as the I.E.

(b) The **Horizon Sight Index Error** is the error applicable to angles measured with reference to a natural horizon through the horizon sight, and, of course, independent of the bubble. It is exactly the same as in the marine sextant, and can be determined in the same way by sighting on the horizon or the sun. Of course, the bulb of the bubble light must be drawn partially out so that it does not obstruct the line *CH* in Fig. 101.

(c) **Corrections** for I.E. can be made if absolutely essential. If this is to be done, the following is the recommended procedure : In order to make both bubble I.E. and horizon I.E. the same, the sextant is held very close to water-level. The direct sea horizon as seen through the horizon sight should bisect the bubble in the centre of its chamber. If this is not so, the horizon sight is adjusted by means of small screws behind the prism (*H* in Fig. 103). Then the natural horizontal (with zero dip) having been made coincident with the bubble level, both will be subject to the same I.E. This common I.E. may be eliminated in most types by adjustment of the mirror— which is a delicate operation. (*Note.*—It is, however, recommended that all errors should be corrected by the makers.)

11. THE USE of the bubble sextant in the air. (**a**) In all cases (i) The handle is held in the left hand, and the drum operated by the right hand.

(ii) The exact G.M.T. of each observation of a heavenly body is taken, either from a chronometer watch or an accurate watch or stop watch set from a chronometer.

(iii) A number of sights are always taken and their values (and their times) averaged.

(iv) When using the bubble, the heavenly body is always brought into the centre of it by suitably rotating the drum, the bubble itself being roughly in the centre of its chamber. (*Note.*—Exact centre of the chamber is not necessary.)

(v) The size of the bubble should be about three times the diameter of the sun which is less than one-sixth of the diameter of the visible field of the bubble chamber. (*Note.*—A larger bubble is too prone to touch the sides and is also hard to sight on, whereas a very small bubble appears to become slightly sticky and sluggish. In bumpy conditions a bubble smaller than that recommended above is advisable.)

(vi) When the bubble is moving badly due to bumpy conditions, its mean position must be kept central, and the heavenly body brought on to it. (In any case, vibration effects on the bubble can be avoided by not allowing the instrument to touch any part of the aircraft.)

(vii) When the bubble is used, obviously no correction for dip or for semi-diameter is necessary.

(viii) Practice is essential for speed and accuracy of observations.

(ix) No observation should ever be taken through glass windows, unless they are of special optical quality, and flat sided.

(x) One of the most important facts which should be remembered when taking a bubble sextant observation in the air is that the human body, if unsupported, will amplify acceleration and deceleration effects on the bubble. It is therefore essential for the observer to assume a thoroughly comfortable position well supported so as to avoid any possibility of swaying. This is particularly important in the case of an aircraft being flown by an imperfect automatic pilot.

(b) Observing Sun's Altitude using the Bubble. A bubble of the correct size is obtained by the adjustment screw. Shades are suitably interposed between the sun and the mirror. Then with one eye close to and looking down (from position O, Fig. 101) into the mirror, the shaded image of the sun is seen, and through the mirror (via collimating lens and reflecting prism) the bubble is also seen. By rotating the drum, the two are made coincident, the bubble being in the centre of its chamber. The exact time is taken and the scale read. This is repeated about another five times and the results averaged. The whole set of readings should only take about three or four minutes. Bad air conditions may make it necessary to take a larger number of observations.

(c) Observing Star's Altitude at Night using the Bubble. With a suitable bubble, the bubble-light is pushed right in and adjusted to the lowest degree of brightness with which the bubble can easily be seen. Then by looking up (from position M in Fig. 101) through the mirror the star (or planet) can be seen directly and the reflected image of the illuminated bubble can also be seen. The star is brought into the centre of the bubble (in approximately the centre of its chamber) by suitably rotating the drum, and the time is noted. It must be remembered that the white part of the bubble (due to the light above it) is not its centre. A number of readings are taken as for the sun.

(d) Observing with the Horizon Sight. Altitudes with relation to the sea horizon may be taken, in the same way as with the marine sextant. The same uncertainty exists with regard to the correct dip to be applied to allow for the aircraft's height.

12. **THE METHODS** employed in taking sextant observations. With experience it will be realized that the actual procedure of taking sextant observations in the air is not quite as simple as it might appear. There are various methods which can be used. The method adopted will depend on a large number of factors, such as the following: whether the aircraft is being flown manually or by an automatic pilot, and if the latter, whether the automatic pilot has a tendency to "hunt" quickly or slowly; the degree of air turbulence if any; the "stickiness" or conversely the "activity" of the bubble of the sextant used; the stability of the aircraft,

its inertia, and its moments of inertia, etc. Most existing automatic pilots are not perfect but suffer from a tendency to apply control one way and then the other, causing the aircraft to move along a wave-like path both directionally and vertically. This may be so slow and/or small that it is not noticeable and yet it will affect bubble-sextant readings. Sights taken abeam will be affected by "hunting" of the rudder mainly, with minor interference effect from the elevator and aileron periodic movements. Sights taken ahead or astern will be affected mainly by the periodic movements of the elevator. The movements are usually somewhat complex wave motions.

Two methods of observation are submitted but it is pointed out that there are many variations. Development in the near future may modify the situation considerably.

The first method which we will call the "self-averaging" sight is applicable to cases with an automatic pilot of which the "period" of any "hunt" it may have is short so that in reasonable conditions the wandering of the bubble in relation to the heavenly body due to take this "hunt" can readily be seen and followed. The body is then brought so that it swings evenly each side of the centre of bubble. When this is so the chronometer is read and the sight accepted. Six such sights should give a very good result. It can only be done when the period of the movement is small and therefore discernable and cannot be done in very bumpy weather. It is, of course, more difficult to do for sights on the bows or quarters where the wave motions due to rudder and elevator are combined.

The second method, "snap sighting," is less reliable than the above, particularly if only six sights are taken. It is, however, applicable in all cases where the above method cannot be used and, if 10 or 12 sights are averaged and "personal tendencies" are avoided, it will give entirely satisfactory results. In it the procedure is simply to bring the bubble to the centre of the bubble and, when satisfactorily in that position, the time is taken and the sight accepted. The description "snap sighting" should not be taken too literally.

One means of testing to a considerable extent the accuracy of one's observations in a particular aircraft with a particular sextant is to take a long series of sights (about 50) and to plot the altitudes obtained graphically against time. If the first of the above two methods has been used with skill and care, the points so plotted should all fall within a very narrow band (less than 15′ wide in good conditions) and that the average of any six consecutive points lies very near the centre of the band. If, however, the second method has been employed it will often be found that the width of the band of points plotted is much greater (as much as 100′ of arc wide). It may also be found that the average of 5 or 6 consecutive sights may in some few cases lie well off the centre-line of the band, but that the average of a larger number, say 10 or 12, is nearly always near the centre line.

13. IMPROVED TYPES. (a) **Averaging Devices** incorporated in the sextant are now in use. There are two types. The first gives the arithmetic mean of a specified number of sights (usually six). The principle of a simple adding machine is employed. When each sight is taken, a lever is pressed which mechanically adds one-sixth (in the case of six sights averaging) of the altitude. The final summation so obtained is, of course, the mean of the six altitudes. The chronometer may be read for each sight and the six times averages; or the time of the first and last sight only averaged.

A second type of averaging device is, however, theoretically superior. In it no single sights are taken and averaged but instead the heavenly body is held constantly in the centre of the bubble for a given time (1 or 2 min.). The sextant mechanically computes the mean altitude during this period.

(b) **Daylight Star Sights.** It is well known that stars can be seen in daylight by an observer standing in the optical blackness at the bottom of a deep mine shaft. The same principle has been applied in a recent development in an attempt to make it possible to take sextant sights of bright stars in daylight.

(c) **Gyro-erected Bubble Sextant.** Among recent developments in sextant design this appears to be one of the most promising. It is designed as an aircraft fixture. In the optical system between the object glass and the bubble chamber are two gyro-controlled erecting prisms, one rotatable on an athwartship axis and the other on a fore and aft axis. These prisms counteract the rolling and pitching movements of the aircraft. But acceleration effects still remain. A pendulous device which moves the bubble chamber bodily, or a double bubble arrangement is therefore necessary.

Such instruments have been successfully produced, but as they are complex and expensive it may be some time before their adoption becomes general.

(d) **Gyroscopic Artificial Horizons.** Recent development in the precision with which gyroscopes can be produced make it possible that sextants using a gyro instead of a bubble as a datum may soon be possible. If such an instrument could be made to the necessary degree of accuracy and reliability it would undoubtedly be superior in many ways to the bubble type.

CHAPTER VII

ASTRONOMICAL NAVIGATION

SECTION 1

THE CELESTIAL SPHERE AND ITS PARTS

1. HEAVENLY BODIES. (a) The heavenly bodies are as follows—

(i) **The Sun** is fixed in relation to the stars and gives the Earth its heat and light.

(ii) **The Stars** like the sun are fixed in relation to each other and are each giving out their own heat and light, but they are at immense (almost infinite) distances from the Earth.

(iii) **The Planets** have no heat or light of their own but obtain

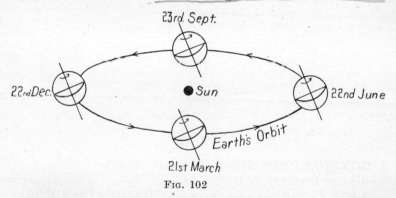

FIG. 102

their apparent brightness by reflection of the sun's light. All planets travel around the sun, at various distances from it, and each rotates on its own axis. The Earth is a planet. Of the other planets Mercury and Venus are closer to the sun than the Earth, and Mars, Jupiter, Saturn, Uranus, Neptune, and Pluto are further away. The Earth is about 92,900,000 miles average distance from the sun.

(iv) **The Satellites** are bodies rotating about the planets. The Earth has one satellite, the Moon, which is the only one of practical interest. Of the other planets Mars has two moons, Jupiter eleven, and Saturn nine. The Earth's Moon is under 240,000 miles from it.

(b) Of the **Movement** of the planets, the Earth's is the one of highest importance to us. Fig. 102 shows the Earth revolving about its axis, and its path round the sun (called its Orbit). If the approximate direction of the Earth's North Pole is taken as the top, then the Earth's Orbit is a left-hand circuit, and the direction of its own rotation about its axis is the same. The path traced out by the Earth is approximately an ellipse.

(c) The plan employed in this chapter in dealing with astronomical navigation is on the following lines: (i) The means of referring to heavenly positions are defined.

(ii) The derivation of the measurement of time is explained.

(iii) Details about heavenly bodies and recognition of stars are discussed.

(iv) The information given by the Almanac for finding the position of any heavenly body at any time is mentioned.

(v) Then the principles of taking altitudes, of celestial position lines, and of the methods of calculation are explained.

(vi) Finally the rising and setting of heavenly bodies is treated.

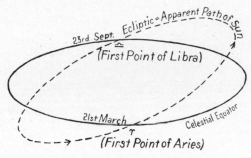

FIG. 103

2. CELESTIAL DEFINITIONS.

In order to facilitate reference to the position of heavenly bodies an immense sphere is considered to exist with the Earth as its centre point. This is the Celestial Sphere (see Fig. 104). Then an observer at the centre (the Earth) sees all heavenly bodies on this sphere. Like the Earth, this sphere is divided up by circles for convenience of reference, and datums are chosen.

(i) An **Orbit** is the path traced out by a planet around the sun, or a satellite around its planet. The Earth's orbit (see Fig. 102) like most others is nearly elliptical in shape, having the sun at one of the foci. The Earth takes about $365\frac{1}{4}$ mean solar days to complete one circuit in its orbit.

(ii) **Perihelion** is that point on the orbit of the Earth where it is nearest to the sun. The Earth is at Perihelion on about 1st-3rd January.

(iii) **Aphelion** is that point on the orbit of the Earth where it is furthest from the sun. It is at Aphelion on about 1st-3rd July.

(iv) **Perigee** is that point on the orbit of the Moon where it is nearest to the Earth.

(v) **Apogee** is that point on the orbit of the Moon where it is furthest from the Earth.

(*Note.*—Perigee and Apogee are at times used with reference to the sun in place of Perihelion and Aphelion.)

(vi) The **Celestial Poles** (P and P_1 in Fig. 104) are those points where the Earth's axis (NS) extended cuts the celestial sphere.

(vii) The **Celestial Equator** (ABG in Fig. 104) is the Great circle

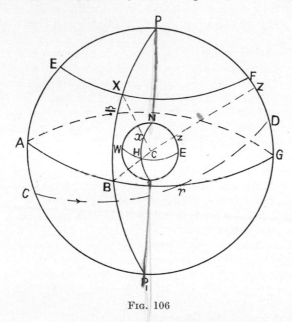

FIG. 106

on the celestial sphere which lies in the plane of the Earth's equator. It corresponds to the Earth's equator. The name Equinoctial, sometimes applied to it, seems unnecessary.

(viii) The **Ecliptic** (CD in Fig. 104; also see Fig. 103) is the Great circle on the celestial sphere which lies in the plane of the sun's apparent orbit round the Earth. Actually, of course, the Earth moves round the sun, but to an observer on the Earth, the sun appears (from observations at his local noon) to move slightly up or down his meridian; and also, in relation to the stars, to move around the Earth in the same direction as the Earth's rotation. The apparent path thus traced out by the sun lies in the plane of the ecliptic.

(ix) The **Obliquity of the Ecliptic** is the angle between the planes of the celestial equator and the ecliptic. It equals about $23\frac{1}{2}$ degrees $(23°\ 27\frac{1}{4}')$. It is equal to the tilt of the Earth's axis.

(x) The **First Point of Aries** (Υ) is the fixed point in the celestial sphere chosen as a datum. It is the point where the ecliptic cuts the celestial equator in passing from South to North. The diametrically opposite point on the celestial equator is called the First Point of Libra ($\triangleq$).

(xi) The **Equinoxes** are the two times of the year when the sun is vertically over the equator giving day and night of equal duration. Obviously they occur when the sun is at the first point of Aries and the first point of Libra (on about 21st March and 23rd September, respectively).

(xii) The **Solstices** are the two times when the sun is at those two points on the ecliptic half-way between the points of intersection of the celestial equator and the ecliptic (that is, between the Equinoxes). The northern summer solstice is on about 22nd June when the sun is at an angular distance of about $23\frac{1}{2}$ degrees North of the equator giving the longest period of daylight; and the northern winter solstice is on about 22nd December.

(xiii) The **Geographical Position** of a heavenly body is that point where the line joining the body to the centre of the Earth, cuts the Earth's surface. x is the geographic position of the heavenly body X in Fig. 104. Occasionally the sun's geographical position is called the **Sub-Solar Spot,** the Moon's the **Sub-Lunar Spot,** and the Star's the **Sub-Stellar Spot.**

(xiv) The **Zenith** of an observer is that point on the celestial sphere made by extending a straight line from the centre of the Earth through the observer to cut the surface of the celestial sphere. The zenith is vertically over the observer's head. In Fig. 105 the point Z is the zenith of the observer at z.

The **Meridian of the Observer** is the celestial meridian passing through his zenith and is in the same plane as his terrestrial meridian.

(xv) The **Nadir** is that point on the celestial sphere diametrically opposite the zenith—that is, vertically below the observer's feet.

(xvi) A **Parallel of Declination** (EXF in Fig. 104) is any small circle on the celestial sphere, whose plane is parallel to the plane of the celestial equator. It is the celestial equivalent to the Earth's parallel of Lat.

(xvii) A **Celestial Meridian** (PXP_1 or PFP_1 in Fig. 104) is any semi-great circle on the celestial sphere between the celestial poles. It is obviously similar to a meridian on the Earth.

(xviii) The **Declination** (Dec.) of a heavenly body is the arc of the celestial meridian measured from the celestial equator to the body. Declination is really celestial latitude. In Fig. 104, BX is the declination (North) of the body X, which equals the Lat. (Hx) of its geographical position x. It is measured up to 90 degrees North or South of the celestial equator.

The difference between the declination of a body and the Lat. of an observer (written Lat. $\sim$ Dec.) is the arc of the celestial meridian between the parallel of Dec. of the body and the parallel of Dec. of the observer's zenith.

(xix) The **Polar Distance** of a heavenly body is that arc of a celestial meridian between the body and the celestial pole. Obviously it equals $90° \pm$ Dec., and is similar to the colatitude of its geographical position. In Fig. 104, PX is the polar distance of X.

(xx) The **Right Ascension** (R.A.) of a heavenly body is the arc of the celestial equator between the celestial meridian of the body and the First Point of Aries (the fixed celestial datum point). It is always measured to the eastward from the First Point of Aries and is expressed in hours, minutes, and seconds (up to 24 hours). R.A. is really the celestial longitude of the body. In Fig. 104, $\varphi\, GAB$ is the R.A. of the body X (and $=$ about 22 hours).

The R.A. of an observer's meridian (written RAM) is arc $\varphi\, G$ in Fig. 104 where z is the terrestrial position of the observer.

The **Sidereal Hour Angle** (S.H.A.) of a heavenly body is the arc of the celestial equator between the First Point of Aries and the celestial meridian of the body. It is always measured westward from the First Point of Aries and is expressed in degrees and minutes. In Fig. 104, $\varphi\, B$ is the S.H.A. of the body X. S.H.A. $= (360° -$ R.A. in arc).

(xxi) The **Hour Angle** (H.A.) of a heavenly body is the arc of the celestial equator between the meridian of the body and the meridian of the observer. It is usually measured towards the West from the observer's meridian in hours, minutes, and seconds. But in modern practice it is measured in degrees and minutes East or West of the observer's meridian (e.g. in Bygrave slide rule). H.A. is really equivalent to difference of longitude.

The **Greenwich Hour Angle** (G.H.A.) of a heavenly body is the arc of the celestial equator between the meridian of Greenwich and the meridian of the body, measured westward from Greenwich and expressed in degrees and minutes.

The **Greenwich Hour Angle of Aries** (G.H.A. φ) is the arc of the celestial equator between the meridian of Greenwich and the First Point of Aries, measured westward from Greenwich in degrees and minutes. The *Local Hour Angle of Aries* (L.H.A. φ) is the arc of the celestial equator measured westward from the meridian of the observer to the First Point of Aries. Then G.H.A. $=$ G.H.A. φ $+$ S.H.A., and L.H.A. $=$ G.H.A. $\pm$ Long.

(xxii) The **Meridian Passage** of a heavenly body is the act of its crossing the plane of the meridian of the observer.

The Transit of a heavenly body is the same as the meridian passage. When a heavenly body is in Transit its celestial meridian is the same straight line as the observer and the centre of the Earth.

A meridian passage "above the pole" (or upper meridian passage) or a superior transit (or upper transit) is when the heavenly body crosses the actual celestial meridian of the observer.

A meridian passage "below the pole" (or lower meridian passage) or an inferior transit (or lower transit) is when the heavenly body crosses the anti-meridian of the observer (that is, the meridian 180° from the observer's meridian).

(xxiii) Two bodies are in **Conjunction** when they are of the same R.A. or Long.

Two bodies are in **Sextile** when they differ in R.A. or Long. by 60 degrees.

Two bodies are in **Quadrature** when they differ in R.A. or Long. by 90 degrees.

Two bodies are in **Opposition** when they differ in R.A. or Long. by 180 degrees.

(xxiv) The **Prime Vertical** is the plane of the Great circle passing through the observer and the true East and West points of the Observer's Rational (Celestial) Horizon. That is, it is the plane of the Great circle passing due East and West through the observer.

The **Vertical Circle** of a heavenly body in relation to an observer is the Great circle which passes through the heavenly body and the zenith of the observer.

(*Note.*—Observer's Celestial Horizon, Altitude, Zenith Distance, etc., will be defined in Section 4.)

SECTION 2

TIME

(*Note.*—Angles measured in hours, minutes, and seconds may be converted into degrees and minutes by the help of special tables or by the relationship: 1 hour = 15°; 4 minutes of time = 1°; 1 minute of time = 15 minutes of arc, etc.

Incidentally the top of the Haversine tables given in Nautical Tables where angles are given in time and arc, provides a convenient conversion table.)

3. The **ROTATION OF THE EARTH** provides a convenient basis in deriving units and measurement of time. Its rotation through 360

degrees in relation to some fixed datum point provides a convenient
unit of time—the Day. For the Solar Day the datum against
which the rotation is measured is the sun, and for the Sidereal Day
the datum is the First Point of Aries. These two are not the same.
For, whereas the First Point of Aries is definitely a fixed datum in
relation to the heavens as seen from the Earth, the sun is not. This

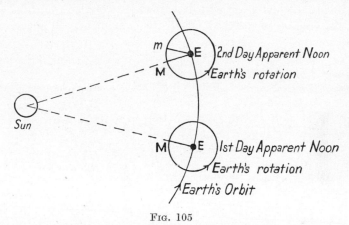

FIG. 105

is because the Earth is moving around the sun (one revolution per
year) in the same direction as its own rotation, thus making the
Solar Day longer than the Sidereal Day (see Fig. 105). A lunar Day
which is the time between successive transits of the moon across a
meridian, is of course even longer. Solar time is the regulator of
humans, and, in fact, nearly all animals on Earth. Other means of
measuring time, such as by pendulums and balance-wheels in clocks,
etc., are all subordinate to the fundamental method based on the
Earth's rotation.

4. SOLAR TIME. The **Solar Day.** From the above it is clear that
the **Apparent Solar Day** is the interval of time between two successive transits of the sun across the observer's meridian. This is
divided into 24 hours of Apparent Time of the True Sun.

Unfortunately the True (or Apparent or Real) Sun as seen from
the Earth gives Apparent Solar Days of irregular length. This is
because the Earth varies its angular speed in its orbit. This irregular
day would be unsatisfactory in use as a means of measuring time
and therefore the Mean Solar Day is used. The **Mean Solar Day** is
the average length of all the Apparent Solar Days throughout a
number of years. The **Mean Sun** (Astronomical Mean Sun) is the
imaginary sun which moves at a uniform speed along the celestial

Equator, so that any two successive transits through a given meridian take a time of exactly one Mean Solar Day.

(*Note.*—The Dynamic Mean Sun is the imaginary sun which moves at a uniform speed along the Ecliptic.)

Now the Solar Day is divided up into 24 hours, but instead of numbering these hours from 0 at the time of Sun's transit of the meridian, 12 hours are added so that the time of transit is 1200 (noon) and the day really starts from midnight. In the case of

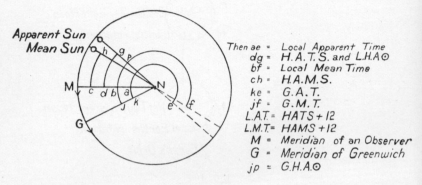

Then ae = Local Apparent Time
dg = H.A.T.S. and L.H.A☉
bf = Local Mean Time
ch = H.A.M.S.
ke = G.A.T.
jf = G.M.T.
L.A.T. = HATS + 12
L.M.T. = HAMS + 12
M = Meridian of an Observer
G = Meridian of Greenwich
jp = G.H.A☉

FIG. 106

Apparent Time the true sun's transit is used, and in the case of Mean Time the mean sun's transit is used.

Now if 12 hours were not added, then obviously time would equal Hour Angle of the sun. This H.A. is called Hour Angle of the True Sun (HATS) if found from the true sun, and Hour Angle of the Mean Sun (HAMS) if found from the mean sun.

So far we have seen the derivation of two times at a given meridian, the Apparent Time and the Mean Time. Now the difference between the apparent and the mean time is a quantity called the **Equation of Time** (E.T.) which is given in the Nautical Almanac. Then Apparent time = Mean time ± E.T.

Now, as time is measured from midnight of the meridian instead of noon of the meridian it is convenient for calculations to add 12 hours to the value of the Equation of Time, giving the **factor E**. Then, for example when E.T. = −14 min. 05 sec., E = 11 hrs. 45 min. 55 sec.; and

HATS = Mean Time of Meridian + E = HAMS + E.T.

HAMS = Apparent Time of Meridian − E = HATS − E.T.

5. LOCAL, AND GREENWICH SOLAR TIMES.
In the last few paragraphs time has been said to be divided into the unit of one day

by two successive transits through a given meridian. Time, which is really the sun's (true or mean) H.A. from the meridian plus 12 hours, may of course be found for any meridian. Thus—

(a) (i) A **Local Apparent Day** is the interval between two successive transits of the true sun across the meridian of the observer. Twelve hours are added, by convention, to the actual time of sun's transit to give Local Apparent Time. In Fig. 106 where the observers meridian is M, his Local Apparent Time (LAT) is ae; and the Hour Angle of the True Sun from his meridian is dg.

(ii) A **Local Mean Day** is the interval between two successive transits of the mean sun across the meridian of the observer. Twelve hours is again added to give Local Mean Time. In Fig. 106, with the observer at M, his Local Mean Time ($L.M.T.$, but often called $S.M.T.$—Ships Mean Time—by nautical navigators) is bf; and the Hour Angle of the Mean Sun (HAMS) is ch. In Fig. 106 the real sun is shown ahead of the mean sun. M and G rotate with the Earth in the direction indicated.

(b) **Greenwich Mean Time.** Obviously, at a given instant each meridian has its own L.M.T. For convenience, when dealing with matters of an astronomical or world-wide nature, and as a standard, one particular time is chosen for use. This is **Greenwich Mean Time** (G.M.T.) which is the Local Mean Time of the meridian of Greenwich (which is the Prime meridian from which longitudes are measured). It is expressed in the 24-hour notation. Thus—

10 o'clock in the morning = 1000 hours G.M.T.

and 3 hrs. 15 min. and 4 sec. in

the afternoon = 15 hrs. 15 min. 04 sec. G.M.T.

or, just 15 15 04 G.M.T.

If the G.M.T. is known at a particular instant and the longitude, then the observer can find his L.M.T. at that instant simply by adding or subtracting his Long. (in time) to or from the G.M.T.

Thus—

G.M.T. + East Long. = L.M.T.

G.M.T. — West Long. = L.M.T.

Whether to add or subtract the Long. is fairly obvious but to save the necessity of thinking about it the following rule proves helpful—

"If longitude is East G.M.T. is least.
If longitude is West G.M.T. is best."

In Fig. 106, G is the meridian of Greenwich, then at the instant depicted jf is the L.M.T. of Greenwich, that is, the G.M.T.

The **Greenwich Apparent Time** is the Local Apparent Time (i.e. by true sun) at the meridian of Greenwich. It equals ke in Fig. 106.

6. STANDARD AND ZONE TIMES. Standard Time is the time of L.M.T. of a particular meridian which is accepted as the standard for use in a definite area. Obviously it would be absurd for adjoining towns to keep the clocks indicating the L.M.T. of their own meridians. Therefore a Standard Time is laid down for a country (or part of a country if of wide latitude) for use entirely in that country. A country may, of course, choose any meridian as its standard, but most countries (and many ships at sea) adopt the time of the zone in which they are situated, according with the **Zone System of Uniform Times.**

Zone Time (Z.T.) is the L.M.T. of the central meridian of the zone. Zones are as follows: Each zone is 15 degrees of Long. wide; that is, it extends $7\frac{1}{2}°$ on each side of its central meridian. One basic principle of the system is that each zone time differs from G.M.T. by a whole number of hours, and so the central meridian of each zone is 15° from the next. Zones are numbered from Greenwich, which is 0, up to 12 East and West. To the East they are marked minus (−) and the West plus (+). Zone No. 12 is common to + and −.

Then to find the zone in which is an observer, he must find that meridian of which the longitude is a multiple of 15, to which he is nearest. Thus: At 1145 G.M.T. find the zone Z.T. of an observer at Long. 64° 30′ W.

$$\text{Nearest multiple of } 15 = 60$$

$$\text{Zone of Long. } 60° \ 00′ \ W. = + \frac{60}{15} = + 4$$

∴ Zone Time at 64° 34′ W. = G.M.T. − 4 = 0845 Z.T.

(To find G.M.T. from Z.T.; G.M.T. = Z.T. + zone no. if West.

or G.M.T. = Z.T. − zone no. if East.)

7. CIVIL TIME. So far, time has been considered mainly from an astronomical point of view. But for civil purposes a time standard called Local Standard Time (LST) is laid down legally. As mentioned above the standard used is the time of the zone in which the area is situated except in a few cases (e.g. India is $5\frac{1}{2}$ hours ahead of G.M.T.). In nearly all countries the 24-hour notation is not used for everyday purposes, but instead two 12-hour periods are used. From midnight to noon is 0–12 a.m. (anti-meridian) and from noon to midnight 0–12 p.m. (post meridian). The faces of watches, clocks, and chronometers are divided into twelve hours.

8. DATE. (a) The **Date,** which is simply the designation of a particular day, is in most things quite as important as the time of the day. For practically all purposes, both astronomical and everyday, the year is divided into twelve months of various lengths—which is common knowledge.

Each Local Mean Time (including G.M.T.) has its own local date for each day. The date at Greenwich (Greenwich Date = G.D.) is accepted as a standard. It may quite often be necessary to find the G.D. corresponding to a given date and time at a place differing from Greenwich. Thus: find the G.M.T. and G.D. at 0730 hrs. on 3rd January, 1936, Eastern Australian Time (Zone − 10).

$$\text{G.M.T.} = \text{E. Aust. T.} - \text{Zone}$$
$$= 0730 \text{ on } 3/1/36 - 10 \text{ hrs.}$$
$$= 2130 \text{ G.M.T. } 2/1/36 \text{ G.D.}$$

The Local Date was 3/1/36 and the G.D. was 2/1/36.

Similarly, to find a Local Date (L.D.) in one part of the world for a certain Local Standard Time (Z.T.) and L.D. at another part, the procedure is as given in the following example. Find the Local Standard Time and Local Date at Samoa (Zone + 11) at 1200 hrs. on 1/2/36 Local Standard Time at Fiji (Zone − 12).

$$\text{Z.T. and L.D. at Zone} + 11 = \text{Fiji Time} - 23 \text{ hrs.}$$
$$= 1200 \text{ on } 1/2/36 - 2300$$
$$= 1300 \text{ hrs. on } 31/1/36.$$

(b) **Change of Date** at Greenwich takes place at midnight G.M.T. and at any other place at midnight of the Standard Time in force at that place. There is, however, one other change of date which takes place. If an observer moves across the 180° meridian he obviously must change his date—for when in East longitude his Local Time is ahead of Greenwich, and when in West longitude his Local Time is behind Greenwich. The meridian 180° East and West, with various modifications to include whole groups of islands on one side or the other, is called the Date Line. The date to the west of this line is one day ahead of the date just to the east of it. Thus an observer moving towards the East puts his local time back by one day when crossing the Date Line.

9. SIDEREAL TIME AND FACTOR R. (a) The **Sidereal Day** is the period of time between two successive transits of the First Point of Aries across the meridian of the observer. This sidereal day is divided into 24 hours of sidereal time. Then, 24 hrs. Sid. Time = 1 Sid. Day = 23 hrs. 56 min. 04·091 sec. of Mean Solar Time, which is 3 min 55·9 sec (solar) shorter than a solar day. But the sidereal day, unlike the mean and apparent solar days, which start at midnight, starts at the actual upper meridian passage of the first point of Aries, and does not have 12 hours added to it. So it is obvious that the **Local Sidereal Time** (L.Sid.T.) at a meridian is equal to the Right Ascension of that meridian. Strictly speaking, the Local Sidereal Time of the meridian is the Hour Angle of the first point of Aries measured westward from the meridian; and it is equal to the Right Ascension of the meridian measured eastward from the First Point of Aries. Similarly Greenwich Sidereal Time is really the Greenwich Hour Angle of Aries.

(b) **The RAM** (= L.Sid.T.) is, as can be seen in Fig. 107, equal to the sum of the Hour Angle of the Mean Sun and the Right Ascension

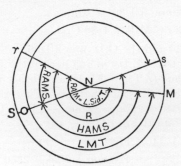

S = Meridian of Mean Sun
s = Meridian of Mean Sun +180° or 12 Hrs.
M = Meridian of Observer
LMT = HAMS + 12 Hrs.
R = RAMS + 12 Hrs.
RAM = RAMS + HAMS = R + LMT(-24)

FIG. 107

of the Mean Sun. But in practice the L.M.T. is usually known or easily found, and not the HAMS. If the L.M.T. and the RAMS are added, then 12 hours will have to be subtracted to give the RAM (L. Sid. T.). To avoid this, 12 hours are added to the value of the RAMS to give the **factor R.** Then HAMS + RAMS = R + L.M.T. = RAM or Sidereal Time, which is all shown in Fig. 107.

(*N.B.*—In all computations of time 24 hours are, of course, deducted if the time is over that amount.)

In Fig. 108 the method of finding the Hour Angle of a Star is simply illustrated. HA* = RAM − RA* = (L.M.T. + R) − RA*.

9A. (a) **PRECESSION AND NUTATION.** Up to this stage the First Point of Aries has been regarded as a definitely fixed datum point, but unfortunately this is not quite a fact. Owing to Precession and Nutation (already mentioned in para. 25 (**b**) of Chapter I), the direction of the Earth's axis is not constant and therefore the plane of the equator is not constant. **Precession** is a slow continuous variation of the direction of the Earth's axis. **Nutation** is a periodic variation or wobble of the direction of the Earth's axis and has, principally, two periods combined, one of eighteen years and one of about fifteen days. The cause of precession and nutation is the fact that the Earth is slightly unbalanced and rotates under the varying gravitational influences of the sun, moon, and planets.

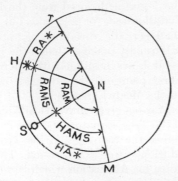

H = *Meridian of a Heavenly Body*
S = *Meridian of Mean Sun*
M = *Meridian of Observer*
HA✳ = RAM ~ RA✳

FIG. 108

As the direction of the Earth's axis alters, the plane of its Equator varies, and the celestial equator, being in the same plane, varies with it. This results in irregularities which up to this stage we have disregarded. But as the plane of the celestial equator varies it obviously does not cut the Ecliptic either in exactly the same place or at a quite constant angle. That is—

(i) The first points of Aries and Libra are not definite fixed datum points in the celestial sphere but move around the celestial equator due to **Precession.** This movement is called the Precession of the Equinoxes. (The Equinoxes coincide with the first points of Aries and Libra.) Now the rate at which the first points of Aries and Libra move is about 50·27″ per year. This is called the Constant of Precession. That is, it takes over 25,000 years for one complete revolution of precession. The direction of movement of the first point of Aries is towards the west.

The change of the exact position of the first point of Aries on the

Equator due to **Nutation** is of the order of about $\pm$ 1·2 seconds. This irregular variation is called Nutation in Right Ascension.

(ii) The Obliquity of the Ecliptic is not a constant angle.

(b) **Mean and Apparent Places.** Now as the plane of the Equator is not a definite fixed plane it is necessary that one be chosen. Therefore the Plane of the Equator at the beginning of the year 1900 is adopted as a fundamental plane of reference. If precession effect for the appropriate time and nutation effect is applied to this the plane of the **True Equator** and the position of the First Point of Aries can be found.

The **Mean Equator** is the Equator deduced from the 1900 fundamental plane by making due allowance for precession but not making any allowance for the small periodic variations of nutation. The Mean Equator for the year is usually taken as that of the 1st January.

The **Mean Place** of a star is its position with reference to the Mean Equator (and the first point of Aries defined by the intersection of the Ecliptic and the Mean Equator).

The **Apparent Place** of a star (as given in Nautical Almanac) is its position with reference to the True Equator (and first point of Aries defined by the intersection of the Ecliptic and the True Equator) including allowance for nutation as well as precession. The Apparent Place also includes allowance for **Aberration** which is a distortional effect due to the Earth's velocity in its orbit. (*Note*.—The constant of Aberration for the sun is $20\frac{1}{2}''$, which is the distance moved by the Earth in the time the light takes to travel from the sun to the Earth (498·4 seconds).)

(*Note*.—For theoretical astronomical work much data are expressed in relation to the Equator and first point of Aries of the year 1950).

(c) **Uniform and True Sidereal Time.** It is obvious that as the first point of Aries is—due to precession and nutation—not a definite fixed datum, the length of a Sidereal Day does not accurately define one revolution of the Earth relative to the fixed stars. Also its length is not quite regular owing to nutation (and a very slight acceleration of precession which may be neglected). But a chronometer can, of course, only keep a uniform time. Therefore a chronometer showing sidereal time actually keeps **Uniform Sidereal Time** which differs from **True Sidereal Time** by omitting the effect of nutation. As Nutation in R.A. is never more than about 1·2 seconds the difference between Uniform and True Sidereal Time cannot exceed that value.

It is often convenient to keep a chronometer set and rated to keep the Local Uniform Sidereal Time of Greenwich. This is called **Greenwich Sidereal Time.** Then, summarizing we have: True

Sidereal Time is based on the time of rotation of the Earth measured in relation to the first point of Aries which moves due to Precession and Nutation. This differs from the real time of Earth's rotation (measured against fixed stars) by the algebraic sum of the Precession effect and the effect of Nutation in R.A. at any time.

Uniform Sidereal Time is based on the time of rotation of the Earth measured in relation to a theoretical first point of Aries which moves only under the effect of Precession.

10. THE YEAR. (a) The **Sidereal Year.** Although, owing to the movement of the First Point of Aries, the sidereal day is not quite a fixed quantity the Sidereal Year is quite definite. The Sidereal Year is the time required for the sun to move through one complete and exact circuit of the Ecliptic. The revolution is measured in relation to a definite fixed direction, and not in relation to the direction of the first point of Aries which is not stationary. The Sidereal Year equals 365·25636 Mean Solar Days.

(b) The **Tropical Year** is the time required for the sun to move through one revolution along the Ecliptic measured in relation to the first point of Aries. Now, as the first point of Aries "backs" 50·27″ per year, the Tropical Year is the time to revolve through (360° — 50·27″), that is, slightly less than the one complete and genuine revolution. Therefore the Tropical Year is less than the Sidereal Year, and equals 365·2422 Mean Solar Days. (365 days 05 hrs. 48 min. 45·51 sec.)

(c) The **Civil Year** or calendar year of the Gregorian calendar is based on the Tropical year, and consists of 365 mean solar days on a normal year and 366 mean solar days on a Leap year. Leap years occur when the number of the year is exactly divisible by 4, except the century years, which are only Leap years when exactly divisible by 400. This averages out, over a period of 400 years, at 365·2425 mean solar days; which differs only slightly from the Tropical.

(d) The **Solar Year** is the name sometimes given to the Besselian Year and it is used for convenience in astronomy owing to the difference between the Tropical year and the Civil year at a particular time. The first Besselian year started in 1900. It is equal in length to a Sidereal Year but begins at a moment not coincident with the beginning of the Civil year. It is of no practical interest to the navigator.

11. SUMMARY. (a) The following are the values of various time periods expressed in Mean Solar Time—

1 Sidereal year	= 365·25636 Mean Solar days.
1 Tropical year	= 365·2422 Mean Solar days.

1 Civil year = 365·2425 Mean Solar days (average over 400 years).

1 Besselian year (Solar year) = 1 Tropical year in length, beginning at time deduced accurately from the beginning of the year 1900.

1 Mean Solar day = 24 hrs.

1 Apparent Solar day = 24 hrs. ± the change in the Equation of Time in the particular 24 hours.

1 Uniform Sidereal day = 23 hrs. 56 min. 04·091 sec.

1 True Sidereal day = 23 hrs. 56 min. 04·091 sec. ± a correction for Nutation in R.A.

Time of one true revolution of Earth = 23 hrs. 56 min. 04·01 sec.

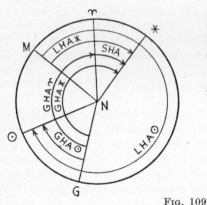

G = Meridian of Greenwich
M = „ „ Observer
⊙ = „ „ True Sun
♈ = „ „ Aries
✳ = „ „ Star

Fig. 109

(b) (i) Apparent Solar Time is found by observations.
Mean Solar Time is kept by clocks.
Apparent Solar Time ~ Mean Solar Time = Equation of Time.

(ii) True Sidereal Time is found by observations.
Uniform Sidereal Time is kept by clocks.
True Sidereal Time ~ Uniform Sidereal Time = Nutation in R.A.

11A. ARC. It has been shown in the last few paragraphs that time is really a measurement of the angle of rotation of a meridian of the Earth in relation to some datum such as the Sun or the First Point of Aries. Obviously it is more logical and convenient for the navigator to measure such an angle as a direct value in degrees and minutes. The Air Almanac works on these lines.

Fig. 109 shows how Hour Angles are obtained using the Air Almanac. It seems likely that the use of Sidereal Time, Factors R and E, etc., will die out as far as navigation is concerned. From Fig. 109 it can be seen that

LHA of a star $= $ GHAΥ $+$ SHA of the Star $\pm$ Long.

and LHA of the sun $= $ GHA of the sun $\pm$ Long.

The Moon and Planets are dealt with in the same way as the Sun.

SECTION 3

HEAVENLY BODIES

(*Note.*—In para. 1 of this chapter heavenly bodies were dealt with summarily. In this section more detail is given.)

12. The **STARS** are, as already mentioned, heavenly bodies having fixed positions in relation to each other, and being enormous distances from the Earth. Each contains its own heat and light, by virtue of its own fiery nature. Owing to the immense distance between the Earth and any of the stars, the movement of the Earth in its orbit does not cause any apparent movement of the stars. But, of course, the rotation of the Earth on its axis makes the stars appear to move from east to west at the rate of one revolution per 23 hrs. 56 min. and 04 sec. approximately.

The **Magnitude** of a star is its degree of apparent brightness. This apparent brightness depends on the actual inherent brightness of the body and inversely on its distance from the observer. Magnitudes are expressed numerically, the smaller the number the larger the magnitude. Thus, Sirius the brightest star in the heavens has a magnitude of $-$ 1·6. Stars of a magnitude of 6 are just visible to the human eye. In navigation the brightest stars are usually used for sights, but the smaller stars are valuable as an aid for recognition of others.

The position of a star is, as we have already seen, expressed by its Sidereal Hour Angle (which is really its celestial longitude) and its Declination (which is really its celestial latitude).

The names of stars are sometimes a little confusing. In all cases a star is given a Greek letter, and the Latin name of the group of stars in which it lies. And, in some cases, the star has a name of its own given to it centuries ago. This name is usually used in preference to the letter and name of the group. Thus the star Sirius is α Canis Majoris, and Canopus is α Argus.

13. RECOGNITION of stars is, of course, necessary at times in air navigation when star sights or bearings are required. There are two means of identifying a star, firstly by its position in relation to the other stars which is constant, and secondly by its position in relation to an observer on the Earth at a given time.

(a) **Recognition** by its position in relation to other stars is the best means of identifying any of the brighter stars. This entails considerable memory work and initial study of the heavens at night. As we all know, the stars distributed all over the sky can be grouped conveniently as an aid in recognition. These groups are called Constellations. In old times these groups were given names according to very imaginative figures which they were supposed to represent. The names are preserved, but it is recommended that the navigator should not strain his imagination by attempting to see these figures in the constellations.

In learning to recognize stars by sight it is suggested that it is best to learn first the more important constellations and then the positions of other stars can be referred to them as an aid. And at all times it must be remembered that the body with the greatest R.A. is furthest to the Eastward. Probably the most useful constellation to know is Orion, the brightest group in the sky (see Fig. 111). Then the constellation Ursa Major, the Pole Star (Polaris in Ursa Minor), and the constellation Cassiopeia in the northern hemisphere (see Fig. 110), and the constellation Crux ("The Southern Cross") and its two pointers (α and β Centaurus) in the southern hemisphere (see Fig. 112) should be learnt. The square of Pegasus is also useful. The Milky Way, or Galaxy, which is an irregular zone around the heavens containing millions of very distant stars resulting in a hazy or nebulous light, is valuable in identifying stars. It should be noted whether a star lies in or near the Milky Way.

Polaris, the Pole Star, is found, incidentally, by extending a line from Merak through Dubhe (of Ursa Major) for a distance about five times the distance of Merak from Dubhe. Polaris lies within about 63′ of the North celestial pole.

Having learnt Polaris and the stars of Ursa Major, Orion, and Crux, the following guides may be helpful—

Aldebaran (α Tauri) lies to the north of a line running through the "belt" of Orion towards the N.W., at a distance from the "belt" of about one and a quarter times the distance Rigel-Betelgeuse.

Altair (α Aquilae) lies on a line drawn through γ and β Cassiopeia, and is just south of the Milky Way. It has a clear bluish-white

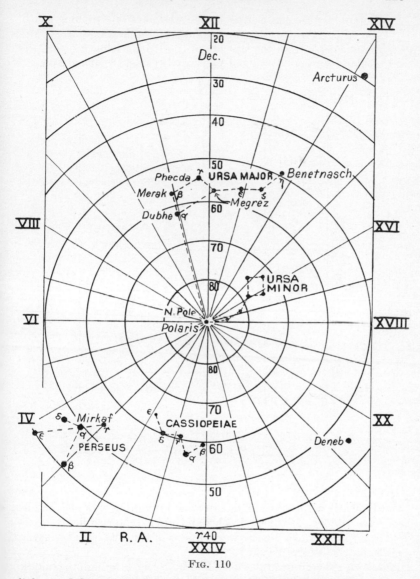

Fig. 110

light, and forms a straight line with two fairly bright stars, one on each side of it.

Antares (α Scorpii) has a slightly reddish light. It is a summer star in England.

Arcturus (α Boötis) lies on the continuation of the curve of the tail of Ursa. It is a very bright star, and has a reddish-yellow light.

Canopus (α Argus) is a little to the west of a line running south from Sirius (see Sirius). It is the second brightest star in the heavens, but is not visible from the latitude of the British Isles.

Capella (α Aurigae) lies about half-way between Orion and Polaris,

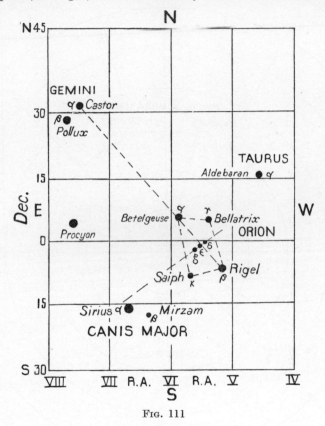

Fig. 111

and is nearly on a straight line drawn through Megrez and Duhbe (of Ursa Major). It is very bright, and has a yellowish light.

Caph (β Cassiopeia) is the western star of the "W" of Cassiopeia. It lies in the Milky Way.

Castor (α Geminorum) lies on a line from Rigel through the middle star of Orion's belt. It has a white light. Between Gemini and Polaris there is a noteworthy lack of bright stars.

Deneb (α Cygni) lies approximately on a line from γ Pegasi through β Pegasi, and is in the Milky Way.

Denebola (β Leonis) forms an equilateral triangle with Arcturus and Spica (see same) and lies to the west of them.

Fomalhaut (α Piscis Australis) lies on a line drawn south through the two western stars of the square of Pegasus (Scheat and Markab) (see Markab). It lies on the opposite side of the south pole from Crux.

Markab (α Pegasi) forms the S.W. corner of the square of Pegasus.

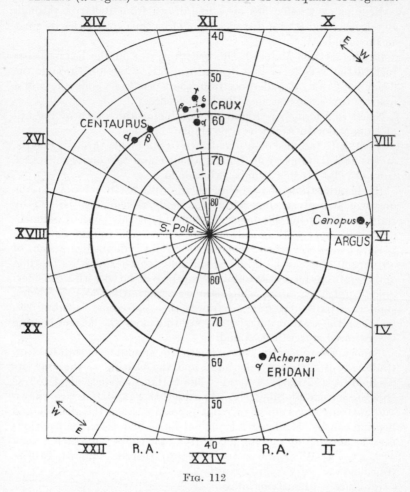

Fig. 112

Nath (β Tauri) is about half way along a line drawn from Capella to a point between Betelgeuse and Bellatrix, and is in the Milky Way.

Polux (β Geminorum) lies to the S.E. of Castor. It has a slightly golden tinge.

Procyon (α Canis Minoris) lies south of a line drawn from Bellatrix through Betelgeuse, at a distance (east) from Betelgeuse about three times the distance between Bellatrix and Betelgeuse. It is just to the east of the Milky Way, and has a pale yellow light. Procyon forms the N.E. corner of a large equilateral triangle made with Betelgeuse and Sirius (see same).

Regulus (α Leonis) lies on a line drawn from Bellatrix through Betelgeuse, and is at a distance from Orion just over twice as great as Procyon is.

Sirius (α Canis Majoris), the brightest star in the heavens, lies just to the S.W. of a line drawn in a S.E. direction through the "belt" of Orion, at a distance from the "belt" of about one and a quarter times the distance Rigel-Betelgeuse.

Spica (α Virginis) is found by continuing the curve of the tail of Ursa Major to Arcturus by a similar distance.

Vega (α Lyrae) lies on a line drawn from Capella through Polaris, and is at a distance from Polaris about equal to Polaris's distance from Capella. It has a bluish-white light.

(b) **Identification** of stars by their positions in relation to the observer at a given time without actually recognizing the star by sight is a commendable method. Not only is this method independent of memory work but also it makes it possible to take sights in a partly clouded sky when recognition by sight is doubtful. A sight of any bright star can be taken as suitable, together with its bearing, and then from the results obtained it can be deduced with a considerable degree of certainty which star was used. Alternatively when a sight of a particular star is required the approximate reading can be set on the sextant and then by sighting along the correct bearing the required star will be found.

Knowing the time, the approximate Lat. and Long. of the observer, the angle of elevation (altitude), and the bearing of the star, its declination and its H.A. (and $\pm$ its S.H.A.) can be calculated as will be seen later. Similarly, when its S.H.A. and Dec. are known and also the observer's approximate position, then the altitude and bearing can be calculated for a given time. The actual calculations may be avoided by making use of (i) a Star Globe; (ii) such a book as Harvey's "What Star is It?"; or (iii) Altitude-Azimuth Tables; (iv) diagrams, of varying accuracy.

(c) **Aids** in Identifying Stars.

(i) **Star Globes** provide not only an aid in learning to recognize stars by sight (as in (a) above) but also a means of identifying a star by its bearing and altitudes (as in (b) above). A star globe usually consists of a sphere on which is printed a graticule of parallels of Declination and meridians of Right Ascension, the Ecliptic and the stars in their appropriate places. Different symbols for the stars give an indication of their magnitude. This sphere is rotatable in all directions in a hole in a box. This hole in which the sphere lies is of such a size that it is a close but free fit around the sphere and that the plane of the circumference of the hole exactly bisects the sphere. That is, only the upper half of the globe is visible. Then the circumference of the hole corresponds to an observer's horizon. Let in to this circumference is a brass ring which is free to rotate horizontally (i.e. around the hole) and on which is carried, at right angles to it, a semicircle of brass. Around the circumference of the hole a scale of bearings is marked off in degrees, and the brass semicircle over the globe is graduated up to 90 degrees from each side. This latter scale is a latitude and/or altitude scale. In some types two brass semicircles are provided, and sometimes also a sliding pointer.

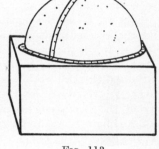

Fig. 113

Now to set the globe for an observer at a given position, the brass ring is rotated till the plane of the semicircle coincides with the zero and 180° of the bearing scale. This will then make the semicircle equivalent to the meridian of the observer. Then the celestial sphere must be rotated into its correct position in relation to this meridian at a given moment. This is done as follows : With the pole (of the same name as the observer's latitude) under the 90° mark of the semicircle scale the globe is rotated till the R.A.M. (calculated for the given time) as indicated on the scale around the celestial equator on the globe is reading against the zero or 180° mark of the bearing scale (i.e. coincident with the brass semicircle). If the observer's latitude is north, the R.A.M. is read against the 180° of the bearing scale, and then the pole is moved towards the zero of the bearing scale (by rotating the sphere) till it coincides with the Lat. of the observer on the scale of the brass semicircle. Or if the observer's Lat. is south, the pole (S) is moved towards the 180° graduation on the bearing scale till it coincides with the Lat. The net results of this are that the observer's position is exactly on top of the globe (under the 90° graduation of the semicircle) and that the observer's celestial meridian is oriented in relation to the bearing scale. All the stars then visible on the globe can be seen from the observer's position at the given time. Then without moving the globe the bearing and altitude of any star can be found by rotating the brass semicircle till it coincides with the star, and reading off from the bearing and the altitude scales. Alternatively the name of a star can be found by setting the semicircle in the known direction and looking under the altitude on the altitude scale to find the star. If no star is found the observation must have been of a planet.

Star globes are usually of such dimensions to be impracticable for use in the air.

(ii) " **What Star Is It ?**" by H. W. Harvey is a very small book used to identify stars from the data of a known altitude and bearing, and observer's position and time. It is suitable for use in the air. This little book contains two sets of tables. On the left-hand pages Hour Angles are tabulated against bearings and altitudes, together with instructions as to which way to apply the H.A. so obtained to the R.A.M. to get the star's R.A. On the right-hand pages Declinations are tabulated against bearings and altitudes. Thus the approximate R.A. and the Dec. of the star are obtained, and a star having (according to an Almanac) this R.A. and Dec. will be the star observed. To avoid the inconvenience of having to refer to an Almanac the approximate R.A.s and Decs. of a large number of stars are given in the back of the book.

The tables only give values for every 10 degrees of bearing and 5 degrees of altitude. As this may cause doubt at times accurate interpolation may be necessary.

In any case the navigator should, as a check, try to estimate the magnitude of the star observed. This can be done with considerable accuracy with practice.

(iii) **Altitude-Azimuth Tables** provide means of finding a star's R.A. and Dec. when the observer's position and time, and the star's altitude and bearing are known. The principle is the same as in "What Star Is It ?" but the Altitude-Azimuth tables are much more detailed, and therefore voluminous.

(iv) **Planispheres** are useful mainly as pictorial representations of the heavens in learning to recognize stars by their relative positions. But, if made suitably, approximate bearings and altitudes can be obtained.

A Planisphere usually consists of an inner disc on which a graticule and stars are printed, which rotates in an outer envelope. This envelope has an oval-shaped hole cut in its upper side through which a certain area of the inner disc can be seen. The area of this hole represents the field of an observer's visible heaven and its edges define his horizon. Its oval shape is to allow for the distortion of the projection. When the disc is rotated to the correct position, then the position of the observer is at the centre of this hole. Obviously, therefore, the planisphere is made for use at a particular latitude.

To set the planisphere the R.A.M. is calculated and the meridian of this R.A.M. as printed on the disc is made coincident with a mark

on the envelope. The stars visible through the hole will be those
visible in the sky at that time on that meridian at the designed
latitude. A rough idea of the bearing of any star can be obtained by
noting its direction from the centre of the hole (which is the observer's
position) and the approximate altitude may be estimated by its

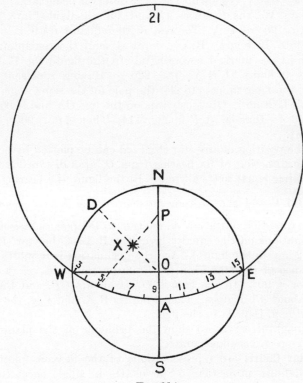

FIG. 114

distance from the edge of the hole, remembering that the centre of
the hole is at 90 degrees from the edge.

In models designed for the layman the edges of the envelope are
cut away and graduated into 24 hours; and the rim of the disc is
graduated with days and months. Then to set the disc, the required
date is made coincident with the required time.

(v) **Star Diagrams** work on the same principle as the planisphere.
A star diagram can be constructed simply, to represent roughly
the heavens as seen from a particular position at a particular time,
to act as an aid in identifying stars. Fig. 114 shows a star diagram.
The circle *NESW* is drawn to represent the observer's celestial

horizon, about the observer's position O. Next the celestial equator is drawn. As it cuts the observer's horizon at points due E. and W. of him, it must pass through the points E. and W. Also the distance from the observer to the equator (OA) must be in the correct proportion (remembering that the radius $OS = 90°$). In the figure the latitude 30° 00″ N. is shown. Then the observer being 90° ($= 6$ hrs.) from E. and W., the distances AE and AW are divided into 6 hours of R.A., or 90° of H.A. The rest of the equator EBW is suitably divided into 12 hours. R.A.M. is at A, and the remaining R.A. graduations are marked accordingly. In the figure the R.A.M. is taken as 9 hours (L.H.A. ♈ = 225°). Having represented the Equator, the next thing is to plot the pole (of the same name as the observer's latitude). Obviously it is on the line ON and is 90° from the Equator—that is, at P in Fig. 114. Then $AP = 90'$, and OP = Co. Lat.

Now the position of any star observed can be plotted by laying it off in the direction of its bearing from O, at a distance from the horizon circle equal to its altitude. In the figure the bearing of the star is 317 T and the altitude 50 degrees (i.e. $DX = \dfrac{50}{90}$ of DO).

Then the direction of the star in relation to the pole as measured on the graduations on the equator gives the R.A. of the star (R.A. = about 5·2 hrs. in the figure). And the declination is proportional to the distance of the star from the Equator, remembering that pole − equator = 90°. In the figure, XC is about $\frac{1}{2}CP$, and therefore Dec. = about 45 degrees. Then from its R.A. and Dec. the star is identified (e.g. Capella in the figure).

This diagram serves to show the principle of the planisphere. It is, of course, very inaccurate.

(vi) **Star Charts** are representations of the heavens plotted on various definite projections. Star charts in single sheet form or made up into atlas form are available for sale, and are valuable in learning to recognize stars. Each edge of the chart is usually marked with the horizon which it represents, and R.A. and Dec. are also shown.

TABLE I

Small letters	Name in English	GREEK ALPHABET					
		Letters	Name	Letters	Name	Letters	Name
α	Alpha	η	Eta	ν	Nu	τ	Tau
β	Beta	θ	Theta	ξ	Xi	υ	Upsilon
γ	Gamma	ι	Iota	o	Omicron	ϕ	Phi
δ	Delta	κ	Kappa	π	Pi	χ	Chi
ε	Epsilon	λ	Lambda	ρ	Rho	ψ	Psi
ζ	Zeta	μ	Mu	σ	Sigma	ω	Omega

14. THE SUN, as we all know, is the source of heat and light, and provides the greatest attractive force on the Earth. It is exactly similar in nature to the fixed stars. It is about 865,000 miles in diameter.

The Solar system consists of a number of planets, and their satellites, and also comets and meteors, moving around the sun which is the centre of the system. The mass of the sun equals about 99·85 per cent of the total mass of the whole solar system. From this it can be deduced that the centre of gravity of the system must be very nearly coincident with the sun, and that the system is fairly stable as a whole.

15. THE PLANETS are bodies which do not possess their own heat and light but derive it from the sun, around which they revolve. They are enumerated in Table II.

TABLE II

PLANETS

Name	No. of Satel- lites	Average Distance from Sun in Millions of Miles	Approx. Diameter	Time of Rotation on Axis	Period of Orbit approx.
				H. M. S.	
1 Mercury	/	36	3000	24 00 50	87·97 days
2 Venus	/	67	7660	23 21 22	224·7 ,,
3 Earth	1	92·9	7926·68	23 56 04	365·256 ,,
4 Mars	2	141	4200	24 37 23	686·98 ,,
5 Jupiter	11	483	85000	09 55 20	11·86 EarthYears
6 Saturn	9	886	72370		29·46 ,, ,,
7 Uranus	4	1782	31700		84·02 ,, ,,
8 Neptune	1	2792	35200		164·7 ,, ,,

The planets closer to the sun than the Earth are called Inferior Planets, and those more distant than the Earth are called Superior Planets. Rotating in a manner similar to the planets and at a distance from the sun greater than Mars and less than Jupiter, are the Asteroids. Asteroids of which there is a large number are groups consisting of very many tiny planets from about 20 to 400 miles in diameter.

From a practical point of view the only planets of interest in navigation are Venus, Mars, Jupiter, and Saturn. The following well-known points should be remembered as an aid in identifying planets—

(i) Planets do not twinkle like stars but have a steady radiance.

(ii) If the fixed star constellations are well known, the addition of another bright body will be noticed.

(iii) Venus is much brighter than any star and hence cannot be mistaken. It is never more than 47° (= 3 hrs. 08 min.) from the sun, and it is therefore not visible more than 3 hrs. 08 min. after sunset, or before sunrise. When it is visible at evening twilight (i.e. when its R.A. is greater than that of the Sun) it is called the Evening Star, and when visible at morning twilight it is called the Morning Star.

(iv) Mars has a reddish glow. It is not as bright as the other planets and it varies considerably (from magnitude of 0 to about + 1·8).

(v) Jupiter is large and white with a magnitude of brightness from about − 2·0 to − 1·2, averaging − 1·6, which is equivalent to Sirius the brightest star.

(vi) Saturn has a yellowish tinge.

16. The **SATELLITES** are bodies which rotate around some of the planets. Like planets they derive their apparent light by reflecting

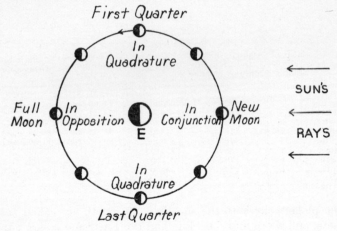

FIG. 115

the sun's light. In Table II the number of satellites to each planet is shown. The only satellite of practical importance to the navigator is the Earth's **Moon,** a comparatively small body of about 2153 miles in diameter.

The Moon is about 240,000 miles from the Earth on an average but varies owing to its elliptical orbit. When the moon is in Perigee it is about 221,000 miles from the Earth's centre, and when in Apogee it is about 252,000 miles. It rotates around the Earth at a speed in its orbit of about 2300 m.p.h. Then, the **Sidereal Period** of the moon which is the time of one complete and true revolution in its orbit in relation to the fixed stars has a mean value of 27 days 7 hours 43 minutes. But during this time the Earth has moved a considerable distance in its orbit around the sun. Then if the direction of the sun in relation to the Earth is taken as a datum, the time for the Moon to complete one revolution around the Earth in relation to this datum is longer than the Sidereal Period. It is called the **Synodic Period** and equals about 29 days 12 hours 44·4 minutes average. It is really the time of one apparent revolution of the Moon. Both the Sidereal and the Synodic Periods vary, the variation of the latter being by far the greater.

The **Phases of the Moon** are illustrated in Fig. 115. At New Moon, which is the beginning of a "Lunation," the Moon has its dark side towards the Earth, and at Full Moon (about fifteen days later) it has its illuminated side towards the Earth. When the Sun and Moon are in the same direction in the relation to the Earth they are in Conjunction. When they are 180 degrees apart they are in Opposition. And when they are 90 degrees apart they are in Quadrature. It must be noted that "First Quarter" and "Last Quarter" do not refer to the portion of the Moon which is illuminated, but to its position in its orbit. Actually about half the disc of the Moon is illuminated at these times.

The plane of the Moon's orbit is never more than slightly over 5° from the plane of the Ecliptic, and therefore its declination is never more than about 28° N. or S.

17. THE ALMANAC. Data concerning the heavenly bodies are published in various almanacs. Of them the Air Almanac is best suited for the air navigator.

(a) The **Official Nautical Almanac** in its full form is a complex volume for the use of astronomers. An Abridged Nautical Almanac is published (H.M. Stationery Office) for navigators. It gives declinations, R.A.s, E, R, semi-diameters, parallax, pole star tables, sunrise and set and moonrise and set tables, etc., together with an explanation. Considerable interpolation is necessary in many cases.

(b) **Brown's Nautical Almanac** gives data similar to that of the official Almanac and also much additional information. Some of this is of purely maritime interest, but the book is very valuable.

(c) The **Air Almanac** (H.M. Stationery Office) is designed for ease and speed. This results in some loss of accuracy, but this in most cases is small and possibly justifiable. It differs mainly in the way it gives the H.A.s of heavenly bodies. These are given directly in degrees and minutes instead of in hours, minutes, and seconds. That is, R.A.s, R, and E are cut out. The H.A.s of the sun, moon, and planets are given directly as values west of Greenwich (GHA). The H.A.s of the stars are given as values west of Aries (S.H.A.), and this is added to the tabulated HA of γ west of Greenwich

(GHA γ) to give the H.A.s of the stars west of Greenwich (GHA*). Thus one very short method is used for the sun, moon or planets, and a second slightly longer method is used for stars. Sunrise and sunset, moonrise and moonset, a very practical twilight table (for ZD of 96°), and an abbreviated pole star table are included. A little more accuracy could be obtained with benefit.

(d) **Ephermerides Aeronautiques,** the French Air Almanac, gives H.A.s similarly in degrees and minutes of arc, but in all cases (including sun, moon, and planets) it works as the British Air Almanac does in the case of stars. This, of course, is longer, but avoids using two different methods. The American Almanac is similar to the British, but gives additional data.

SECTION 4

APPLIED ASTRONOMICAL NAVIGATION

18. ALTITUDE AND ZENITH DISTANCE. The first idea to be thoroughly understood in astronomical work is the relationship between Altitude and Zenith Distance.

Altitude (Alt.) is the vertical angle between the direction of a body and the horizontal plane through the observer (AZC in Fig.

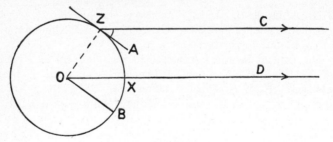

FIG. 116

116). Zenith Distance (Z.D.) is the arc of the Great circle on the celestial sphere between the body and the Zenith of the observer. It equals the arc of the Great circle on the Earth between the geographical position of the body and the observer's position (ZOX or ZX in Fig. 116). *Note.*—The Zenith of an observer is the point on the celestial sphere vertically over the observer's head.

Now, in Fig. 116, OD is the direction of the heavenly body which is being observed by an observer at Z. As the body is at an immense distance from the Earth ZC and OD may be taken as parallel. Then as ZA is the horizontal plane through the observer at Z then

AZC is the Alt. of the body. Now if OB is drawn parallel to ZA, then $ZOB = 90$ degrees. And it is obvious that the angle

$$DOB = \text{the angle } CZA = \text{Alt.}$$
$$= ZOB - ZOX \quad = 90° - \text{Z.D.}$$

that is, $\qquad$ Alt. $= 90° - $ Z.D.

or $\qquad$ Z.D. $= 90° - $ Alt.

Thus, when alt. is known the Z.D. which is simply the Great circle distance of the observer from the geographical position of the body, can be found.

19. ALTITUDE AND POSITION LINE. If, in Fig. 117, CX is a vertical post and A is an ant, then for a given Alt. of the top of the post as observed by the ant there is only one distance at which the ant must be from the base of the post. That is, if the Alt. is CAX then the ant must be at a distance equal to AX from the base of the post. From this it can be seen that the ant must be on a circle about the base of the post X, of a radius equal to XA. This Circle of Position of the ant is the circle on which it is known (knowing the Alt.) that the ant must be.

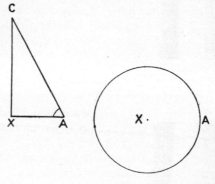

Fig. 117

Now, if instead of flat ground and a post, a sphere and a heavenly body are substituted, then the same principle will apply. In Fig. 116, the heavenly body corresponds with the top of the post C of Fig. 117 and X the geographical position of the body in Fig. 116 corresponds with the base of the post X in Fig. 117. Then for a given Alt., Z must be at a certain fixed distance from X. That is Z must be on a Circle of Position about X, the radius of which equals the Great circle distance XZ, which is the Z.D. This Circle of Position is a small circle (unless the Z.D. is 90°, when it is a Great circle) of which X is one of its poles. When an altitude is found by sextant it results in the general case in finding this Circle of Position on which it is known the observer must be. Of course, if plotted on a projection this circle will be distorted in accord with the nature of the projection. On a Mercator's projection the circle will obviously be elongated on the side away from the Equator.

Now, at any point on a Circle of Position the direction of the geographical position of the observed body is at right angles to the circle. In practice, a small arc of a Circle of Position may be represented by a straight line (at right angles to the bearing of the observed body) provided that the Z.D. is very great compared to the length of the arc. This point is of great practical importance, for it is this line that is the astronomical Position Line obtained by a sextant sight. It is sometimes called a Sumner Position Line.

Of course it must be remembered that if the Alt. is very large, making the Z.D. very small, the curvature of the Circle of Position will be too great to allow even a small arc of it to be represented by a straight line. If the Z.D. is not more than about $1\frac{1}{2}°-2°$ then the Circle of Position may be plotted on a Mercator's chart by a circle around the geographical position of the observed body. If a plotting chart is used (or squared paper) slightly larger Z.D.'s may be plotted by a circle without undue distortion.

Now, having described the fundamental idea of how a Position Line (or Circle of Position) is obtained from an Alt., the errors and corrections to be applied to Observed Altitudes (Obs. Alt.) will be given.

20. CORRECTIONS TO OBSERVED ALTITUDE. (a) The **Visible Horizon** is the circle around the observer drawn through all points where the line of sight from the observer's eye is tangential to the Earth's surface (AB in Fig. 118). The Visible Sea Horizon is a small circle about the observer but the Visible Land Horizon may be at irregular distances from the observer depending on the ground heights.

The **Sensible Horizon** is the circle around the observer on the horizontal plane through the observer's eye. (DE in Fig. 118.)

The **Rational Horizon** (or Celestial Horizon) is the circle on the celestial sphere on the plane through the centre of the Earth parallel to the plane of the Sensible Horizon. (FG in Fig. 118.)

(b) The **Observed Altitude** (Obs. Alt.) of a body is the angle in the vertical plane between the centre of the body and the visible horizon (or the bubble centre in an air sextant) as measured by a sextant. (XOB in Fig. 118 + sextant errors, etc.) Obs. Alt. is the uncorrected reading. The **Apparent Altitude** (A. Alt.) of a body is the angle in the vertical plane between the centre of the body and the sensible horizon of the observer. (XOE in Fig. 118.)

The **True Altitude** (T. Alt.) of a body is the angle in the vertical plane between the centre of a body and the rational (or celestial) horizon. (XCG in Fig. 118.)

The difference between Apparent and True Altitude is negligible in practice, except when the observed body is comparatively close to the Earth—such as the Moon (see "Parallax" below).

(c) The **Corrections** to be applied are as follows:

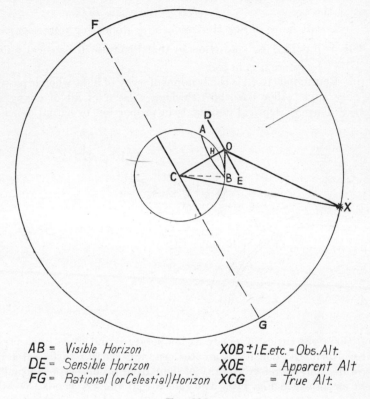

AB = *Visible Horizon*   XOB ±I.E.etc. = Obs.Alt.
DE = *Sensible Horizon*   XOE   = Apparent Alt
FG = *Rational (or Celestial) Horizon* XCG   = True Alt.

FIG. 118

(i) **Index Error** of the sextant is the first correction always. It is applied as explained in Chapter VI.

(ii) **Dip** is the vertical angle between the Sensible Horizon and the Visible Horizon (EOB in Fig. 118) due to the height of the observer (HO). As is obvious from the figure, dip makes the Obs. Alt. too great and therefore it must always be applied as a "minus" correction. It can be shown simply (knowing Earth's radius, etc.) that dip $= 1 \cdot 063 \sqrt{h}$, where dip is in minutes and h in feet. But this does not include terrestrial refraction (see below). When refraction is included, dip in min. $= 0 \cdot 98 \sqrt{h}$.

Now, in Fig. 118—

The angles $COB + BOE = 90°$

and   „   „ $COB + OCB = 90°$

$\therefore$ $OCB = BOE$

that is, the arc $HB =$ the angle BOE

or distance of Sea Horizon = dip—(omitting refraction).

This is modified by refraction so that distance in nautical miles $= 1·15 \sqrt{h}$, where h is in feet.

(iii) **Refraction** (Ref.) is the bending of a ray of light when it passes (at any angle other than 90°) through a layer of air of changing optical density. Optical density is in proportion to actual density

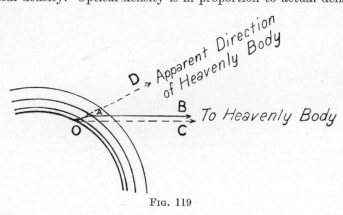

Fig. 119

and therefore varies inversely as temperature and directly as pressure. Normally, density is greater near the Earth's surface due to pressure, and therefore the ray of light from an observer is usually bent as shown in Fig. 119. The rule is that the ray bends towards the normal in the denser medium (the "normal" being the line at right angles to the boundary layer between the two mediums of differing density). Refraction is of two kinds, thus—

Astronomical Refraction is the error due to the bending of a ray of light from the heavenly body in its passage through the atmosphere of varying optical density. In Fig. 119 the observer O sees the body apparently in the direction OD, whereas actually he is looking along the curve OA, and thence along AB which is the true direction of the body. OC is parallel to AB. Then the angle DOC is the refraction. The figure is, of course, exaggerated. Values for Ref. become extremely doubtful at some Alts., and no Alt. below 10° should be used unless absolutely necessary.

Refraction Tables given in nautical tables usually give values for normal conditions of pressure and temperature (usually 1015 milli-bars and 50° F.). But, of course, Refraction decreases with height. Thus at 20,000 ft. it is only about half its sea-level value. The Air Almanac and all new aeronautical tables give Refraction Tables to cover all navigable heights. Refraction is always "minus" to Obs. Alt., and must be applied to both marine-type and bubble-type sextant observations.

Terrestrial Refraction is the bending of the ray of light between an observer and the visible horizon or other terrestrial object. It has no connexion with astronomical navigation, but is of great prac-tical importance in problems of dis-tance of horizon and dip.

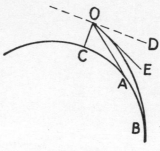

In Fig. 120 the observer O is at a height OC above the surface. If there was no Ref. his line of sight to the horizon would be OA. Then DOA would be his dip and CA his distance from the visible sea horizon. But act-ually Ref. causes his actual line of sight to the horizon to be a curve such as OB. Then he apparently sees the horizon in the direction OE, and apparent dip $= DOE$, and distance to sea horizon $= CB$.

Fig. 120

As stated above, theoretical dip $= DOE =$ theoretical distance to horizon $= CA$ $= 1 \cdot 063 \sqrt{h}$.

But actual dip $= 0 \cdot 98 \sqrt{h}$, and

actual distance to sea horizon $= 1 \cdot 15 \sqrt{h}$, in fact.

Now it may be of practical value to know the distance from which a peak of a certain height can be seen. To determine the "Circle of Maximum Range of Visibility" may be necessary, and is shown in the following example: Find maximum distance at which a moun-tain 3300 ft. high can be seen from an aircraft approaching it at 1800 ft.

Distance of sea horizon from 3300 ft. = 66   naut. miles ⎱ From Tables
  „   „   „   „ 1800 ft. = 48·7 „   „   ⎰ or calculated.

Total = 114·7 naut. miles

114·7 nautical miles is the range of visibility required and a circle of this radius drawn around the position of the mountain on the map or chart may be of value in conditions of extreme visibility.

(iv) **Semi-diameter** is measured as an angle at the observer between the direction of the observed body's centre and its Upper Limb

(U.L. or ☽) or edge, or its Lower Limb (L.L. or ☉) or edge. Then if an Alt. be measured to the body's L.L. obviously the semi-diameter must be added to give the Alt. of the body's centre, which is what is required. The stars being mere pin points of light have no appreciable semi-diameter, but the sun and the Moon have and, therefore, when using a sea horizon and sighting to the Sun's L.L. (or the Moon's U.L. or L.L. as necessary depending on the phase of the Moon), allowance must be made. Semi-diameters for the Sun and the Moon

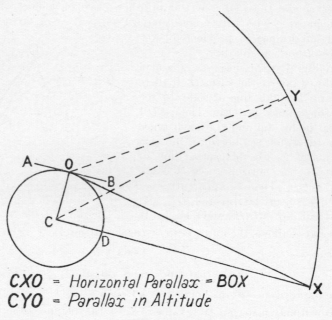

$$CXO = Horizontal\ Parallax = BOX$$
$$CYO = Parallax\ in\ Altitude$$

Fig. 121

are given in the Nautical Almanac for each day. The Moon's semi-diameter must be corrected for parts of a day. Semi-diameter is applied as a plus correction if Alt. is measured to the L.L., and as a minus correction if Alt. is measured to the U.L.

Now when the Alt. of a body is 90° the observer is nearer to the body than is the centre of the Earth by a distance equal to the Earth's radius. Therefore the semi-diameter appears to be larger. This increase in semi-diameter, due to the observer being closer than the centre of the Earth to the observed body, is called Augmentation of Semi-diameter, and depends on the Alt. It is largest in the case of the Moon, but only then is it large enough to warrant consideration.

(v) **Parallax** (Plx.) is the effect of the observer's position being off the line between the heavenly body and the Earth's centre. Thus in Fig. 121 the True Altitude of X in relation to the Rational Horizon (CD) is zero. But in relation to the Sensible Horizon AB through an observer at O, it has an Alt. of minus $OXC = -BOX$.

And tan $OXC = \dfrac{OC}{CX} = \dfrac{\text{Earth's Radius}}{\text{Distance to the body}}$.

Obviously if the distance to the body becomes very great, parallax becomes very small. In the case of the stars it is negligible, and even with the sun it never exceeds about 9″ and therefore can be disregarded in air work. But for the Moon it is considerable (up to about 61′) and must be taken into account.

Now Horizontal Parallax (H.P.) is the angle subtended at the observed body by the Earth's Radius, that is, it is the angle when the body's T. Alt. is zero ($OXC = BOX$ in Fig. 121). But as the Alt. of a body increases the parallax effect decreases. Thus reduced parallax effect is called **Parallax in Altitude** (P. in A.). In Fig. 121 Y is a heavenly body, and $CY = CX$. Then OYC, the Plx. in Alt., is less than OXC, the H.P.

H.P. for the Moon is given in the Nautical Almanac, and Nautical Tables provide conversions of various H.P.s into P. in A. The Air Almanac tabulates P. in A. directly.

Parallax is always applied as a plus correction to A. Alt. to give T. Alt., and in practice is only applicable to observations of the Moon.

(d) Summarizing corrections, we have (shown by examples)—

(i) For sun sight,

With marine-type sextant on sea horizon

Obs. Alt. ☉ =	55°	30′
I.E. (+ or −) =	+	4′

	55°	34′
Dip (always −) 100 ft. =	−	9·8′

	55°	24·2′
Ref. (always −) −		0·6′

	55°	23·6′
Semi-diam. (+ for L.L.) =		16·2′

A. Alt. (of Sun's Centre ☉) = 55° 39·8′

and as Plx. is neglected = T. Alt.

With bubble sextant

Obs. Alt. =	55°	49·4′
I.E. (+ or −) =	−	9·0′

	55°	40·4′
Ref. (always −) =	−	0·6′

A. Alt. (of Sun's Centre ☉) = 55° 39·8′

and as Plx. is neglected = T. Alt.

I.E. is known; Dip and Ref. are taken from Inman's or Norie's; and Semi-diameter from the N.A.

(ii) For moon sight,

With marine-type sextant

Obs. Alt. U.L. =	44°	28·8′
I.E. (+ or) = +		4·0′
	44°	32·8′
Dip (always −) 100 ft. = −		9·8′
	44°	23′
Ref. (always −) = −		1′
	44°	22′
Semi-diam. (− for U.L.) = −		16′
A. Alt. =	44°	06′
P. in A. (always +) = +		40′
T. Alt. =	44°	46′

With bubble sextant

Obs. Alt. =	44°	16′
I.E. (+ or −) = −		9′
	44°	07′
Ref. (always −) = −		1′
A. Alt. =	44°	06′
P. in A. (always +) = +		40′
	44°	46′

(iii) For star sight (and planet sight using planet's centre)

With marine-type sextant

Obs. Alt. =	38°	07′
I.E. (+ or −) = −		3′
	38°	04′
Dip (always −) 100 ft. = −		9·8′
	37°	54·2′
Ref. (always −) = −		1·2′
A. Alt. or T. Alt. =	37°	53′

With bubble sextant

Obs. Alt. =	37°	46′
I.E. (+ or −) = +		8·5′
	37°	54·5′
Ref. (always −) = −		1·2′
A. Alt. or T. Alt. =	37°	53′

(*Note.*—In Inman's and in Norie's, corrections for use with the Sun or with the Moon for sights with reference to the sea horizon are combined to save time.)

21 (a) METHODS OF OBTAINING ASTRONOMICAL POSITION LINES OR POSITIONS from the data obtained by sextant observations may be grouped under the following headings—

    (i) by normal calculation (Long Methods),
    (ii) by precomputed tables,
    (iii) by calculation with special "Position Line" tables (Short Methods),
    (iv) by slide rules,
    (v) by mechanical devices,
    (vi) by diagrams, graphs, etc.

Under heading No. (i) may be included the Hilaire or Intercept method with Altitude worked by the haversine formula and Azimuth by Cosec or Log haversine formula, the Longitude method, Meridian Altitude method, Equal Altitudes method, Ex-meridian Altitude method, Latitude by Pole Star method, etc.

Under heading No. (ii) are methods which give the answer (with some small interpolation) rather than a means of calculating the answer. Some give both Altitude and Azimuth, or others only give one of these required items. Included in this class are Air Publication 1618 Astronomical Navigation Tables for Altitude and Azimuth, U.S. Hydrographic Office Altitude Azimuth Tables (H.O. 214), Ball's Altitude Tables, Davis's Altitude and Azimuth Tables, Davis's Azimuth Tables, Burdwood's Azimuth Tables, etc.

Under heading No. (iii) come all the so-called "short" methods which work on the Intercept principle but are calculated in all cases (except Goodwin's printed 1906) by the formulæ of Napier's rules, the spherical triangle being divided into two right-angled spherical triangles. Some solve the triangle for Altitude only, while with others both Altitude and Azimuth can be calculated. The earliest of this type of table appears to be by Souillagouet in about 1900. Then came Smart in England, Ogura in Japan, and Bertin in France.

There are dozens of these Position Line tables, such as: Sine method (Smart and Shearme), Aquino's, Ogura's, Hughes's (Comrie's), Ageton's, Dreisonstok's, Gingrich's, Weems's, Myerscough and Hamilton's, etc.

Under heading No. (iv) falls one of the best of all methods, the Bygrave slide rule. There are many other slide rules which have been produced or are theoretically available, but at present the Bygrave is the only one which is entirely satisfactory.

TABLE III

In making the following comparison between various methods of solving the spherical triangle in air navigation no account has been taken of the items common to all methods such as the calculation of Hour Angle, etc. But Hour Angle, Declination, and the like are counted as items to be written. In all cases the method of assessment is the same.

Name of Method	No. of Items Written	No. of Additions or Subtractions	No. of Rules	Position Used	No. of Different Tables	Particular Case
Air Ministry Altitude-Azimuth .	5 or 7	0 or 1	1	Assumed	1 or 2	22 Selected Stars
,, ,,	8	1	1	,,	2	Sun Planets and Other Stars
Ball . . .	6	1	0	,,	2	Alt. only
Davis or Burdwood .	8–11	1 or 2	4	,,	3–5	Alt. and Azimuth
" . .	5	1	1	. . .	1	Azimuth only
Hughes (Comrie)	17	4	4	Assumed	3	
,, . .	28	7	7	D.R.	3	
Ageton . .	20	5	5	,,	1 (7 Entries)	
Dreisonstok .	17	4	3	Assumed	2	
Gingrich . .	16	3	4	,,		
Weems . .	12	3	4	,,	3	
Ogura . .	15	3	3	,,	5	
Myerscough and Hamilton .	15	3	3	,,	1 (3 Entries)	
Smart & Shearme	10	2	1	,,	2	Alt. only
Smart & Shearme with A, B, & C	15	3	3	,,	5	Alt. and Azimuth
Pinto . .	16	3	3	,,	5	
A, B, & C . .	8	1	2	. . .	3	Azimuth only
Bygrave . .	8	2	2	D.R.	1	
Haversine formula .	13	4	1	D.R.	2	Alt. only
Haversine formula with Davis & Burdwood .	15	5	2	,,	3	Alt. and Azimuth

Under heading No. (v) are some very satisfactory methods, although they are in most cases expensive. Included in this group are the Hagner Position Finder (a "spherical CDC"), the Kaster spherant, the U.S. Army Spherical Calculating Machine, etc.

Under heading No. (vi) are included Weems's Star Curves, the Baker Navigating Machine, Becker diagram, Favé, Veater diagram, Rust's Azimuth diagram, Weir's Azimuth diagram, Towson's Great Circle diagram with tables, and nomograms of all kinds, etc.

(b) **General.** In many of the methods mentioned, both altitude and azimuth are found, but in others it is customary to find Altitude by one method and Azimuth by another method (or by observation with a compass or bearing plate). Thus, the most generally used of all methods at sea is the Intercept method calculating the zenith distance by the haversine formula and taking the Azimuth for Davis's or Burdwood's tables. With one or two exceptions it is necessary in all methods firstly to determine the Greenwich Date and then the Greenwich Mean Time, which are required in taking data out of the Air Almanac. In the descriptions of the methods which follow it must be clearly understood that the terms "observation" and "time of observation" mean the average of a series of observations and the average times respectively. Examples are given for the sun, moon, stars, and planets. But when, as in most cases, only one is shown, it does not mean that the method does not apply to the others.

In all those methods where an Assumed Position is used the Intercept obtained is likely to be larger than if the D.R. Position is used. As errors occur when a large intercept occurs at large altitudes, it is a good rule to avoid the use of Assumed Position at altitudes over 70°. In any case altitudes over about 75°–80° should never be taken.

A number of the methods mentioned above and shown hereafter are far from suitable for air use. In judging the merits of the various means of solving the astronomical triangle in the air the following desirable qualities should be kept in mind. They should be (i) quick, accurate, and reliable; (ii) simple, requiring minimum of brain work and writing; (iii) of small weight and size.

Table III is a fair comparison of air methods, although some people might count the number of items, etc., differently. It shows that the complete Altitude-Azimuth tables for the Selected Stars take first place, and that these same tables when used for the sun, moon, etc., share second place with the Bygrave slide rule, which latter has the advantage of working from the D.R. Position.

22. The **MARC ST. HILAIRE** or Intercept method by Haversine formula. **(a)** In this the observation of the heavenly body is taken and time noted. This is corrected as explained in para. 20 of this Chapter to give True Altitude from which True Zenith Distance (T.Z.D.) is found. Then, by the haversine formula, the Z.D. between the heavenly body and any D.R. Posn. near the observer is calculated for the time of the observation. Obviously then, if the T.Z.D. observed is greater than this Calculated Zenith Distance (C.Z.D.) then the observer must be on a position line further from the heavenly body than is the D.R. Posn., and vice versa. The difference between the T.Z.D. and C.Z.D. is called the Intercept. If the T.Z.D. is greater the Intercept is laid off "away" from the D.R. Posn., and if T.Z.D. is the smaller the Intercept is laid off "towards" the direction of the observed body from the D.R. Posn. Now if the true bearing or Azimuth of the body from the D.R. Posn. is calculated by the cosecant or log. haversine formula, or taken from Azimuth tables, then the Intercept can be marked off along this line of bearing through the D.R. Posn., and through the mark a position line can be drawn at right angles to the bearing. Provided the Z.D. is fairly large, this straight position line will represent fairly accurately an arc of the circle of position.

Fig. 122 shows the triangle to be solved. The PZX notation is standardized. P is the elevated Pole, Z is the observer's Zenith, and

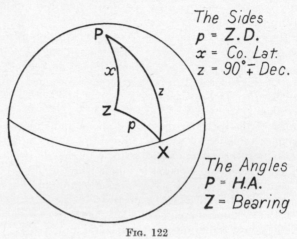

The Sides
$p = Z.D.$
$x = Co.\ Lat.$
$z = 90° \mp Dec.$

The Angles
$P = H.A.$
$Z = Bearing$

Fig. 122

X is the position of the observed body. The side $p\ (= ZD)$ is calculated for the triangle when $Z =$ D.R. position of observer. Then the angle $Z\ (=$ bearing of $X)$ is calculated or found from tables. The formulæ used are—

Hav. $p =$ Hav. $(x \sim z) +$ Sin x Sin z Hav. P

and Hav. $Z = ($Hav. $z -$ Hav. $(x \sim p))$ Cosec x Cosec p

or L Hav. $Z =$ L Hav. $x +$ L Hav. $p + \frac{1}{2}$ L Hav. $(z + (x \sim p))$
$+ \frac{1}{2}$ L Hav. $(z - (x \sim p))$.

(b) Examples (using the Air Almanac). (i) On the 1st January, 1939, at about 1430 Hrs. Zone Time (in Zone $+$ 5) the Obs. Alt. of the Sun's centre by bubble sextant was 18° 00·2′ at 19 hrs. 31 min. 23 sec. by the chronometer watch. I.E. of Sextant $= + 3′$. Error of Watch $= 14$ sec. Slow. Ht. $= 1000$ ft. D.R. Position $= 37° 22′$ N. 70° 05′ W.

D.R. Posn.

Zone Time and Date $= 1430$ hrs. on 1st January, 1939, 37° 22′ N.
Zone $+ 5$ 70° 05′ W.

G. Time and G.D. $= \underline{1930}$ hrs. on 1st January, 1939.

		H. M. S.			
Watch	=	19 31 23	Obs. Alt.	=	18° 00·2′
Error slow	+	14	I.E.	= +	3′
G.M.T.	=	19 31 37			18° 03·2′

GHA	=	111° 38′	Ref. (by A) =	−	4′
	+	24′	T. Alt.	=	17° 59′2′
	=	112° 02′	∴ T.Z.D.	=	72° 00·8′
Long. W	=	− 70° 05′			

HATS	=	41° 57′ W.	L Hav. =	1̄·10767
Lat.	=	37° 22′ N.	L Cos =	1̄·90024
Dec.	=	23° 02′ S.	L Cos =	1̄·96392

$$\overline{2}\cdot 97183$$

Antilog. = 0·09372

Lat. ∼ Dec. = 60° 24′ N. Hav. = 0·25303

N. Hav. C.Z.D. = 0·34675

∴ C.Z.D. = 72° 09·1′

T.Z.D. = 72° 00·8′

Intercept = 8·3′ towards.

Now Sun's True Bearing can be taken from Azimuth tables or calculated as follows—

(By Cosec formula.)

Dec.	=	23° 02′ S.	
90° ∼ Dec.	=	113° 02′	Hav. = 0·69563
Colat.	=	52° 38′	
C.Z.D.	=	72° 09·1′	
Colat. ∼ C.Z.D.	=	19° 31·1′	Hav. = 0·02873

Diff. = 0·66690

Log = 1̄·82406

Colat.	=	52° 38′	L Cosec = 0·09976
C.Z.D.	=	72° 09·1′	L Cosec = 0·02143

1̄·94525 = L. Hav.

True Bearing

∴ True Bearing = N. 139° 44′ W. = 220 T approx.

Then the straight Position Line is drawn at right angles through a point bearing 220° T from the D.R. Position and at 8·3′ from it —as shown in Fig. 123.

(ii) On 1st January, 1939, at about 2100 hrs. Eastern Australian Time (in Zone − 10) the Obs. Alt. of the Moon's estimated centre

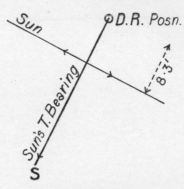

FIG. 123

by bubble sextant was 45° 04·5′ at 10 hrs. 58 min. 32 sec. by the chronometer watch. I.E. of sextant = − 4·5′. Watch Error = 1 min. 03 sec. Slow. D.R. Posn. 34° 28′ S. 154° 17′ E. Height of aircraft 15,000 ft.

<table>
<tr><td></td><td></td><td>D.R. Posn.</td></tr>
</table>

			D.R. Posn.
Zone Time and Date	= 2100 hrs. on 1st January, 1939.		34° 28′ S.
Zone	= − 10		154° 17′ E.
G. Time and Date	= 1100 hrs. on 1st January, 1939.		

		H. M. S.			
Watch	=	10 58 32	Obs. Alt.	=	45° 04·5′
Error Slow	= +	1 03	I.E.	= −	4·5′
G.M.T.	=	10 59 35			45° 00′
			Ref. 15,000 ft.	= −	1′
GHA	=	225° 15′	A. Alt.	=	44° 59′
	+	2° 19′	P. in A.	= +	41′
	=	227° 34′	T. Alt.	=	45° 40′
Long. E.	= +	154° 17′	∴ T.Z.D.	=	54° 20′
LHA	=	381° 51′			

	=	21° 51' W.	L Hav. = $\bar{2}$·55533
Lat.	=	34° 28' S.	L Cos = $\bar{1}$·91617
Dec.	=	15° 23' N.	L Cos = $\bar{1}$·98415

$$\text{Sum} = \bar{2}\text{·45565}$$

Antilog = 0·02856

Lat. ∼ Dec.   =   49° 51'   Hav. = 0·17760

0·20616 = Hav.
—————— C.Z.D.

∴ C.Z.D. = 54° 00·5'
T.Z.D. = 54° 20'

Intercept =   19·5 Away

Moon's True Bearing = $333\frac{1}{2}$° T (from Tables or calculated).

Then the Intercept of 19' is marked off in the direction $(333\frac{1}{2}° - 180°)$ T = $153\frac{1}{2}$° T from the D.R. Posn. and through the mark, at right angles to the bearing, the Position Line is drawn.

(c) The Advantage of the St. Hilaire method is that it applies to all cases, and is accurate.

Its disadvantage is that its rather tedious calculations make it slow, and liable to errors due to the human factor. It is, however, the most used and most useful method and the navigator should keep in practice in working by this method, even although he may use another method, or other methods, in addition.

Prime Vertical Observations. When the Lat. has been found by any method such as Mer. Alt., Ex-Mer. Alt., or Polaris observations (in each case, requiring no plotting on the map or chart), it may be desirable to find the Long. rather than a position line. This may be done by taking an observation of a body on the Prime Vertical, that is, when it bears 090° T. or 270° T.

The **Prime Vertical** is the plane of the Great circle passing through the observer and the True East and West points of the observer's Rational (or Celestial) Horizon.

In Prime Vertical observations the normal procedure is to work the sight by the St. Hilaire method and then to call the Intercept the departure from the D.R. Long. This Dep. is converted to d. Long. $\left(= \dfrac{\text{Dep.}}{\text{Cos Lat.}} \right)$ and so the Long. is found without plotting. In theory the bearing of the body must be 090 T or 270 T, but about 3–4 degrees away from these bearings would not cause an appreciable error (unless the Intercept is unusually large).

Tables are provided in Inman's to assist Prime Vertical Observations. HA and Alt. are tabulated against Dec. and Lat. when body is on Prime Vertical.

Of course, Dec. and Lat. must be of same name to allow body to be on Prime Vertical.

23. The **LONGITUDE METHOD.** (a) In this the D.R. Lat. is used, and the Longitude of the intersection of the Position Line and this

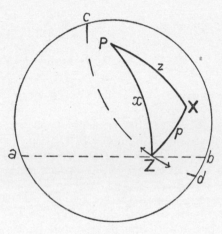

Fig. 124

parallel of Lat. is calculated by the Log Haversine Formula or the Cosecant Formula. It must be clearly understood that only the point through which the position line passes is found, and not a position. (Inman's Tables, etc., give tables for correction when the D.R. Lat. is accepted, giving a position which may be in error. This is not recommended.) This method is sometimes called the "Chronometer" method.

In Fig. 124 the *PZX* triangle is to be solved. It is necessary to find the Long. of *Z* where the position line *cd* crosses the parallel *ab*, which is the D.R. Lat.

$z = 90 -$ Dec. of the body

$x = 90 \pm$ D.R. Lat. = D.R. Colat.

$p = $ T.Z.D. $= 90 -$ T. Alt. $= 90 - ($Obs. Alt. $\pm$ Corrections$)$

It is required to find P, the Hour Angle.

Then the formula to be used is—

L Hav. P = L Cosec x + L Cosec z + $\frac{1}{2}$L Hav. $(p + (x \sim z))$
$\qquad$ + $\frac{1}{2}$L Hav. $(p - (x \sim z))$

$\qquad$ = L Sec Lat. + L Sec Dec. + $\frac{1}{2}$L Hav. $(p + (\text{Lat.} \sim \text{Dec.}))$
$\qquad$ + $\frac{1}{2}$L Hav. $(p - (\text{Lat.} \sim \text{Dec.}))$

or Hav. P $\quad$ = (Hav. p — Hav. $(x \sim z)$) Cosec x Cosec z

$\qquad$ = (Hav. p — Hav. $(\text{Lat.} \sim \text{Dec.})$) Sec. Lat. Sec. Dec.,
$\qquad$ where p = T.Z.D.

Then, having thus found the H.A., the Long. of the observer can be found as follows—

$$\text{L.H.A.} \sim \text{G.H.A.} = \text{Long.}$$

Thus the Long. is found at which the position line cuts the D.R. Lat. The direction of the position line through this point is at right angles to the bearing of the body observed from it.

If, of course, the D.R. Lat. is known with a considerable degree of certainty, the Long. found may be accepted together with the Lat. to give a fix.

(b) *Example.* On 1st January, 1939, at about 0550 Zone Time (in Zone — 5) the Obs. Alt. of Procyon in the West by bubble sextant is 18° 40′ at 00 hr. 48 min. 37 sec. by the chronometer watch. I.E. of sextant = + 5·5′. Watch Error 38 sec. slow. Ht. of aircraft 10,000 ft. D.R. Posn. 35° 00′ N. 73° 00′ E.

$\qquad$ Zone time $\quad$ = 0550 on 1st January, 1939.
$\qquad$ Zone $\qquad$ = − 5
$\qquad$ G.M.T. & G.D. = 0050 on 1st January, 1939.

			D.R. position	= 30° 00′ N.
				= 73° 00′ E.

				H.	M.	S.
Obs.	=	18° 40·5′	Watch	= 00	48	37
I.E.	= +	5·5′	Error (slow) = +			38
		18° 46′	G.M.T.	= 00	49	15

Ref. at
$\quad$ 10,000 ft. $\;$ = − $\qquad$ 2

T. Alt.	=	18° 44′		
∴ T.Z.D.	=	71° 16′	Hav.	= 0·33942
Lat.	=	35° 00′ N.		
Dec.	=	05° 23′ N.		
Lat. $\sim$ Dec.	=	29° 37′	Hav.	= 0·06532
			Diff.	= 0·27410

		Log.	$= \bar{1}\cdot43791$
Lat.	$= 35^\circ\ 00'$ N.	L. Sec.	$= 0\cdot08664$
Dec.	$= 05^\circ\ 23'$ N.	L. Sec.	$= 0\cdot00192$
			$= \bar{1}\cdot52647$
			$=$ L. Hav. L.H.A.*

$\therefore$ L.H.A.* $= 70^\circ\ 52'$ W.

Now at 00   49   15 G.M.T.

G.H.A.γ	$= + 109^\circ\ 47'$
	$2^\circ\ 19'$
$+$ S.H.A.*	$= + 245^\circ\ 58'$
G.H.A.*	$=\ \ \ \ 358^\circ\ 04'$ W.
L.H.A.*	$= -\ \ \ 70^\circ\ 52'$ W.
$\therefore$ Longitude $=$	$287^\circ\ 12'$ W. $= 72^\circ\ 48'$ E.

Stars True Bearing (from Azimuth Tables, or calculated) $= 263^\circ$ T. Then the Posn. Line is drawn through the point $35^\circ\ 00'$ N. $72^\circ 48'$ E. in a direction of $(263 + 90)^\circ = 353^\circ$ T. (see Fig. 125).

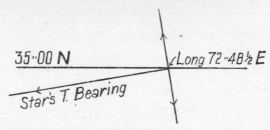

FIG. 125

24. MERIDIAN ALTITUDE METHOD. (a) This is of no use in the air but is of theoretical interest. A stationary observer with a marine type sextant observes the sun (or other body) when it is nearly on the meridian. As its Alt. increases he continues to screw the sextant micrometer so as to keep the L.L. of the sun exactly in contact with the sea horizon. The moment that increase in Alt. stops and he finds it unnecessary to turn the micrometer to a larger angle he notes the time and the sextant reading. Then

Lat. $=$ T.Z.D. (from the Obs. Alt.) $\pm$ Dec.

Thus,   if T. Alt. $= 51^\circ\ 50'$, T.Z.D. $= 38^\circ\ 10'$, Dec. $15^\circ\ 20'$ S.,

and the observer knows he is in North Lat.,

then Lat. = 38° 10′ − 15° 20′ S. = 22° 50′ N.

and Long. = G.A.T. of Observation.

Thus, 1400 G.A.T. means that the observer is 2 hrs. West Long. = 30° 00′ W. But this is not accurate in practice.

This method of observing maximum altitude of a body, as it crosses the observer's meridian, requires only a minimum of calculation. But it requires accurate observation and therefore cannot be used for air work.

(b) If a Mer. Alt. is taken by a moving observer it may be found (depending on his speed and direction and the rate of change of Dec.) that the maximum Alt. is obtained before or after the body has crossed the meridian. The interval between the times of the body's meridian passage, and the maximum Alt. depends on the rates of change of Lat. and Long. and Dec.

This Interval (in seconds) = 15·28 (G/S Cos Tr. ± Rate of Change of Dec. per hour) (Tan Lat. ± Tan Dec.) (1 + 0·002 G/S Sin Tr.)

Now, if in practice it is desired to take a Mer. Alt. observation when moving, it is best to work out beforehand the exact time of meridian passage and at that time the Alt. is observed.

Provided the D.R. Long is fairly accurate this is quite a practical method even for air work. But if used the aircraft should be flying low and the sea horizon used, for as only one sight is taken the bubble horizon would not be sure enough. But in any case the method is not very attractive for practical use.

To find the **time of meridian passage** of (for example) the Moon on 27th January, 1936, on an aircraft on Tr. 220 T. with G/S 100 kts. Its position at 1915 G.M.T. of that date is 30° 10′ N. 73° 00′ W.

Firstly, find the time of Moon's Mer. passage of a meridian somewhere near where the navigator thinks he will be at the time of Mer. passage. This is done simply as follows: The G.M.T. of Moon's Mer. passage at Greenwich is taken out of the N.A., together with the "Difference" between the values given for the date and the preceding date if Long. is East or the date and the following date if the Long is West. This difference is the difference of time of Moon's Mer. transit at Greenwich.

Then L.M.T. of local Mer. passage = G.M.T. of Greenwich Mer. passage.

$$-\left(\frac{\text{E. Long.}}{360} \times \text{diff.}\right) \text{ or } +\left(\frac{\text{W. Long.}}{360} \times \text{diff.}\right)$$

Thus,

$$\text{G.M.T.} = \frac{\text{H. M.}}{14\ 59}$$

$$\frac{\text{W. Long}}{360} \times \text{diff.} = \frac{73}{360} \times 51 = \frac{+\quad 10}{}$$

$$\text{L.M.T. of Transit of } 73\ 00'\ \text{W.} = \quad 15\ 09$$

$$\text{Long.} = + 04\ 52$$

$$\text{G.M.T. of Transit of } 73°\ 00'\ \text{W.} = \quad \underline{\underline{20\ 01}}$$

But at 2001 G.M.T. the D.R. position is 29° 03′ N. 74° 16′ W., and H.A. Moon = 01° 16′ W. Then the difference in rate of change of Observer's Long. and rate of change of Moon's Long. is the rate of change of H.A.

Rate of change of Observer's Long.

= G/S Sin Tr. × Sec. Mean Lat.

= 100 Sin 40° × Sec. 29° 00′ approx.

= 73·8′ per hour West.

And rate of change of Moon's Long.

$$= \frac{360 \times 60}{24 + \text{diff.}} = \frac{21600'}{24\cdot035} = 898\cdot8' \text{ per hour (W.)}$$

Therefore rate of change of H.A.

= (898·8 − 73·8) per hour (W.) = 825′ per hour (W.)

= 13·7′ per minute (W.)

∴ Time of Mer. passage of Observer

$$= \text{Time of Mer. passage of } 73°\ 00' + \frac{\text{H.A.}}{\text{rate of change of H.A.}}$$

$$= 20\ 01 + \left(\frac{76}{13\cdot7}\right) = 20\ 01 + 5\tfrac{1}{2} = \underline{\underline{20\ 06\tfrac{1}{2}}} \text{ G.M.T.}$$

(This should be checked by finding in the normal way the time of Moon's Mer. passage through the D.R. meridian at that time.)

A graphical solution where G.M.T.s of transits are plotted for a series of D.R. Positions is also quite satisfactory.

25. EQUAL ALTITUDES METHOD of finding Longitude. In the last para. it was said that the Long. can be found by taking the time of maximum Alt. But as the rate of change of Alt. is very small when near the maximum it is very difficult for the observer to tell the exact moment of maximum Alt. By taking the exact times at which the sun is at equal Alts. on each side of the meridian greater accuracy is obtained—for the rate of change of Alt. is greater. Then the average of the two times gives the time meridian passage and thence the observer's Long. If the interval between the times of observation is large then allowance must be made for the change in Dec. of the body observed.

This method must be carried out using a marine-type sextant, and is, of course, of theoretical interest only to the air navigator. But a combination of Mer. Alt. and Equal Altitudes observations by a stationary observer will give both Lat. and Long. with very little work.

26. EX-MERIDIAN METHOD. (a) This is commendable for use in the air. It gives the observer's Lat. without much calculation, and can be used whenever the observed body is near the observer's meridian. The principle is that the T.Z.D. = Lat. $\pm$ Dec. $+ a$, where $a = $ a correction required due to there being slight H.A. This correction is obtained from "Ex-Meridian tables" (in Inman's and Norrie's tables or, more briefly in Bairnson's Ex-Mer. tables), the use of which is simple and explained by accompanying notes.

In using Ex-Mer. tables the following rule must apply (for the sake of accuracy): The H.A. in minutes must be **less than** degrees of Z.D. This H.A. may be East or West, i.e. the observation may be taken before or after the body crosses the meridian.

Then, in practice, the procedure is as follows—

(i) Approximate time of Mer. passage of the body is first calculated.

(ii) Near this time a series of observations are taken and averaged in the usual way. This observation is then corrected.

(iii) G.D. and G.M.T. are found, and then the actual H.A.

(iv) Then, by entering Ex-Mer. tables, the "Reduction" factor, a, is found.

(v) This may then be used to find Lat. direct. If the navigator is in doubt as to which way to apply the factor a he should remember that an Ex-Mer. Alt. is less than the Mer. Alt. and therefore must be added to the T. Alt. or subtracted from the T.Z.D. thus—

$$\text{Lat.} = (\text{T.Z.D.} - a) \pm \text{Dec.}$$

Or, when Dec. is of same name and greater than Lat.,

$$\text{Lat.} = \text{Dec.} - (\text{T.Z.D.} - a)$$

(*Note.* If H.A. is comparatively large it is more accurate to actually lay off a Posn. line through the point where the Lat. (as just found) cuts the line of bearing from the D.R. Posn. to the body observed—at right angles to this line.)

(b) *Example.* On 1st January, 1939, at about 2020 hrs. Zone Time (in Zone + 3) the star Rigel has an Obs. Alt. of 47° 10′ as measured by bubble sextant at 11 hr. 25 min. ·08 sec. by chrono-meter watch. I.E. of sextant = − 5′. D.R. Posn. 34° 30′ N. 20° 00′ W. What is the latitude as found by Ex-Meridian tables?

Zone Time and Date =		20 20 on 1st January, 1939 D.R.Posn.		
Zone	= +	3		34° 30′ N.

G.M.T. and G.D.   =   23 20 on 1st January, 1939. 20° 00′ W.

	H.	M.	S.			
Watch	23	25	08	Obs. Alt.	=	47° 10′
Error Fast	−	2	00	I.E.	= −	5′
G.M.T.	23	23	08			47° 05′

GHA♈	=	90° 42′	Ref.	=	1′
	+	47′			
+ SHA*	=	282° 06′	T. Alt	=	47° 04′
			∴ T.Z.A.	=	42° 56′
GHA*	=	373° 35′			
Long. W.	= −	20° 00′			

LHA   =   353° 35′ W.
      =   6° 25′ E. = 25 min. 40 sec. E.
            Dec. = 8° 16′ S.

Then, Table I (in Inman's)	=	0·080
Table II	=	$\bar{3}$·496
Sum	=	$\bar{3}$·576 = Log a
Table III (antilog a)	=	25·9′
Table IV	= −	·1
	=	25·8′ = 26′ approx. = a,
		the Reduction − to Z.D.
And T.Z.D.	=	42° 56′
∴ Reduced Z.D.	=	42° 30′
Dec. (opp) −	=	08° 16′ S.
		34° 14′ N. = Latitude.

(c) The advantage of this method is that it is quick, simple and accurate. But, of course, it can only be taken when the observed body is near the observer's meridian.

27. LATITUDE BY POLE STAR OBSERVATIONS. (a) "Polaris" has a Dec. of about 88° 57′ N., that is, it is within 63′ of the North Pole. Now if its Dec. was 90° exactly then Lat. would equal its

T. Alt., as can be seen in Fig. 126. But as the Dec. is not 90°
corrections must be made. Tables are provided in the Nautical
Almanac for arriving at this correction. In these tables, Table I = r
Cos h, where r = 63', and h = HA of Polaris. Table II corrects for
the fact that Table I assumes that the triangle is a plane, but really
is spherical. Table III corrects for variation of RA and r of Polaris.
The Local Sidereal Time (or RAM) must be found to enter the Tables.

With the Air Almanac there is even less work to be done, but
unfortunately some accuracy is lost. Only one table is necessary in
most cases and *refraction is included in it*. A small auxiliary table
called "Adjustment to Pole Star Table" corrects for changes of
refraction with altitude. The argument for entering the main table
is the Local Hour Angle of Aries.

(b) *Example.* On 1st January, 1939, at about 20° 00' hr. Zone
Time (Zone + 3) the Obs. Alt. of Polaris by bubble sextant is
30° 45' at 11 hr. 06 min. 13 sec. by chronometer watch. I.E. = − 3'
Watch Error = 38 sec. fast. Ht. of aircraft 400 ft. D.R. Posn.
30° 00' N. 40° 03' W. What is the latitude?

(i) Using the Air Almanac.

Zone time and date = 2000 hr. on 1st January, 1939.   D.R. Posn.

Zone	= + 3			30° 00' N.
G.M.T. and G.D.	= 2300 on 1st January, 1939.			40° 03' W.

				H.	M.	S.
Obs. Alt.	= 30° 45'	Watch	=	23	06	13
I.E.	= − 3'	Error fast	= −			38
	30° 42'	G.M.T.	=	23	05	35

Q	= − 58'	GHA	=	85° 42'
Adjustment	− 1'		+	1° 24'
∴ Lat.	= 29° 43' N·			87° 06'
		Long. W.	= −	40° 03'
		LHA	=	47° 03'

(ii) Using the Nautical Almanac—

				H.	M.	S.
Obs. Alt.	= 30° 45'	Watch	=	23	06	13
I.E.	= − 3'	Error fast	= −			38
	30° 42'	G.M.T.	=	23	05	35
Ref.	= 1·6'	Long.	= −	02	40	12
T. Alt.	= 30° 40·4'	LMT	=	20	25	23
Table I	= − 57·7'	R	= +	06	42	47
Table II	= Nil	RAM	=	03	08	10
Table III	= + ·7'					
	29° 43·4' N. = Latitude.					

28. (a) POSITION LINE TABLES ("Short" methods) by various authors are used considerably nowadays. All are based on the Intercept method. Mathematically they are all on a similar principle. This is exemplified in the Sine Method described below. Other methods use other notation, and have other small differences. In nearly all cases the working is shorter than the haversine formulæ

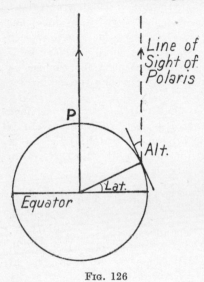

FIG. 126

method, but familiarity and a thorough understanding of the method are necessary.

(b) The **Sine Method** (Smart and Shearme Tables) for Calculated Altitude only. In this method the spherical triangle is divided into two right-angled spherical triangles, as in Fig. 127, which are then solved by pre-computed tables. These tables are now included in Inman's and are also published separately (J. D. Potter 5s.). They are based on one of the formulæ expressed by Napier's Rules (see para. 22 of Chapter I). The method is similar to the St. Hilaire in that an Intercept is found and laid off. But instead of the D.R. position, a "chosen position" is used. This chosen position is as near as possible to the D.R. position, but is in whole degrees of Lat. and is of a Long. which makes the H.A. an even multiple of four minutes, i.e. an exact degree of arc. This makes it possible to use the tables without interpolation.

Now in Fig. 127 the arc of a Great circle is drawn through Z to cut PX the celestial meridian of the heavenly body (or PX produced) at right angles. Then $ZT = p$, and $PT = U$. And $ZX = CZD$, and $(90° - ZX) =$ Calculated Alt. $= a$. Now the parts of the right-angled spherical triangle ZTX are given in Fig. 128. There are two points to note—

$$90° - ZX = 90° - CZD = \text{Calc. Alt.} = a,$$

and $$TX = PT \sim PX = U \sim (90° \pm \text{Dec.})$$

Then by Napier's rules—

$$\text{Sin } a = \text{Cos } p \text{ Cos } TX$$
$$= \text{Cos } p \text{ Cos } (U + 90 \pm D)$$
$$= \text{Cos } p \text{ Sin } (U \pm D)$$

And $\quad$ L Sin $a =$ L Cos $p +$ L Sin $(U \pm D)$

$\underline{\underline{\text{L Sin } a = V + \text{L Sin } (U \pm D)\text{, where } V = \text{L Cos } p.}}$

V and U are taken from the tables, and this little formula is solved giving Calculated Alt. Then Calc. Alt. $\sim$ T. Alt. $=$ Intercept., "towards" if T. Alt. is greater, and vice versa. A note at the foot

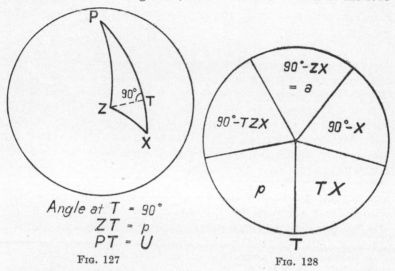

Angle at $T = 90°$
$ZT = p$
$PT = U$

FIG. 127 $\qquad\qquad\qquad$ FIG. 128

of each page states that U and D are plus $(+)$ when Lat. and Dec. are of same name.

This method is accurate and fairly quick, and the tables (separate) are light and convenient. As printed at present H.A. is in hours and minutes, which is, of course, inconvenient when used with the Air Almanac.

(c) **Ogura's Tables (Japanese)** are similar in principle to the Sine method and were first produced at about the same time. But they also include three additional tables, D, E and F similar to the ABC tables of Burton's, Norie's, etc., to find the azimuth.

(d) **Aquino's Tables** are on similar lines. In this method the spherical triangle is divided by a perpendicular from X dropped on to the observer's meridian. A full explanation is given in an introduction to the tables and will not be repeated here.

This method is more complicated than the sine method, but it completely solves the triangle. Thus Azimuth tables are not required. But the navigator must acquire complete familiarity with the tables—the notation is rather complex, and the interpolation necessary is a little difficult.

(e) **Hughes's Tables** compiled by L. J. Comrie, M.A., Ph.D., have a perpendicular dropped from Z (the Observer's Zenith) on to the meridian of the observed body at Q. Then the notation used is—

d declination.

$K =$ declination of Q.

$D = $ Log. cosec $ZQ \times 10^3$.

$E = $ Log. tan $(K \sim d) \times 10^3$.

$Z_1 = $ Azimuth of Q.

$A = $ Log. sec. $ZQ \times 10^5$.

$B = $ Log. sec. $(K \sim d) \times 10^5$.

$C = $ Log. cosec calc. alt. $\times 10^5$.

$Z^2 = $ diff. in Az. of Q and observed body.

These tables can be regarded as completely reliable typographically and mathematically, but they are not quite as simple as some of the other "short" methods. If required, a D.R. Position instead of the "chosen" or "assumed" position can be used with Hughes's tables but the overall work required is considerably increased.

(f) **Ageton's Tables.** (U.S.A., H.O. No. 211.) These tables are very popular in America. Like Aquino's, these tables are bases on a triangle divided by a perpendicular dropped on to the meridian of the observer. The greatest advantage of the method is that it uses the D.R. Position. But unfortunately it is, like Aquino's, rather complex, and interpolation is necessary. When K falls near $90°$ inaccuracy results, and such sights cannot be satisfactorily reduced. Complete familiarity is absolutely necessary.

(g) **Dreisonstok's Tables** (U.S.A., H.O. No. 208), by Lt. Comdr. J. Y. Dreisonstok, U.S.N. Once again the triangle is divided by a perpendicular dropped on to the meridian of the observed body. The procedure is very similar to that of Hughes's tables, which were, in fact, based partly on Dreisonstok. But Dreisonstok's tables are, if anything, not so well laid out as Hughes's, but are encompassed in a smaller and lighter book.

(h) **Gingrich's Tables.** In these the perpendicular is once again dropped on to the meridian of the observed body. The method of computing the Altitude is exactly the same as in Hughes's tables, but the Azimuth is found in a different and slightly more simple way.

(i) **Pinto's " Simplex " Tables.** These well-known Portuguese tables by J. Carlos Pinto are on the usual lines using Napier's rules for the determination of Altitude, and Azimuth is found by A B C tables.

(j) **Myerscough and Hamilton's Tables** (Pitman). These excellent British tables have the spherical triangle divided by a perpendicular on to the meridian of the observed body. They differ from the usual, however, in that there is only one table—and this is entered three times. They are very clearly printed and an explanation is given on each page. Unfortunately, a little interpolation is necessary. A short Ex-Meridian table is included among the miscellaneous tables given.

(k) **Weems's Tables,** by Lt. Comdr. P. V. Weems, are exactly the same as Gingrich for the determination of Altitude, but Azimuth is found by means of a Rust's Azimuth Diagram provided with the tables.

(l) **A, B and C Tables** are not in the same category as the ordinary "short" methods of solving the spherical triangle, but they do provide a short means of finding the Azimuth. They are included in Norie's and Burton's Nautical Tables, and are given as the means of finding Azimuth in some of the "short" methods.

(m) **Goodwin's Position Line Star Tables.** This is one of the older "short methods," but it is not based on the same principle. Instead, it firstly provides a "short" means of reducing an Altitude by the longitude method (see para. 23) when (i) the body is near the Prime Vertical or (ii) its rate of change of Altitude is fairly uniform (as when Dec. is greater than Lat.). It does, in fact, work on the Rate of Change of Zenith Distance with a correction for change of declination from the figure used in compiling the tables. Secondly, a means is provided of reducing Ex-Meridian Altitudes to latitude. The tables are applicable only to 17 Selected stars.

29. PRE-COMPUTED TABLES. A number of tables have been published which give the solution of the spherical triangle directly for a large number of cases. Between these cases, which are usually for whole degrees of latitude and for certain values of Hour Angle, interpolation is, of course, necessary. But even so Pre-computed Tables are the logical method; they are simple and short; and they are less prone to cause mistakes than other methods. A number of versions of these tables give both the required answers, namely, Altitude and Azimuth, in which case they are termed Pre-computed Altitude Azimuth Tables. Others give Altitude only (Altitude) tables) and some only give the Bodies' True Bearings (Azimuth tables).

(a) British Air Ministry **Astronomical Navigation Tables. AP1618.** These are Pre-computed Altitude-Azimuth Tables in their most modern and, so far, most satisfactory form. Designed for use with the British Air Almanac they provide an almost work-free solution for 22 selected stars, and for the sun, moon, planets, and stars of declinations up to 29 N. or S. declination only one simple interpolation is necessary. The use of an Assumed Position (or Chosen Position) is necessary. Unfortunately, stars not included in the list of 22 and of greater declination than 29 cannot be used with the tables.

Undoubtedly the most advantageous use of the tables compared with other methods is for the cases of the 22 listed stars. This feature is further appreciated if a Siderograph (Chronometer keeping sidereal time but graduated in degrees and minutes of arc of G.H.A. ♈) is used.

Refraction, for an assumed flying height of 5000 ft., is included in the altitudes given. No correction for this must be made to the Obs. Alt. A supplementary table, amongst others, gives the adjustment required for heights differing considerably from 5000 ft.

Two examples follow. One shows the procedure in the case of one of the 22 selected stars, and the other is for the planet Venus.

Example i. On 26th March, 1940, at about 2110 hr. Local Standard Time (Newfoundland = + 3) the Obs. Alt. of Pollux by bubble sextant is 59° 42′ at a GHA of 194° 20·6′ by siderograph (sidereal chronometer) of which the error is 2·6′ Fast. I.E. = − 1′.

Height 5000 ft. D.R. Position 49° 50′ N. 51° 09′ W.

Watch	=	194° 20·6′	D.R. 49° 50′ N. 51° 09′ W.	
Error	= −	2·6′	Assumed 50° 00′ N. 50° 53′ W.	
GHA♈	=	194° 18′	O. Alt.	= 59° 42′
SHA	=	244° 35′	I.E.	= − 1′
GHA*	=	078° 53′	T. Alt.	= 59° 41′
Long. W.	= −	50° 53′		
LHA*	=	28° 00′	Tab. Alt.	= 59° 33′
			t	= Nil for 1940
Az.	= N. 125° W.		Corr. Tab. Alt.	= 59° 33′
	= 235° True		T. Alt.	= 59° 41′
			Intercept	= 8′ Towards

Example ii. On 27th March, 1940, at about 2100 hr. Zone Time (Zone −2) the Obs. Alt. of Venus is found by bubble sextant observation to be 13° 31′ at Watch Time 19 hr. 03 min. 15 sec. I.E. = + 2′. Watch Error 34 sec. slow. Height 4500 ft. D.R. 54° 15′ N. 33° 20′ E.

Zone Time and Date 2100 hr. on 27th March, 1940.

Zone — 2

1900 G.M.T. on 27th March, 1940, G.D.

	H.	M.	S.
Watch	= 19	03	15
Error	=		34
G.M.T.	= 19	03	49
GHA *	=	61° 38'	
Incr.	= +	57'	
GHA *	=	62° 35'	
Long. E.	= +	33° 25'	
LHA *	=	95° 00'	
Dec.	= 20° 17' N.		
Az.	= N. 74 W. = 286 True Bearing		

D.R.	= 54° 15' N. 33° 20' E.
Ass.	= 54° 00' N. 33° 25' E.
O. Alt.	= 13° 31'
I.E.	= + 2'
T. Alt.	= 13° 33'
Tab. Alt.	= 13° 16'
Corr.	= + 14'
Corr. Tab. Alt.	= 13° 30'
T. Alt.	= 13° 33'
Intercept	= 3' Towards

(b) **Ball's Altitude Tables.** These old-established tables are similar in principle to the second part of A.P. 1618 but give altitude only. An "Assumed Position" is used, being the whole degree of latitude nearest to the D.R.Lat., and a longitude nearest to the D.R. Long., which makes the L.H.A. of the observed body a whole degree. Actually L.H.A. is in hr. and min. Therefore it is entered to an exact 4 minutes of time which is the same as a whole degree of arc. The tables can also be used, by three different methods, to to determine the Azimuth, but the procedure is somewhat cumbersome.

Three volumes (rather large) are available: (i) Lat. 31°–60° N. or S., Dec. 0°–24°; (ii) Lat. 0°–30° N. or S., Dec. 0°–24°; and (iii) Lat. 24°–60° N. or S., Dec. 24°–60°. (Price 12s. 6d. each. J. D. Potter.)

(c) **Davis's Altitude-Azimuth Tables, Davis's Azimuth Tables,** and **Burdwood's Azimuth Tables** all give tabulated values of the required answer with arguments of whole degrees of Declination and of every 4 or 10 minutes of Hour Angle, for each whole degree of latitude.

30. The **BYGRAVE POSITION LINE SLIDE RULE.** This is one of the best of the mechanical methods of solving the spherical triangle. It is similar in principle to the tabular methods given in para. 28 in that it makes use of Napier's rules of circular parts. The slide rule consists of an outer (lower) cylinder around which is marked in a spiral a Log. Cosine scale, and an inner (upper) cylinder around which is marked in a spiral a Log. Tan scale. The inner cylinder is free to rotate in the outer cylinder. Around the outer cylinder is a long collar which is free to be rotated. It has a large cut-away opening, at the bottom of which it carries a pointer marked S against which the outer (L Cosine) scale is read, and at its top another pointer marked L is provided for reading the inner (L Tangent) scale. It is against this latter pointer (L) that all results are read. This slide rule then constitutes a means of adding and subtracting L Cosines and L Tangents, that is, of multiplying and dividing Cosines and Tangents. Instructions for using the slide rule are printed on it, for normal and unusual cases.

In Fig. 129 the astronomical triangle is shown with the arc XT drawn from X at right angles to the meridian of the observer. Of course the point T may not fall between P and Z but on a point of PZ produced. The notation used on the slide rule is given in Fig. 129.

In using the slide rule there are always three stages to be worked out, each stage requiring three movements and one reading, as follows—

(i) S is set to zero (against the stop) on the lower scale;
Upper scale is set to d against L;
S is set to H on the lower scale;
and y is read off against L on the upper scale.

In doing this, Tan d is divided by Cos H to give Tan y, and y is read off the Tan scale, thus solving the formula—

$$\text{Tan y} = \frac{\text{Tan d}}{\text{Cos H}} \text{ which is deduced as follows}$$

$$\text{Sin } (90° - \text{H}) = \text{Tan d Tan } (90 - \text{y}) \text{ by Napier's Rules,}$$
$$\text{see Fig. 130}$$

$$\text{Cos H} = \frac{\text{Tan d}}{\text{Tan y}}$$

$$\text{tan y} = \frac{\text{Tan d}}{\text{Cos H}} \text{ (y and c are then combined to give Y.)}$$

(ii) S is set to y on the lower scale;
Upper scale is set to H against L;
S is set to Y on the lower scale;

and A is read against L on the upper scale, (if Y is more than 90° then A is more than 90°). In doing this Cos y and Tan H are multiplied, and are divided by Cos Y to give Tan A, and A is read off the Tan scale, thus solving the formula—

$$\text{Tan A} = \frac{\text{Cos y Tan H}}{\text{Cos Y}},$$

which is deduced as follows—

$$\text{In } XTP, \text{ Sin } (90° - \text{y}) = \text{Tan } TX \text{ Tan } (90° - \text{H}),$$
$$\text{see Fig. 130.}$$

$$\text{Cos y} = \frac{\text{Tan } TX}{\text{Tan H}}$$

$$\text{Tan } TX = \text{Cos y Tan H}$$

In XTZ, $\text{Sin } (90° - Y) = \text{Tan } TX \text{ Tan } (90° - A)$,

see Fig. 131.

$$\text{Cos Y} = \frac{\text{Tan } TX}{\text{Tan A}}$$

$$\text{Tan A} = \frac{\text{Tan } TX}{\text{Cos Y}} = \frac{\text{Cos y Tan H}}{\text{Cos Y}}.$$

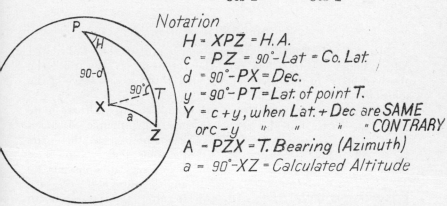

Notation

$H = XPZ = H.A.$

$c = PZ = 90° - Lat = Co. Lat.$

$d = 90° - PX = Dec.$

$y = 90° - PT = Lat. of point T.$

$Y = c + y$, when $Lat. + Dec$ are SAME

or $c - y$ "   "   "   " CONTRARY

$A = PZX = T. Bearing (Azimuth)$

$a = 90° - XZ = Calculated Altitude$

Fig. 129

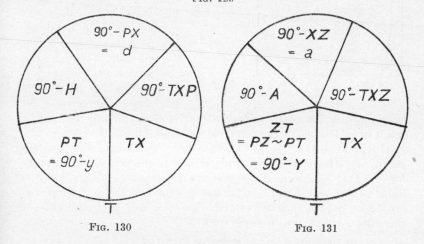

Fig. 130   Fig. 131

(iii) S is set to A on the lower scale;
  Upper scale is set to Y against L;
  S is set to zero (against the stop);
  and a is read off against L on the upper scale.

In doing this Cos A is multiplied by Tan Y to give the Tan of the

Alt. (a) and this is read off the Tan scale by bringing the collar back to zero, thus solving the formula—

$$\text{Tan } a = \text{Cos } A \ \text{Tan } Y,$$

which is deduced as follows—

$$\text{In } XTZ, \ \text{Sin } (90° - A) = \text{Tan } a \ \text{Tan } (00° - Y),$$

see Fig. 131

$$\text{Cos } A = \frac{\text{Tan } a}{\text{Tan } Y}$$

$$\text{Tan } a = \text{Cos } A \ \text{Tan } Y$$

Then if T. Alt. found by observation is greater than Calculated Alt. a found by the slide rule, the Intercept is "towards" the observed body, in the direction A (found in the second stage of the solution).

The above description refers to the simplest case. Others more complicated arise but this serves to show the principle. Being a logarithmic rule the scale for some angles becomes of such a size to be inaccurate, and therefore it is necessary to alter the procedure to avoid these values. This is done when A is between 85° and 90° (95°), etc.—full instructions being printed on the slide rule.

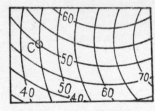

Fig. 132

In addition to the printed instructions the slide rule also gives conversions of time and arc, also Refraction values, Moon parallax, etc., and a small ivorine tablet is provided on which to write.

The great advantage of this rule is that it solves the problem completely (Bearing and Calculated Alt.), quickly and accurately for any D.R. position. But it has one disadvantage. When old it is liable to slip, and if this is not noticed an undetected and dangerous error may result. It is regrettable that some very positive means of preventing this is not incorporated.

31. (a) WEEMS'S STAR ALTITUDE CURVES produced by P.V.H. Weems, of U.S.A., are one of the greatest aids to air astronomical navigation. By taking observations of two stars simultaneously and noting the G. Sid. T. of observation a fix in Lat. and Long. can be obtained from the curves of the stars. In Fig. 132 the principle is illustrated roughly. Parts of Circles of Position around the geographical positions of stars A and B are drawn on the chart, and these constitute Altitude Curves. Now suppose at a given moment the Alt. of A is 50° 00′ and the Alt. of B is 45° 00′ then the observer is obviously at the position C. Weems's Star Altitude Curves are constructed on Mercator's projection to avoid distortion. No meridians or parallels are shown but the scales of Lat. and Long. are printed up the sides and along the bottom and top respectively. The Long. scale is marked off in Local Sidereal Time which is the same as R.A. Then the procedure is simply as follows: Observations of the two stars are taken at the same time, and the Greenwich Sidereal Time noted from a Sidereal chronometer (or from G.M.T. by ordinary chronometer + R). The point at which the two curves of Obs. Alt. intersect is found. With dividers its distance from the top or bottom is taken and measured on the Lat. scale at the side to give Lat. of observer; and its distance from the side is also taken and measured on the L. Sid. T. scale at the bottom or top. Then Long. of observer = L Sid. T $\sim$ G. Sid. T. Thus Lat. and Long. have been found with practically no work. In the near future LHAΥ will replace Local Sidereal Time on the curves, and, of course, GHAΥ will replace G.Sid.T.

Weems's Curves are made up in book form or in strips for use in a roller map holder. They are constructed for three stars, being "Polaris" and two other stars, suitable for use in the area for which they are intended.

No correction, other than I.E., need be applied to bubble sextant observations when using these curves—for Refraction is included in them. This important point must be remembered. The best way of obtaining the observations simultaneously, and at the same time using averages of a number of readings, is to take the sights as in the following example—

Arcturus		Polaris	
G. Sid. T.	Obs. Alt.	G. Sid. T.	Obs. Alt.
H. M. S.		H. M. S.	
08 24 08	42° 20′	08 24 34	46° 40′
08 24 59	42° 19′	08 25 18	46° 45′
08 25 52	42° 28′	08 26 15	46° 37′
08 26 37	42° 26′	08 26 55	46° 40′
08 27 12	42° 28′	4)33 43 02	4)186° 42′
5)42 08 48	5)211° 21′	= 08 25 45·5	= 46° 40·5′
= 08 25 45·6	= 42° 16·2′		

Thus the average of five Arcturus sights is at almost exactly the same time as the average of four Polaris sights.

The curves are correct for a considerable period of time owing to the fact that the R.A. and Dec. of stars change only very slowly. Weems's curves are constructed for six-year intervals, and at three years before or after the date for which they are constructed the error due to change of R.A. and Dec. will amount to a maximum of about $2\frac{1}{2}'$, which is regrettably large. It is of practical importance for the navigator to check for which date the curves are correct and to avoid using curves at more than three years from this date.

The curves can also be used to plot a position line on a map or chart. The Lat. and Long. of two points on the curve of the Alt. found by observation are found in the same way as was the position of observer above, giving two positions through which the straight position line may be plotted on the map or chart.

(*Note.*—Similar curves cannot be made for the sun, moon and planets, for their R.A.s and Decs. change so rapidly that they would be out of date in no time, but see para. 35).

(b) **Baker Navigating Machine.** This is based on the same principle as Weems's Star Curves, but instead of having the curves on the charts it provides curves of altitude on a transparent screen which can be moved over a chart below it until it is correctly superimposed as indicated by a time scale (for L.H.A.). The arrangement looks rather like the roller-type strip-map holder.

32. GRAPHICAL METHODS are numerous and are based on various different principles. Owing to the necessity of a very large scale in order to obtain accuracy they are not suitable for air use.

(a) The **Veater Diagram** provides a solution of the spherical triangle by simply representing values by curves on a Mercator's projection.

(b) The **Becker Diagram.** This diagram by Professor L. Becker, Ph.D., of the University of Glasgow, provides a complete solution of the spherical triangle. Two sets of curves are plotted on squared paper representing the polar co-ordinates of the observed body X in relation to the pole P, or in relation to the observer's zenith Z. The formulæ giving the relationship between these polar co-ordinates and the linear co-ordinates used in the construction are derived through Napier's rules—a Great-circle arc having been drawn from X to meet the meridian of the observer at right angles and so divide the triangle into two right-angled spherical triangles.

The use of the diagram is quick and simple requiring only the aid of a pair of dividers, but unless the diagram is made very large the accuracy obtained is not good enough for practical air purposes.

(c) There are many other diagrams and graphs providing solutions. The **Favé Diagram,** a long-standing French method, appears to be on the same principle as the above.

(d) **D'Ocagne Nomogram.** This consists of a squared diagram, the spacings of which are in accordance with the haversine formula. The vertical lines represent (i) L.H.A. or (ii) Azimuth, and the horizontal lines represent (i) Zenith Distance or (ii) Polar Distance.

(e) There are a number of diagrams which solve the Azimuth only. **Rust's Diagram,** an American method, appears to be one of the best for air use. **Towson's Great-circle Tables,** which are used with the aid of a diagram, can also be used to find Azimuth. **Weir's Diagram** is used in sea navigation quite extensively.

(f) The **Immler-Askania Calculator.** Just as the Baker Navigating Machine uses altitude curves with mechanical aid, so the Immler-Askania Reckoner uses Altitude nomograms and Azimuth nomograms with mechanical aid. These nomograms are carried on drums which are controlled by small hand-cranks and suitable gearing.

The Fuss-Askania and Le Sort are both apparently on similar lines.

The Brill instrument and the Voigt instrument are two more graphical-mechanical methods of solution.

33. MECHANICAL METHODS are of two classes: (1) those which provide a physical solution rather than mathematical; (ii) those which are mechanical ready reckoners similar in principle to the calculating machines used by accountants. Examples of the former are the Willis Altitude-Azimuth instrument, the Kaster Spherant, and the Hagner Position Finder. The Baker and Immler-Askania machine are also sometimes regarded as mechanical solutions, but this strictly speaking is not so. They are both graphical solutions handled mechanically.

The physical solutions have graduated circles and quadrants on which values of L.H.A., Dec., and Lat. are set and on one of which the answer is read. In the German Spherotrigonometer, as used on the Graf Zeppelin, two sights can be solved together.

In the calculating-machine class of mechanical solution there is the U.S. Army machine—a most elaborate and, it is believed, satisfactory device. It is obviously expensive and heavy.

34A. The **SINGLE ASTRONOMICAL POSITION LINE.** It very often happens, particularly during daylight when the sun is the only heavenly body available for observations, that one position line only can be obtained. If no D/F or terrestrial bearings are available to use with it, no Fix is obtained. But nevertheless the single astronomical position line can be of value alone.

(a) **Ground Speed** can be found if the bearing of the observed body is nearly the same as the Track (within about 10°) and its reciprocal,

resulting in a position line nearly at right angles to the Track. In
Fig. 133 at 1000 the aircraft leaves land at A on a Track AB.   At

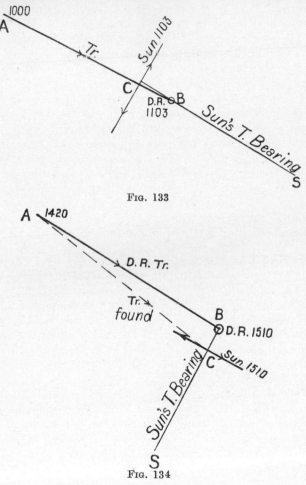

FIG. 133

FIG. 134

1103 in D.R. position B an observation of the sun gives the Intercept BC "away." Then the G/S is $\dfrac{AC \times 60}{63 \text{ min.}}$.

(b) **Track** can be found if the bearing of the observed body is
approximately at right angles to the Track resulting in a Position
line nearly coinciding (within about 10°) with it. Thus, in Fig. 134
the aircraft leaves land A at 1420 hr. on a Track AB. At 1510 in
D.R. position B an observation of the sun gives an Intercept BC
"towards." Then the Track made good is AC.

(c) **Latitude** of observer can be found if the bearing of the observed body is approximately 180 T or 360 T, that is, if it is nearly on the observer's meridian. Then the observation is best converted into Lat. by Ex-Mer. tables (or special tables for Polaris sights) as previously explained in para. 26 of this chapter.

(d) **Longitude** of the observer can be found if the bearing of the observed body is approximately 270 T or 090 T, that is, if it is

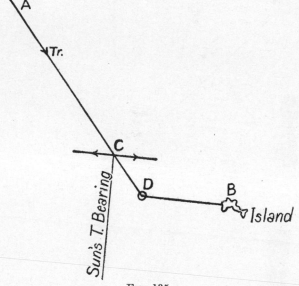

Fig. 135

approximately on the Prime Vertical. The Intercept is best worked out in the usual way by St. Hilaire method and then converted into d. Long. from the D.R. position used. d. Long. $= \dfrac{\text{Intercept}}{\text{Cos. Lat.}}$ as mentioned in para. 27 of this chapter.

(e) A **Land-fall** may be made good by running down a single position line. This is most useful when it is desired to fly to a small island in daylight when a single position line only can be obtained. The procedure is illustrated in Fig. 135. An aircraft is coming from A, and "aims off" to that side of the island on which the sun's bearing will be when the aircraft is near the island. The amount of this aiming off depends on the navigator's accuracy and the distance from the last known Fix. The navigator must be sure that he is not on the wrong side, then he will know which way to turn along the position line. When nearing the island a sun sight gives the position line through C. This is transferred to pass through the island B, and it then cuts the Track at D. The aircraft therefore continues on its Track for a D.R. distance of CD and then to make good a Track of DB parallel to the position line until it arrives at B. The distance DB is, of course, not known but provided it (or CD) is not too great the D.R. errors will not cause the aircraft to completely miss the island. Of course it is better if the time of approaching the island is

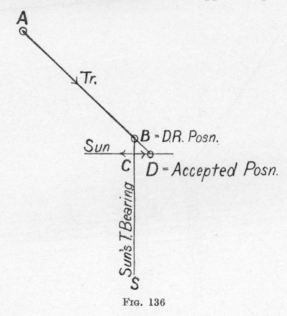

FIG. 136

such that the bearing of the body is at right angles to the track—so checking Track as in subpara. (b) above.

(f) **Guesstimation** may be used if the position line is at an angle of about 45° (+ or − about 15°) to find a position. There are three ways of dealing with this, depending on the reliability of the D.R. Track and G/S. Of course this must be used with a little reluctance and great discretion, but it is of value.

(i) When information, such as good reliable drift sights, makes it reasonably sure that the D.R. Track is the correct Track it should be accepted, and the point where the astronomical position line cuts it should be taken as the Accepted Position of the aircraft. Thus, in Fig. 136, the aircraft is making good the Track AB with reasonable certainty. When in D.R. position B an Alt. of the sun gives an Intercept BC "towards." Then D where the Accepted Track cuts the position line is the Accepted Position, from which further D.R. is carried on until a more definite Fix can be obtained.

(ii) When information makes it reasonably certain that the D.R. G/S is correct (unlikely in practice), it should be accepted, and the point *D* where the D.R. distance-covered $(AB = AD)$ cuts the position line found by observation is the Accepted Position. (See Fig. 137.)

(iii) When no information is available to indicate that either D.R. Track or G/S are particularly reliable, then the only procedure is to assume that the point on the position line nearest to the D.R. position is most likely to be correct. *N.B.*—This estimating of position line results in an Accepted Position only a little more reliable than a D.R. position and must be treated accordingly.

34B. The **ASTRONOMICAL FIX.** A fix can be obtained from astronomical position lines in several different ways.

(a) **Simultaneous Observations** of two or more heavenly bodies (stars at night, or sun and moon by day) separated to give a wide cut are probably the best method. Sights of each body are taken alternatively so that the average times of observation are about the same for each, as

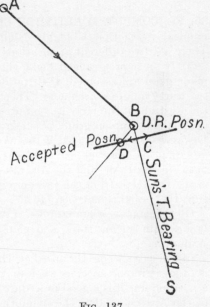

Fig. 137

exemplified in para. 31. Then each is solved separately and the two position lines plotted to give the Fix.

(b) **Consecutive Sights** firstly of one body and then of another are more simple to take, but one of the resulting position lines has to be transferred by the ground distance travelled between the times of the first and second observations. Thus one position line has to be transferred, but as the time is only small no appreciable error is likely to occur through this.

(c) A **Running Fix** by two well-spaced observations of one heavenly body is possible, and is used in marine navigation, but as rather a long time interval is necessary to give a good cut, large D.R. errors may occur making the Fix inaccurate. It is not recommended generally, but in one case it is reasonably good. If a

fast aircraft is travelling towards the East the rate of change
of bearing of a heavenly body observed is very large, and therefore
only a short time interval is required to give a good wide cut. This
results in an accurate Fix.

(d) The **Plotting** of astronomical position lines can, of course, be
done on the map or chart in use, but it is often more convenient to
work on a **Plotting Chart,** which is a sheet of plain paper with a scale
(as illustrated in Fig. 95, and described in para. 5(a) of Chapter V)
and a compass rose.

35. PRECOMPUTED ALTITUDE CURVES. This method of astro-
nomical navigation is highly commendable for particular cases.
There are two different applications—

(i) If on a prearranged flight the Track and G/S which will be
made good are assumed, D.R. positions at short intervals of time,
say thirty minutes, are found. Then for each time and D.R. position
the Altitude of the body is computed. Each Alt. so found is plotted
against the time on graph paper giving a curve of Altitude. Zenith
Distances may be plotted if the navigator prefers them. Then, at
any time on the flight an observation is taken and the difference
between the T.Alt. and the Alt. taken from the curves for that time
is the Intercept from the Precomputed D.R. position at that time;
thus the actual calculation of the position line in the air is avoided.

On the same graph a number of Alt. curves for different heavenly
bodies (sun, moon, stars, and planets) can be plotted, as also can
Azimuths.

(ii) In cases where the speed at which a particular sight is reduced
is of great importance, as when making a landfall by running down
a position line it is a good procedure to plot on squared paper curves
of the Altitude and of the Azimuth of the body to be observed, in
relation to a fixed geographical position (such as that of the desired
landfall). These curves are plotted against time for a period extending to a reasonable extent each side of the E.T.A. Then when near
the E.T.A. (i.e. within the time scale of the precomputed curve)
the sight is taken and the difference between the T.Alt. and the
Alt. from the curve is the Intercept to or from the fixed position
used. The answer is thus quickly obtained and is of direct value.
The work entailed in calculating the curves is not as much as might
be expected, particularly if a Bygrave slide rule or a "Short"
method is used.

36. SENSE FINDING. In the unlikely and most deplorable
event of a navigator wishing to run down a single Position Line,
but not knowing which way to turn, it is in theory possible for him

to take further sights in order to determine whether he has turned the right way. But it must be made clear that with existing means of obtaining altitudes the precision obtained is not sufficient to make this procedure reliable or even possible in any but very good conditions.

The procedure is as follows: A precomputed curve of altitude for the geographical position of the desired destination is plotted against time (G.M.T.). Then when the aircraft reaches the Position Line the destination course is altered one way or the other to give a Track along the P.L. It is important that this new track be exactly towards or away from the destination. Drift and course should therefore be checked carefully. Then at about five-minute intervals a careful set of sextant sights should be taken, and when corrected the T.Alt. should be plotted against G.M.T. on the precomputed altitude curve. About four or five such altitudes should indicate clearly whether they are getting more like the values of altitude at the destination or the reverse. If the former, then the aircraft is going towards the destination and vice versa. Or, if a curve be drawn through the T.Alts. plotted then the destination is ahead if the curves are converging, or it is astern if the curves are diverging.

It must be noted that in some cases the rate of converging or diverging may be small, and in such cases it is essential that a larger number of sights at about five-minute intervals be taken (about ten).

REDUCTION OF SEXTANT SIGHTS
(LIST OF METHODS)

Normal Logarithmic (Haversine formula).
Longitude, or so-called "Longitude by Chronometer."
Meridian Alt.
Equal Alt.
Ex-Meridian Alt.
Polaris.
A.P.1618 Precomputed Alt. Azimuth Tables.
H.O.214 Precomputed Alt. Azimuth Tables.
Ball's Precomputed Alt. Tables.
Davis's Precomputed Alt. Azimuth Tables.
Davis's Precomputed Azimuth Tables.
Burdwood's Precomputed Azimuth Tables.
Souillagouet's Tables.
Smart and Shearme's Tables.
Bertin's Tables.
Ogura's Tables.

Aquino's Tables.
Pinto's Tables.
Dreisonstok's Tables (H.O. 208).
Gingrich's Tables.
Weems's Tables.
Ageton's Tables (H.O. 211).
Hughes' (Comrie) Tables.
Myerscough and Hamilton's Tables.
Goodwin's Tables.
Bygrave Slide Rule.
Wimperis and Horsley Slide Rule (D'Ocagne Nomogram).
Hagner Position Finder.
Kaster Spherant.
Willis Alt-Azimuth Instrument.
Spherotrigonometer.
U.S. Army Calculator.
D'Ocagne Nomograms.
Sundry Other Nomograms.
Becker Diagram.
Favé Diagram.
Veater Diagram.
Rust's Diagram.
Weir's Diagram.
Towson's Diagram and Tables.
Weems's Alt. Curves.
Baker Navigating Machine.
Immler-Askania Calculator.
Fuss-Askania Calculator.
Le Sort Calculator.
Brill Calculator.
Voigt Calculator.
Etc.

SECTION 5

RISING AND SETTING OF HEAVENLY BODIES

37. RISING AND SETTING of Heavenly Bodies. (a) The time of rising or setting of a heavenly body is the moment when the centre of the body is on the observer's celestial (rational) horizon. This occurs when the Zenith Distance of the body from the observer is 90°, but in actual fact Refraction (and Parallax) alters this value so that the time of Theoretical Rising or Setting is the moment when the Z.D. is (90° + Correction). This correction is about 34' for the Sun or Stars, and for the Moon is about − 20 but varies as H. Plx. changes.

Now half the disc of the sun or moon is still visible when the centre is apparently on the horizon. Then, the time of Visible Rising or Setting is the moment when the Upper Limb of the body coincides with the horizon. This occurs when the Z.D. is (90° + Correction + Semi-diam. + Dip).

In the case of the Sun the Z.D. is about (90° + 34' + 16' + Dip) = 90° 50' + Dip, which (omitting the Dip) is the value used for the tables in the Nautical Almanac.

In the case of the Moon the Z.D. is about (90° + 34' + 16' + Dip − H. Plx.). The N.A. bases its Moonrise and Moonset tables on this (omitting Dip).

In the case of the stars semi-diameter is too small to be taken into account, and time of Visible Rising or Setting is when Z.D. is about (90° + 34' + Dip).

(b) The methods of finding the time of Rising or Setting are as follows : (i) From the Nautical Almanac, for sunrise and sunset, and moonrise and moonset. The sunrise and sunset tables are straightforward. In southern latitudes a "corresponding date" must be found from the table given for that purpose. This is necessary as the times are only tabulated for the northern hemisphere.

The moonrise and moonset tables are slightly more difficult to use as allowance has to be made for the longitude of the observer. A full explanation and examples are given in the N.A.

(ii) By Calculating the H.A. of the body, solving the spherical triangle by the Cosec, or Log Hav. formula. Then the Longitude of observer, E or R, etc., being known, the H.A. is converted into G.M.T., Zone or Standard Time as desired.

(iii) By taking the H.A. out of Alt.-Az. tables and thence calculating the time. This is difficult in that Alt.-Az. tables do not give Alts. of less than zero. Therefore it is necessary to make interpolation below the lowest Alt. given, for the value of Alt. = 0° − Ref. − Semi-diam. + Plx. − Dip).

(iv) By taking the H.A. out of the Time Amplitude tables as given in Inman's, and thence calculating the time. These tables refer to the centre of the body without the effects of refraction. Therefore another table is provided to allow for Ref. (about − 34') of the sun or stars (and two-thirds of these corrections applied in the opposite way to allow for the Ref. and Plx. (− 34 + 54 = 20) of the Moon). But Semi-diameter and Dip are not allowed for.

(c) **Amplitudes.** (i) Bearing Amplitude is the angle between the direction of a heavenly body at rising or setting and the line due East and West through the observer, i.e., it is the bearing of the body expressed as an angle N. or S. of E. (rising) or W. (setting). If the Dec. of the body is N. then the bearing will be N. of E. or W. when rising or setting respectively. And similarly if Dec. is S., the bearing will be S. of E. or W.

It can be calculated or taken from Azimuth tables, but the Bearing Amplitude tables provided in Inman's are simpler. These are calculated for Z.D. = 90°, and a correction table is provided to make them apply to the moment when the centre of the body is apparently on the horizon (as seen from sea level).

These bearings at rising or setting are very suitable in checking compass deviation (see para. 8 (i) of Chapter III).

(ii) Time Amplitude is the difference between 18 hours and the Hour Angle at rising, or between 6 hours and the Hour Angle at setting. In either case the H.A. may be greater than or less than 18 hours or 6 hours, depending on the Dec. of the body and the Lat. of the observer. As mentioned in subpara. (b) above the Time Amplitude tables given in Inman's provide a means of finding the time of rising or setting.

(d) Twilight. It is well-known that owing to the effect of the atmosphere around the Earth, considerable light remains for a time after the sun has set. This "Twilight" is almost negligible when the centre of the sun is 18° below the horizon, and therefore Morning Twilight is said to begin, and Evening Twilight is said to end, when the Z.D. of the sun's centre is $(90 + 18)° = 108°$.

Twilight tables are added to the sunrise and sunset tables in the N.A.

In both the Air Almanac and Brown's N.A., however, the values given are based on a Z.D. of 96°. This gives a far more genuine value for the length of twilight for practical flying purposes than does the N.A.

CHAPTER VIII

TIDES

1. THE CAUSES OF TIDES. (a) **Tides** are vertical movements of
the water on the surface of the Earth. They should not be confused
with the tidal streams which run as a result of them. These vertical
movements are generally of a periodic nature—not simple but a
combination of a number of different periodic movements of different
frequencies. Each of these movements which combine to make tide
is called a constituent of the tide, and each has its particular cause.
The constituents, which will be dealt with hereafter, are—

The Mean Lunar Semidiurnal constituent
wave . . . . . . M_2
The Mean Solar Semidiurnal constituent
wave . . . . . . S_2
The Lunar Elliptical constituent wave . N_2
The Luni-Solar Declinational Semidiurnal
constituent wave . . . . K_2
The Lunar Declinational Diurnal constituent waves . . . . . O_1 and part of K_1
The Solar Declinational Diurnal constituent waves . . . . . P_1 and part of K_1

K_1 being a combination of Lunar and Solar Declinational waves of
the same frequency.

Each cause of tide tends to build up a crest of water on the
Earth's surface, and this tends to move round due to the Earth's
relative rotation. In dealing with the causes of tide the simple idea
of a wave crest moving around the Earth in phase with its cause will
in the first instance be considered, and later the effect of the
interference of land masses will be explained.

Two other constituents which will be mentioned are the shallow
water and frictional effects, M_4 and MS_4.

The analysis of tides into constituents, called Harmonic Analysis,
not only gives a means of tidal prediction by re-combination of the
constituents (called Prediction by Harmonic Constants), but it also
helps to give an understanding of tidal theory.

(b) The **Mean Lunar Semidiurnal Constituent** (M_2, Period $= 12 \cdot 42$
hrs.) is a wave motion of the water on the surface of the Earth,
having two crests, 180 degrees apart. It has two causes.

(i) Firstly, the water vertically below the Moon is attracted by it by a stronger force than the other water on the Earth (mutual attraction of any two bodies being inversely proportional to the square of the distance between them) which tends to heap up this water forming a wave crest (high water) immediately below the Moon.

(ii) Secondly, the centrifugal effect of the rotation of the Earth-Moon system causes a heaping-up of water on the side of the Earth which is opposite the Moon. Forget for the present the Earth's rotation. Now the Moon rotates about the Earth once in a lunar month. Its average distance from the Earth remains about the same and therefore the system is in equilibrium. The centre of gravity of the system is on a line between the Earth's centre and the Moon, at a distance of about 3000 miles from the former. As the system is in equilibrium, the C.G. of the Earth must rotate around the C.G. of the whole system as indicated in the figure. All parts of the Earth are thus rotated in a circle resulting in a heaping of surface water on that side of the Earth farther from C.G. of the system.

Now the wave crests move around with the Moon once in a lunar month, but the Earth rotates once in 24 hrs. Mean Solar Time, giving the result that these two waves move once around the Earth in about 24 hrs. 50 min. of Mean Solar Time (24·84 hrs.), so that each crest passes a fixed observer after an interval of 12·42 hrs., and the time difference between crest and trough is about 6·21 hrs.

M_2 is the largest tidal constituent. It does not take into account any irregular effects.

(c) The **Mean Solar Semidiurnal Constituent** (S_2, Period $= 12$ hrs.) is a wave motion of the water of the Earth exactly similar in principle to M_2 but resulting from Solar attraction and Earth-Sun centrifugal effect. Obviously the time for these two waves to rotate once around the Earth is 24 hrs. of Mean Solar Time, so that each wave crest passes a fixed observer after an interval of 12 hrs., giving a time difference of 6 hrs. between crest and trough. Like M_2, it is an average effect.

(d) The **Lunar Elliptical Constituent** (N_2, Period $= 12·66$ hrs.) is a wave motion of dimensions and phase proportional to the variations of M_2 due to the varying distance of the Moon from the Earth. As was explained in Chapter VII, the Moon moves in an elliptical path around the Earth. At its greatest distance from the Earth it is said to be in Apogee, and at the smallest distance in Perigee. Attractive force is greater with reduced distance and also centrifugal force is greater with reduced radius. Therefore, when the Moon is closer to the Earth than its mean position, N_2 is additive to M_2, and when it is further away N_2 is to be subtracted from M_2.

Note.—A Solar Elliptical Constituent due to the varying distance of the Sun from the Earth is too small to be taken into consideration for most practical purposes.

(e) The **Luni-Solar Declinational Semidiurnal Constituent** (K_2, Period = 11·97 hrs.) is a wave combining two modifying effects, namely the effect on the Moon's tidal forces due to its Declination, and the effect on the Sun's tidal forces due to its Declination.

If the Moon was over a pole (Dec. = 90°) there would obviously be a permanent high water at the poles and a low water at the Equator. But there would be no change of level—that is, no tide— due to the Moon. Conversely, if the Moon is exactly over the Equator (Dec. = 0°), the rise and fall of water due to it will be a maximum. A modifying value must therefore be applied to M_2 to allow for Moon's Dec.

Similarly the effect of the Sun's Dec. must be taken into account. The two effects are combined as the constituent K_2.

(f) The **Lunar Declinational Diurnal Constituents** (O_1, Period = 25·82 hrs. and part of K_1, period = 23·93 hrs.) due to Dec. of the Moon result in the equivalent of a wave crest which has periods of rotation around the Earth of about a day. When the Moon has any considerable Dec., every alternate tide at a place is larger than those immediately before and after it. The effect is included in the constituent O_1, and also the constituent K_1 which is partly caused by a Solar Declinational effect. Thus—

(g) The **Solar Declinational Diurnal Constituents** (P_1, Period = 24·07 hrs., and part of K_1) are exactly similar, but are due to the Sun's Dec. and therefore result in a diurnal modification to the semidiurnal wave (S_2) due to the Sun.

2. COMBINATION OF TIDAL WAVES.

All the constituents described above effect the same water resulting in the composite wave which we call Tide. Each constituent has its own frequency, so that the angular distance between constituent wave crests, called Phase Difference, is constantly changing. Figs. 138 and 139 show the constituents M_2 and S_2 combined. In Fig. 138, M_2 and S_2 are approximately in phase, but in Fig. 139 they are out of phase by about 90 degrees. It can be seen that the height of the composite tide at any time equals the algebraic sum of the heights of the constituents. In Fig. 140, the Constituent Waves M_2, S_2, O_1, and P_1 are shown together with their resultant wave, to illustrate how all the Constituents combine to form a Tide.

There are, of course, a great many more constituents than the seven astronomical and two terrestrial mentioned in this chapter.

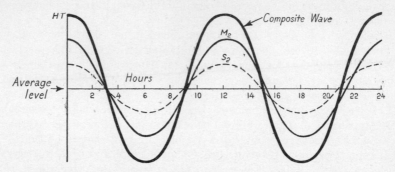

FIG. 138. COMPOSITE WAVE OF M_2 AND S_2 IN PHASE AT 0 HOURS

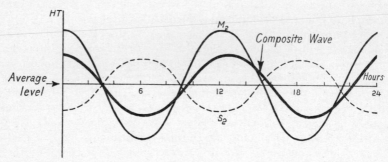

FIG. 139. COMPOSITE WAVE OF M_2 AND S_2 90° OUT OF PHASE AT 0 HOURS

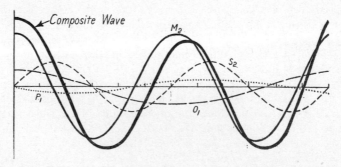

FIG. 140. RESULTANT COMPOSITE WAVE OF FOUR CONSTITUENT WAVES

Tides are divided into as many as thirty-six constituents in some cases in carrying out the predictions for Standard Ports in Admiralty Tide Tables.

3. The **AGE OF A TIDE** and **TERRESTRIAL EFFECTS.** (a) The above constituents all represent the result of astronomical effects. If the surface of the Earth was covered entirely by water, then these lunar and solar tidal waves would (omitting frictional effects) move around so that their crests were exactly in time with the astronomical bodies causing them. Thus, the crest of the M_2 tidal constituent would rotate around the Earth exactly with the Moon, so that at all times it was on a line from the Moon, through the Earth's centre. Now, due to shallow water, coastlines, etc., friction causes a wave crest to lag behind the body causing it. Thus the crest of the M_2 wave lags behind the Moon so that the high water of M_2 does not occur at the time of Moon's transit at a place. Similarly, the crest of the S_2 wave lags behind the sun so that the time of high water of S_2 does not coincide with the time of Sun's transit (local apparent noon or midnight). The other constituents also lag behind their causes. Thus it can be seen that the result of friction is to delay the constituents. Then the **Age of a Tide** is the time lag between the cause and the resultant high water.

The Age of the Tide is generally considered to refer to the composite M_2–S_2 wave, but of course the other constituents also lag behind their causes and therefore have Ages. In practice the Age of the Tide is generally found by noting the interval between the time of Sun's and Moon's transit when they are in conjunction or opposition (at new or full moon, see Fig. 115 and Fig. 138, and the arrival of the next highest high water. The effect of the other constituents may be such that the composite wave of M_2 and S_2 in phase does not give the highest high water, in which case the Age of the Tide must be observed for about a year, and an average taken. The Age of the Tide is purely a local phenomenon and varies considerably. It is as much as six days in South America, and in exceptional cases is negative, i.e. the tide is ahead of its cause. The average Age of Tides throughout the world is taken as one and a half days.

(b) A further **terrestrial effect** is that very small wave motions are induced by friction, and are superimposed on the astronomical tide wave. These wave motions are represented by the constituents M_4 and MS_4. They are generally very small and have a quarter-diurnal period (6·21 hrs. and 6·19 hrs. respectively).

(c) **Meteorological Tides.** The times and heights of high and low water may be affected by the wind, and to a very small extent by changes of the barometric pressure. Only in exceptional cases is the effect considerable, but generally a strong on-shore wind increases and an off-shore wind decreases the height of a tide.

4. DEFINITIONS. **Tides** are vertical movements of the water on the surface of the Earth.

Mean Lunar Semidiurnal Tide is the tide due to a simple harmonic wave caused by the effect of the Moon, and rotating at the same speed, namely once around the Earth in 24 hrs. 50 min. of solar time. It has two crests, 180° apart, and therefore gives two high waters per day, each about 12 hrs. 25 min. apart.

Mean Solar Semidiurnal Tide is the tide due to a simple harmonic wave caused by the Sun, and rotating at the same speed as it rotates, namely once around the Earth in 24 hrs. Having two crests 180° apart, it gives two high waters per day, each 12 hrs. apart.

Spring Tide is the tide due to effects of the Moon and the Sun when they are in opposition (Full Moon) or conjunction (New Moon) $(M_2 + S_2)$ so that the waves due to each are additive. (See Fig. 138.)

Neap Tide is the tide due to the effects of the Moon and the Sun when in quadrature $(M_2 - S_2)$, so that high water due to the Sun coincides with the low water due to the Moon and vice versa. (See Fig. 141.)

Phase Inequality of Height is the difference between the heights of Spring tide and Neap tide at a place. (Compare Figs. 138 and 139.)

The tide is said to **Lag** when the crest of the composite Luni-Solar tide wave is after the time of Moon's transit.

The tide is said to **Prime** when the crest of the composite Luni-Solar tide wave is before the time of Moon's transit.

Phase Inequality of Time is the amount of time by which a tide primes or lags.

Lunar Anomalistic (or Elliptical) Inequality of Heights is the difference of tide heights due to the varying effect of the Moon as it moves around the Earth in its elliptical path (so changing its distance from the Earth).

Solar Elliptical Inequality of Heights is the difference of tide height due to the varying effect of the Sun as the Earth moves around it in an elliptical path (so changing the distance from Earth to Sun).

Lunar Semidiurnal Inequality of Heights is the difference in the range of lunar tides due to the varying tide-producing effect of the Moon with change of Declination. This inequality is greatest when Moon's Dec. is greatest, and is nil when the Moon is over the Equator.

Solar Semidiurnal Inequality of Heights is the difference in the range of solar tides due to the varying tide-producing effect of the Sun with change of Dec. It is greatest when Sun's Dec. is greatest.

Lunar Diurnal Inequality of Heights is the difference of level of successive lunar high waters due to the effect of the Moon's Dec. It is greatest when Moon's Dec. is greatest.

Solar Diurnal Inequality of Heights is the difference of level of successive solar high waters due to the effect of the Sun's Dec. It is greatest when the Sun's Dec. is greatest.

Lunitidal Interval is the time difference between the movements of the moon and the movements of the tides caused by it.

High Water Lunitidal Interval (HWLI) is the difference between the time of Moon's transit and the next following lunar high water.

Mean High Water Lunitidal Interval (MHWI) is the average HWLI which gives a value which cuts out priming and lagging due to Phase Inequality of Time. Obviously on days of Springs and Neaps when there is no phase inequality, MHWI = HWLI.

High Water Full and Change (HWF and C) is the HWLI on days of full and new Moons. As the time of Moon's transit is at noon or midnight on those days, the HWFC equals the local time of high water.

The **Vulgar Establishment** of a place is the same as HWF and C, and is printed in Roman figures on charts, indicating hours and minutes.

Mean Low Water Lunitidal Interval (MLWI) is the average time interval between times of Moon's transit and the next low water. This average interval equals the actual interval on days of Springs and Neaps.

Low Water Full and Change (LWF and C) is the LWLI on days of full and new Moons. As the time of Moon's transit is noon or midnight, the LWF and C equals the local time of low water.

Chart Datum is the plane of reference to which the heights of tides are referred as positive (above) or negative (below) values. The depths shown on a chart are the vertical distances of the sea bottom below this plane of reference. (See Fig. 141.)

Rise is the height of high water. (See Fig. 141.)

Range is the difference between the heights of high water and low water.

Mean High Water Springs (MHWS) are the average heights of high water at Spring tides, at a place. The mean is taken over a long period to eliminate inequalities.

Mean Low Water Springs (MLWS) are the average heights of low water at Spring tides, at a place.

Mean High Water Neaps (MHWN) are the average heights of high water at Neaps, at a place.

Mean Low Water Neaps (MLWN) are the average heights of low water at Neaps, at a place.

Mean High Water (MHW) is the average height of high water at a place, measured over a long period of time to eliminate inequalities.

Mean Low Water (MLW) is the average height of low water at a place, measured over a long period to eliminate inequalities.

Mean Tide Level (MTL) is the mean of the heights of MHW and MLW.

Mean Level (ML) is the best value of MTL available, but may not

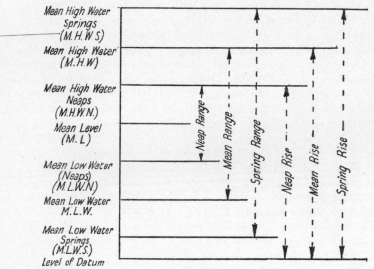

FIG. 141*

be absolutely accurate in cases where an insufficiently long series of observations have been taken.

Mean Sea Level (MSL) is the average level of the sea. (*Note.*— MSL and MTL do not necessarily coincide.)

Mean Spring Range (MSR) is the difference between the heights of MHWS and MLWS.

Mean Neap Range (MNR) is the difference between the heights of MHWN and MLWN.

Mean Range is the difference between the heights of MHW and MLW.

Mean Spring Rise is the height of MHWS.

Mean Neap Rise is the height of MHWN. (It usually equals about $\frac{3}{4}$ Mean Spring Rise.)

Mean Rise is the height of MHW.

* Based on Fig. 178 " Admiralty Manual of Navigation."

Duration of Rise is the difference of time of LW and the next following HW.

Duration of Fall is the difference of time of HW and the next following LW.

Stand of the Tide is a period which sometimes occurs at either high or low water, during which the level of the water remains practically the same.

Equinoctial Tides are those Spring tides occurring at about the time of the Equinoxes, which are abnormally high due to the fact that nearly all the constituents are approximately in phase so that their effects are additive.

Solstitial Tides are those Spring tides occurring at about the time of the Solstices, which are not as high as normal Springs owing to the fact that the other constituents are out of phase with the M_2S_2 wave so that their effects are subtractive from it.

Single Day Tides are those where the diurnal constituents are very large compared to the semidiurnal constituents so that the resultant composite wave gives one HW and one LW only per day.

5. TIDE TABLES. (a) **British Admiralty Tide Tables,** Part I and Part II, give tidal data for many ports in all parts of the world. Abridged editions giving data for ports in the British Isles and Europe are also published. Many other tide tables such as those issued by local port authorities, etc., are also available.

(b) **Part I** of Admiralty Tide Tables gives the times and heights of HW and LW for a number of Standard Ports. Usually a long series of observations have been taken at a port and a complete Harmonic Analysis carried out to determine the constituents. The predictions are then made by the Harmonic method. Sometimes, however, a method called the Equation method is used. Occasionally the method of Variable Differences, based on the tides of a neighbouring Standard port, may be used.

(c) **Part II** of Admiralty Tide Tables gives tidal data of three different types by which predictions of tides can be made, for a very large number of ports called Secondary Ports. The three different methods are: the *Admiralty Method* containing four constituents, the *Tidal Differences* between a Secondary and a Standard Port, and in Section II, the *Harmonic Constants* for a few ports only, expressed as H the amplitude in feet and g the phase-lag or angle in degrees.

Prediction by the harmonic method is the most accurate of the three. In it the time of HW or LW is not found directly but from a curve of the heights of water calculated for a series of particular times. Each height is found at the time by computing the algebraic sum of the height of each constituent at the place required. Each constituent of the same shape as a Cosine curve is expressed in the Tables by H, its Amplitude (semi-range) and g its lag or phase-angle. The calculations required in the Harmonic method are lengthy and cumbersome.

In the new Admiralty method which replaces the old Non-Harmonic method the four constituents M_2, S_2, K, and O are given, expressed as g and H as in the Harmonic method. Now, in the Harmonic method these average constituents are modified for their variations from average by the application of the minor constituents. But in the Admiralty method this variation from average conditions is allowed by the application of various additions and factors. The calculations are moderately complex and the result is moderately accurate.

For ports where the tide is mainly of a semidiurnal nature, the method of Tidal Differences can be used. In it the time of HW or LW is expressed as a difference from a particular Standard Port as given in Part I. The height is expressed by giving a Ratio of Ranges compared with its Standard Port. This method is quick and simple to use.

(*Note*. **Part III** of Admiralty Tide Tables consists of a full explanation of the methods of prediction of tides and tidal streams.)

(d) **From a chart** the time of HW may be found approximately as follows. The Vulgar Establishment printed in Roman figures on the chart nearest to the position required indicates the HWF and C at that place, which is the time of HW on the day of full Moon or new Moon. The date of the last full or new Moon is therefore taken from the Nautical Almanac, pocket diary, or calendar, and, by allowing that the tide is approximately 50 minutes later each day, the time of HW for the date required is obtained.

(e) The **height** of water between times of HW and LW is found by assuming that the tide rises and falls harmonically, like a cosine curve. Tables to assist in this calculation are given in Tide Tables together with an example. The values found are not always reliable.

6. (a) **TIDAL STREAMS** are the horizontal movements of water on the surface of the Earth due to the gradients of the water caused by tides. Water tends to flow from the crest to the trough of a tidal wave. This flow is generally negligible in the open sea, but, as the frictional and constricting effects of the land cause the gradient of the tidal wave to steepen, it reaches more appreciable proportions. Tidal streams generally tend to flow away from the nearest high water—with slight modifications. Thus, when the tide is rising, the stream flows one way (towards the trough and away from the crest of the tide) and when the tide is falling it flows the other way. But, of course, this is not always the case.

On Admiralty Charts, Flood Streams (on a rising tide) are indicated by half-feathered arrows, and Ebb Streams (on a falling tide) by plain straight arrows. The maximum speed of flow of the stream in knots is indicated by a small figure. A constant current is indicated by a full-feathered arrow. The speed given, if not marked "Sp" or "Np" for Springs or Neaps, is the maximum speed on days half-way between Springs and Neaps.

(b) The **Rate of Flow** of Tidal Streams is sometimes tabulated on a chart for particular positions on it. If this is not so, the following approximate guide may be applied to the values given near the arrows indicating the stream—

(i) Average rate of flow = $\frac{1}{2}$(Spring rate + Neap rate).
  Spring rate = twice Neap rate = $\frac{4}{3}$ average rate.
  Neap rate = $\frac{1}{2}$ Spring rate = $\frac{2}{3}$ average rate.

(ii) For 1st hour after slack water, rate = $\frac{1}{3}$ maximum rate of the day.
  For 2nd hour after slack water, rate = $\frac{2}{3}$ maximum rate of the day.
  For 3rd hour after slack water, rate = the maximum rate of the day.
  For 4th hour after slack water, rate = the maximum rate of the day.
  For 5th hour after slack water, rate = $\frac{2}{3}$ maximum rate of the day.
  For 6th hour after slack water, rate = $\frac{1}{3}$ maximum rate of the day.

The maximum rate of the day is found from (i) above.

(c) **Definitions.** A **Flood Stream** is a tidal stream when the tide is rising and when the direction of the stream turns within an hour of HW.

An **Ebb Stream** is a tidal stream when the tide is falling and when the direction of the stream turns within an hour of LW. **Ingoing, Outgoing, Northgoing, Eastgoing,** etc., are terms which are self-explanatory, and being more definite should be used in preference to Flood Stream and Ebb Stream.

Slack Water is that condition when there is no horizontal flow of water at the place. It must not be confused with the Stand of the tide. Slack water refers to the lack of tidal streams only and not the state of the tide.

A **Tide Race** is an area of turbulent sea of rips, overfalls, and breaking seas due to a fast-running tidal stream flowing over a sharply uprising sea bottom.

CHAPTER IX

METEOROLOGY SUMMARIZED

(METEOROLOGY, which is of vital interest to the aircraft captain, really requires a volume larger than the whole of this book to deal with it even moderately. It must be realized that in this chapter only very brief summaries of the following are given: (i) the atmosphere and its variable elements, (ii) the ways of measuring the variable elements of the weather, and (iii) the weather map and forecasting.)

SECTION 1

ELEMENTS OF THE WEATHER

1. THE ATMOSPHERE in which the weather makes itself manifest is not a chemical compound but is a mixture of practically constant constitution together with a variable quantity of water vapour, and of dust and/or smoke particles and salt particles. The atmosphere is divided fairly distinctly into two layers—the Stratosphere, or outer layer, and the Troposphere, or inner layer, separated by a boundary layer called the Tropopause.

(a) The *Stratosphere*, the outer layer, is very stable. In it there is practically no change of temperature with increase of height, and no convection currents of air, but sometimes an appreciable change of temperature is found with change of position horizontally.

In addition to oxygen and nitrogen it contains a number of rare gases in small quantities (helium, neon, xenon, and krypton).

(b) The *Troposphere*, the inner layer, suffers considerable instability and, being that part of the atmosphere in which we live and fly, is of the greatest importance. The three fundamental variables are (i) Air Temperature, (ii) Air Pressure, and (iii) Air Density. Another variable of great importance is the amount of water vapour in the air, called the Humidity.

The fundamental variables—temperature, pressure, and density—are connected by Boyle's Law and Charles's Law giving the formula

$\dfrac{p_1}{\rho_1 \, t_1} = \dfrac{p_2}{\rho_2 \, t_2}$, where p is pressure, ρ is density, and $t =$ temperature Absolute ($=$ Centigrade $+$ 273°).

Or $\rho = \dfrac{p}{Rt}$ where R is a constant.

The average composition of the atmosphere is roughly as follows—
By Volume—Nitrogen 76·9%   Carbonic Acid gas   0·03%
          Oxygen 20·7%   Water Vapour   1·4%
          Argon   0·9%   Hydrogen   0·01%

and dust and salt particles. Of these the most important from a practical weather point of view—the water vapour—varies most.

(c) The *Tropopause*, or boundary between the Stratosphere and Troposphere, varies in its height above the ground. It is highest over the Equator where it is about 16 Km. up (about 10 miles or 52,000 ft.), and is lowest over the Poles where it is about 8 Km. up (about 5 miles or 26,000 ft.).

(*Note.*—The **International Standard Atmosphere** is taken to be such that its temperature is 15° C. (288° A. or about 60° F.) and its pressure is 1013·2 millibars at mean sea-level, and that its temperature falls off at the rate (Lapse Rate) of 6·5° C. per 1000 metres (which is about 2° C. per 1000 ft., or 3·6° F. per 1000 ft.).)

2. AIR TEMPERATURE. (a) This element of the weather affects the others most, but is the least affected by them. That is, the weather is affected fundamentally by the temperature, and this in turn depends on the heat derived from the sun. Now the air being almost transparent to both light and heat waves does not absorb very much heat from the sun's rays passing through it, but is heated mainly by actual contact with the ground. The amount of absorption by the air of heat waves from the sun and of heat waves reflected from the Earth's surface is very, very small.

The units of temperature measurement are degrees Fahrenheit, Centigrade or Absolute. Then $C.° = (F. - 32) \times \frac{5}{9} = A.° - 273$, or $F.° = \frac{9}{5} C.° + 32$.

(*Note.*—Temperature must not be confused with the quantity of heat causing it. Temperature is the *degree of hotness* resulting from the quantity of heat present.)

(b) Heat Absorption and Radiation vary considerably and are important factors. Thus, land absorbs sun's heat quicker than the sea. Also, dry desert land absorbs heat from the sun more quickly than land with abundant vegetation. Similarly the land loses its heat by radiation (at night or when clouds obscure the sun's rays) quicker than the sea; and also desert land cools quicker than well-covered land.

Another very important practical point affecting radiation is the state of the sky. On a night with a clear sky the ground will cool quicker than with an overcast sky, so increasing the possibility of ground fogs. (See Fogs in paragraph 8 of this chapter.)

A further point is that exposed parts such as mountain peaks tend to cool very quickly at night. (See Katabatic Winds in paragraph 7.)

(c) Lapse Rate. The temperature of the air usually decreases with height. The rate of change of temperature with height is the Lapse Rate or, to be more precise, the Vertical Lapse Rate.

(i) The *Normal Lapse Rate* is about 6° C. per 1000 metres which is about 3·3° F. per 1000 ft., or 1° F. per 300 ft.

(ii) But convectional movements of the air have a strong influence on the lapse rate. Hot air rises without actually losing heat, but its temperature falls due to expansion. The best way of visualizing this is to imagine that the heat is spread out in a greater volume of air and therefore the temperature of each part of the mass is lessened. The rate of cooling due solely to the expansion of rising air, per unit height, is its Adiabatic Lapse Rate. ("Adiabatic" means without losing or gaining heat from an outside source.) The *Dry Adiabatic Lapse Rate* is about 1° C. per 100 metres, or 3° C. (5·4° F.) per 1000 ft.

But if the air contains much water vapour, this moisture itself actually contains heat and when it condenses, it gives off its Latent Heat—and therefore, on rising, the drop of temperature is less than for dry air. The *Saturated Adiabatic Lapse Rate* is about 2·6° F. (1·5° C.) per 1000 ft., when at about 50° F.

(d) A large Lapse Rate indicates an unstable atmosphere causing very changeable weather. On the other hand, a very small or even negative Lapse Rate indicates stability, resulting in calm and probably foggy weather.

A negative Lapse Rate (increase of temperature with height) is called an *Inversion*—a condition suitable for the occurrence of fogs.

3. AIR PRESSURE. (a) The pressure at a position is due to the weight of the column of air above that position. Obviously, therefore, pressure decreases with height—on this the operation of altimeters depends. The unit of pressure used hereafter is the millibar (mb.). 1 millibar = $\frac{1}{1000}$ bar and 1 bar = 1,000,000 dynes per sq. cm. (= 29·5306 inches or 750·076 mm. of mercury at 273° A. in Lat. 45°). The older units of inches and millimeters, which are becoming obsolete, were the measurement of the length of a column of mercury which could be supported by the atmospheric pressure. Then 1 inch = 25·4 mm. = 33·9 mb., or 1 mb. = 0·0296 inch. The average pressure at sea-level is about 1013 mb. = 29·9 inches = 760 mm. approx. (1 Atmosphere = about 14·7 lb. per sq. inch = about 1013 mb.)

Pressure varies horizontally forming pressure systems of various shapes and intensities. The Horizontal *Pressure Gradient* is the change of pressure per unit horizontal distance. Pressure changes are generally the result, more or less direct, of varying solar heating. The different types of horizontal pressure distribution are discussed fully in Section 3. In addition, there are pressure distributions of a more general nature—

(b) Pressure distribution over the Earth's surface varies due to two main factors: (i) the unequal heating of the Polar and Equatorial areas. As the sun beats straight down on Equatorial regions there is obviously much more heat absorption there than

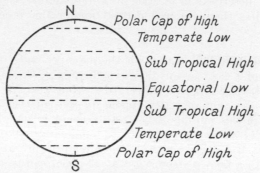

FIG. 142. GENERAL PRESSURE DISTRIBUTION UNINFLUENCED BY LAND AND SEA MASSES

at the Poles where the sun's rays (when there are any) strike the surface at a very shallow angle; (ii) the unequal heat absorption by land and sea. The temperature of the sea is fairly uniform but large land masses become very hot under the influence of the summer sun and very cold in winter.

(c) Now when air becomes heated it becomes less dense, rises and so reduces the pressure. This, in conjunction with the two factors of heating mentioned above, has the following results.

(i) The High Pressure areas known as the "Polar Caps" exist over the Poles, and a Low Pressure belt runs round the Equator. This belt moves up and down a little, following the variation of the sun's declination.

(ii) The Equatorial hot air which rises and flows outwards from the Equator descends at about Lat. 25°–40° tending to cause High Pressure belts at that Lat. north and south of the Equator. Then between the High Pressure belts of these "Horse Latitudes" and the Polar Caps are the Temperate Low Pressure belts.

(Note.—Fig. 142 gives the pressure distribution which would tend to result from factor (i) of sub-para. (b) above alone.)

(iii) Areas of High Pressure develop over large land masses in winter, and are replaced by Low Pressure areas in summer. Of these, the largest is the Great Siberian High of winter which becomes the Great Siberian Low in summer.

(d) Diurnal Pressure Waves resulting from heating due to the sun and cooling at night are very noticeable in the tropics. They move from east to west with the sun, and have a maximum amplitude of about 2 to 3 mb. They have a period of 12 hours, the maxima of pressure being at about 10.00 and 22.00 hr. local time and the minima at about 04.00 and 16.00 hr. Of course, other pressure changes as described in Section 3 will obliterate these diurnal changes unless they are well defined and/or the other changes very small.

4. THE AIR DENSITY. Density is the mass per unit volume, and, in the case of a gas (e.g. air), it varies directly as the pressure and inversely as the Absolute temperature, But there is usually a considerable amount of water vapour present in the atmosphere and therefore this must be taken into account in practice. If the density of dry air at a given Absolute temperature and pressure is known, then the density at any other temperature and pressure together with a known amount of water vapour can be found from the following formula—

$$\rho = \rho_0 \frac{p - \frac{3}{8} e}{p_0} \times \frac{T_0}{T},$$

where ρ_0 = density of the standard dry air at a given Absolute temperature T_0 and a given pressure p_0 in mb.

ρ = density of the air.

T = Absolute temperature of the air.

p = Pressure in mb. of the air.

e = Aqueous vapour pressure in mb.—found from wet and dry bulb readings of a psychrometer (hygrometer).

(*Note.*—Vapour pressure is the pressure which the vapour would exert if it was alone in the space it is sharing with the air.)

The density (ρ) of dry air at 1000 mb. and 290° A. is 1201 grammes per cubic metre. Air containing water vapour is less dense than dry air in accordance with the above formula. (In meteorology, density is normally expressed in grammes per cubic metre.)

The main effect of varying density is to cause convection currents of air, the less dense air tending to rise and the heavy (more dense) air tending to descend.

Density, of course, decreases with height, necessitating a correction to be applied to A.S.I. reading at heights above sea-level.

Also, density varies slightly with change of place or time. The general tendencies of density are—

(i) At any level up to 8 Km. average density increases from the Equator towards the Poles; and also the average is lower in summer than in winter.

(ii) At a height of 8 Km. density remains very nearly constant at a given level.

(iii) At any level above 8 Km. the average density decreases from the Equator towards the Poles; and also there is a slight seasonal change, being greater in summer than in winter.

(iv) Diurnal changes at levels near the ground occur to considerable magnitude in hot countries. Thus, on a really hot day, the density near ground-level on a dry aerodrome may be reduced to such an extent as to make landings and take-offs da gerous.

In addition to its meteorological significance the density is of great practical importance in its effect on an aircraft's aerodynamic performance, the power output of an engine, and on A.S.I. readings, etc. The density of the air at high-level aerodromes or, as already mentioned, on very hot days, is of vital importance in taking off and landing. The unit of density used in British aeronautical design and performance formulae is the gravitational-mass unit called the Slug, which equals 0·00237 for the standard atmosphere at sea-level. $\rho = \dfrac{W}{g}$ slugs where w is the weight per cubic foot and g is the force of gravity.

5. HUMIDITY is the amount of water vapour present in the air. It is of obvious importance to the weather, in causing fog, clouds, rain, etc. Now air at a given temperature can only hold a certain maximum quantity of water in vapour form. Beyond this, which is called the *Saturation Point*, the water will condense out into water particles forming clouds, fog, or rain. *Relative Humidity* is the ratio (expressed as a percentage) of the amount of water vapour present to the amount which would be present if the air was saturated at that temperature. This is of great practical importance. The Relative Humidity of saturated air is 100 per cent, and very damp air is about 85 per cent and over.

Now the amount of water vapour which air can hold varies with its temperature. Hot air can hold much more than cold air. Thus, if air is saturated (Relative Humidity = 100 per cent) and it is heated, its Relative Humidity is lessened (without losing any water vapour); or if it is cooled, the Saturation Point will be reduced and part of the vapour will condense out. The amount of water vapour contained in saturated air is given in paragraph 13.

Humidity is measured by various forms of Hygrometer. (See Section 2.)

6. WIND is simply the flow of air horizontally, and is expressed by a speed and the direction from which it blows.

(a) The tendency is for air to flow from an area of high pressure to an area of low pressure. But owing to the Earth's rotation it (like any other moving body) suffers a deflection, called Geostrophic Deflection. Then, for a given horizontal pressure gradient, a certain wind speed and direction is reached where the Geostrophic effect,

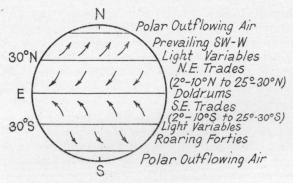

FIG. 143. GENERAL WINDS

combined possibly with a centrifugal effect (called Cyclostrophic Deflection), and the pressure gradient effect will balance out. But this will be dealt with in full later.

The law concerning Geostrophic Deflection states in general that any body moving over the Earth tends to be deflected to the right in the northern hemisphere and to the left in the southern hemisphere. Or, as Buys-Ballot puts it, winds blow anti-clockwise around a low pressure area and clockwise around a high pressure area in the northern hemisphere, and the reverse in the southern hemisphere.

(b) **General Winds** are shown in Fig. 143. The heating effect of the sun gives pressure belts as described in para. 3 of this chapter. Then winds tend to blow from low pressures (or "Lows") to high pressures ("Highs") and, being deflected in accordance with Buys-Ballot's Law, result in the winds shown in Fig. 143. This, of course, is considerably modified in practice owing to heating effects on the large land masses, but over the oceans the "permanent" Trade Winds are very consistent. The belts in which they blow move up and down slightly with the sun's declination and they blow strongest when the sun is of opposite declination. Thus, the North-east Trades are strongest in the southern summer and the

South-east Trades are strongest in the northern summer. Above the Trades are winds in the opposite direction called Anti-Trades (see "Upper Winds"). In the southern temperate zone land does not cause any very great interference and therefore the general tendency to NW. and W. winds is effective, resulting in the famous "Roaring Forties" which blow right around the world in the belt 40° S.–60° S. In the north temperate zone large land masses interfere with the pressure distribution and therefore there is no well-defined westerly wind but nevertheless the wind of greatest frequency and strength is SW.–W.

(c) **Cyclonic Winds** are those which blow around a centre of low pressure and the system is called a Cyclone or Depression. The air tends to flow towards the Low centre and is deflected due to the Earth's rotation to a direction such that this Geostrophic deflection is balanced by the effect of pressure difference. The wind is then rotating around the centre, and centrifugal effect (Cyclostrophic deflection) must be taken into account. Now, as will be explained later, places

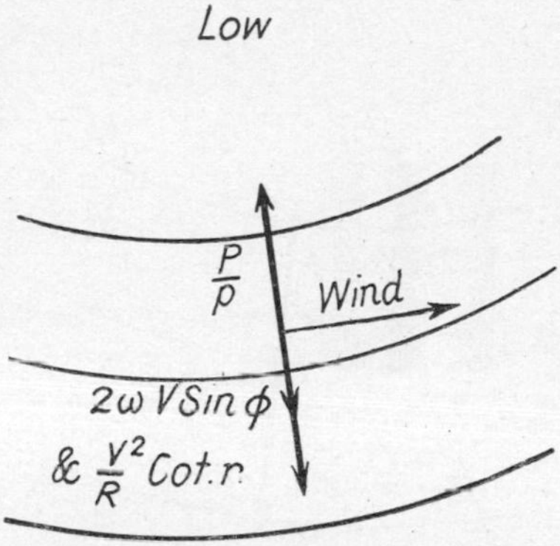

FIG. 144. FORCES ACTING ON A CYCLONIC WIND IN THE NORTHERN HEMISPHERE

of equal pressure can be joined by lines called *Isobars*. Then a wind which blows at such a speed that its direction coincides with the isobars is called the *Gradient Wind*. It usually occurs in a depression at a height of about 1500–2000 ft. If the wind is slower the Geostrophic and Cyclostrophic deflections are weaker and the wind turns inwards toward the low pressure. Whereas if the wind is stronger than the Gradient Wind, the Geostrophic and Cyclostrophic deflections are stronger than the pressure effect and the wind turns away from the low pressure. Fig. 144 illustrates the three forces acting on a Cyclonic Wind in the northern hemisphere. In the southern hemisphere the rotation is reversed.

(i) The value of Geostrophic effect depends on the speed of the wind and on the speed of rotation about a vertical axis at the particular locality. This rotation is obviously a maximum at the Poles and nil at the Equator and equals $\omega \sin \phi$, where ω is the angular velocity at the Poles and ϕ is the Latitude. Then it can be shown that the Geostrophic deflection is a force at right angles to the direction of movement giving an acceleration of $2\omega V \sin \phi$, where V is wind speed. It acts to the right in the northern hemisphere and to the left in the southern hemisphere.

(ii) The value of Cyclostrophic effect depends on the speed of the wind and the radius of curvature of its path. Now if r is the radius of curvature as measured at the centre of the Earth (i.e. Nautical Miles = minutes of arc) then the actual straight line linear radius of curvature = $R \sin r$. Now acceleration due to

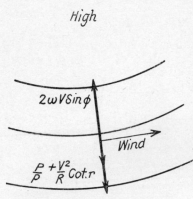

FIG. 145. FORCES ACTING ON AN ANTICYCLONIC WIND IN THE SOUTHERN HEMISPHERE

centrifugal force = $\dfrac{V^2}{\text{radius}}$ = $\dfrac{V^2}{R \sin r}$ and the component of this parallel with the Earth's surface = $\dfrac{V^2}{R \sin r} \times \cos r = \dfrac{V^2}{R} \cot r$, acting at right angles to the direction of motion in a direction away from the centre of rotation.

(iii) The acceleration due to the difference of pressure depends on the pressure gradient P and inversely on the density ρ, and equals $\dfrac{P}{\rho}$.

Then, for a cyclonic Gradient Wind

$$\frac{P}{\rho} = 2\omega V \sin \phi + \frac{V^2}{R} \cot r.$$

(d) **Anticyclonic Winds** are those which blow around a centre of high pressure. The air tends to flow outwards from the high to the surrounding low pressure, and is deflected by Geostrophic effect tending to make it rotate around the centre. But any rotation causes a Cyclostrophic effect which, unlike the cyclonic winds, acts in the same direction as the pressure gradient effect. Fig. 145 shows the forces on a Gradient Wind in an Anticyclone in the southern hemisphere. The rotation is, of course, reversed in the northern hemisphere. From this it can be seen, that, for an Anticyclonic Gradient Wind

$$\frac{P}{\rho} + \frac{V^2}{R} \cot r = 2\omega V \sin \phi.$$

(*Note.*—A Geostrophic Wind is one which blows along a straight

(Great circle) isobar, so that $\dfrac{P}{\rho} = 2\omega V \sin \phi$, there being no Cyclostrophic effect.)

(e) **Change of Wind with Height** can, with experience, be deduced up to moderate altitudes. Up to about 2000 ft. the accuracy obtained is usually good enough to be used in navigation when no proper means of finding the wind are available. At greater heights an experienced and clever observer can deduce good results, which, even if not used directly in navigation, often constitute a valuable guide.

The points considered in deducing a wind are—

(i) The direction of the surface wind and its speed (estimated by sight or from weather reports).

(ii) The direction and estimated speed of movement of cloud shadows over the ground, and the height of the clouds causing the shadows.

(iii) The pressure distribution, known from previous meteorological information or, if not known, roughly estimated.

(iv) The latitude zone (Equatorial, Sub-tropical, Temperate, or Polar).

(v) The probable effects of heating, seasonal and diurnal, on local land masses.

But although a clever navigator can obtain good deductions by considering the above points, experience in the particular latitude zone and locality is of very great value.

In England, which lies in the North Temperate zone, the following characteristics are generally true—

(i) When surface wind is NE., winds above 3000 ft. generally decrease and may even become westerly, but exceptions to this are not infrequent.

(ii) When surface wind is SE., winds veer with height, and speed usually remains about the same.

(iii) When surface wind is SW., winds veer with height and increase speed.

(iv) When surface wind is NW., winds veer only very little but often increase speed considerably.

(*Note.*—A *veering* wind is one which changes its direction clockwise (in either hemisphere). A *backing* wind is one which changes its direction anti-clockwise.)

(f) **Upper Winds.** Comparatively little data have so far been collected concerning upper winds. But it has been discovered that a few important tendencies generally apply, thus—

(i) At high altitudes winds tend to rotate around areas of low temperature in the same way as surface winds rotate around areas of low pressure.

(ii) At high altitudes in the Equatorial belt the rising air tends to lag behind the rotating Earth, and therefore there is a wind from the East. In the sub-tropical zones the upper air tends to flow outwards from the Equator and is deflected in accordance with Buys-Ballot's Law to merge with westerly winds which seem to dominate at very high levels in Temperate and Polar regions.

(iii) Winds due directly to surface heating influences die out even in the strongest cases (such as Monsoons) at about 15,000 ft. Trade Winds have Anti-Trade Winds blowing above them, in directions as much as 180° different, the change being at from 2500 ft. to 16,000 ft. Anti Trades are often called Counter Trades.

(g) **Turbulence** in the atmosphere is due to frictional influences when a wind blows over the Earth's surface and past hills and other obstacles, or when one current of air is moving in relation to adjoining air. It is of interest in estimating the aerodynamic stresses on an aircraft in turbulence "bumps," and in finding the magnitude of downdraughts likely to be encountered when landing in the lee of an obstacle. Eddy motion is superimposed on the existing wind. It has been shown by G. I. Taylor that in Eddy Motion the three components—(i) horizontally downwind, (ii) horizontally across wind, and (iii) vertical—are usually of about the same strength. This fact may be applied to wind speed and direction readings of an anemometer (see Section 2) to find the actual values of the components of the eddy motion imposed on the wind. It appears, however, that this conclusion does not apply close under the lee of a cliff, mountain or ridge where obviously the roly-poly nature of the turbulence makes the components (i) and (iii) greater than component (ii). This can be shown by the fact that if a modern heavy aircraft is flown into such a wind the fluctuations of the A.S.I. will be of greater magnitude than if the aircraft is flown across wind.

(h) **Vertical Currents** may be divided into three groups, thus—

(i) The vertical component of turbulence as described in (g) above.

(ii) Larger scale vertical movements due to winds blowing over high mountain ridges, the vertical component being dependent on the strength of the wind, the slope and the height of the mountain, etc.

(iii) Convection currents due to hot air rising and cold air descending. Temperature instability causes vertical currents which at times reach highly dangerous velocities, as in thunderstorms. An idea of the vertical velocities reached has been deduced from hailstones which have fallen on to the ground. By cracking one such hailstone in half, layers were discovered indicating that it had been carried upwards into freezing air, and fallen, and been

carried up again a number of times. By measuring the diameter
of the hailstone and finding its terminal velocity the strength of the
vertical current which carried it upwards can be deduced. For
example, a hailstone of 2 in. diameter needs a vertical current of
about 117 ft. per second (nearly 80 m.p.h.) to hold it up. Such a
hailstone has fallen and found to have the ice layers indicating
repeated upward movements. Of course, such violent vertical
currents are fortunately rare, but make thunder clouds a danger to
aircraft.

(iv) Slow vertical movements of large masses of air due to the
surface horizontal winds converging, called Convergence, and so
forcing the air upwards; or diverging, called Divergence, and so
tending to draw the air downwards.

7. PARTICULAR WINDS. (a) As has already been mentioned the
following points must always be remembered when dealing with
winds.

(i) Sun's heating, which is most effective on land, causes Low
pressure.

(ii) Cooling, during winter or at night, and is greatest on land,
causes High pressure.

(iii) Wind tends to blow from High to Low and is deflected by
Geostrophic effect.

The winds mentioned hereafter may be grouped into those of
  (i) Local nature,
  (ii) Monsoonal nature
  (iii) Cyclonic or Anticyclonic nature,
or (iv) Katabatic nature.

But classification in some cases is not very distinct.

Another type of wind not elsewhere mentioned is that of the
Land and Sea Breezes. Diurnal heating—unequal—of the land and
sea is the cause. During the day the land heats up causing a Low
pressure and resultant on-shore breeze. At night the land loses its
heat quickly and forms a High pressure relative to the adjoining
sea area, resulting in an off-shore breeze. This diurnal wind is
very common in hot countries when no other well-defined pressure
systems interfere.

(b) Local Winds.

(i) The *Sirocco* is of slightly cyclonic nature in that it is a warm
S. or SE. wind in front of a cyclonic depression moving eastwards
along the Mediterranean generally in late summer. The air in it
originates in the Sahara but soon picks up moisture over the sea.

(ii) The *Levanter* is a strong NE. wind on the east coast of Spain
and easterly in the Straits of Gibraltar in early winter and in spring

and in early summer. It is strongest in the winter period. Generally it occurs with a High over Europe and a Low over North Africa.

(iii) The *Maestro* is a fresh NW. wind in the Adriatic in summer, with fine weather. It is associated with a Low over the Balkans.

(iv) The *Gregale* is a strong NE. wind in the Ionian Sea and adjoining parts, occurring with a generally High pressure but with an abnormally intense High to the north (in Greece), usually in winter.

(v) The *Khamsin* is a hot dry south wind in North Egypt, with a Low approaching along the North African coast and a relatively High pressure in Middle Egypt.

(vi) The *Harmattan* (or the Doctor), of slightly Monsoonal nature, is a very dry and relatively cool wind from the cooling Sahara (in November to March) flowing towards the lower pressure area of West Tropical Africa. It carries with it a dust haze which at times causes very poor visibility.

(vii) The *Shamal* is a NW. wind in 'Iraq in Summer.

(viii) The *Seistan* is a strong moist north wind in East Iran in summer for a period of about four months.

(c) Monsoons are winds of a seasonal nature, caused by the difference of temperature (and consequently, pressure) between land and sea areas at the particular season.

(i) The SW. Monsoon is warm, moist and rainy, strong in the Indian Ocean and Arabian Sea, and light in the China Sea, and blows from about April to September. It is caused by a Low pressure over Central Asia.

(ii) The NE. Monsoon is strong in the China Sea and light in the Indian Ocean, and blows from about November to March. A High pressure over Central Asia assists the natural tendency to the North-east Trade Wind.

(iii) The NW. Monsoon is an extension of the NE. Monsoon across the Equator in the southern summer (November to March) to the East Indies and the North of Australia, and sometimes more to the east. An area of Low pressure in the north of Central Australia seems to be the cause. This wind sometimes backs round to the south-west, particularly in the north of Western Australia.

Monsoonal winds also occur in Africa and the American continents.

(d) Cyclonic Winds are those which blow around centres of Low pressure. They are generally called Depressions in the temperate zones and are of moderate intensities only. In the Tropics they are usually more intense and are called Cyclones which occur mostly at the western edges of the oceans, particularly at the end of the hot season.

They are named—

(i) Cyclones—in Arabian Sea, Bay of Bengal, Mauritius, and Madagascar.

(ii) Typhoons—in the China Sea and Japanese coasts.

(iii) Hurricanes (very intense)—in the Gulf of Mexico, West Indies, Florida, East Australian coast, and Samoa, etc.

(iv) Baguios—in the Philippine Islands (particularly July–November).

(v) Tornadoes, of West Africa, are squalls accompanying cyclonic storms, and occur with rain. In the United States, east of the Rocky Mountains (also in Australia), they are very small and violent rotating winds, usually of less than a few hundred feet in diameter. In America they become very intense with speeds calculated to be up to 200 m.p.h. In Australia the name "Willy Willy" is used for these whirl-winds, but meteorologists prefer to use it to refer to a severe cyclone in Australia. (Anticyclonic Winds are those which blow about an area of High pressure. They are generally of less intensity than Cyclonic Winds.)

(e) Katabatic Winds are caused by air being cooled by contact with cold hill tops, and gravitating down the slopes. Mountain tops, being more exposed, cool much more rapidly than sheltered valleys.

(i) The *Bora* is a cold and sometimes very strong NE. wind in the Adriatic in winter, blowing from the cold mountains situated to the north and north-east of the sea.

(ii) The *Mistral* is a cold dry N. or NW. wind in Southern France (mainly down the Rhône valley), with clear weather. It occurs with a High pressure over the mountains of Switzerland and France, and a Low pressure over the Gulf of Genoa.

(iii) The *Bize* is a cold dry N., NE., or NW. wind in Southern France in winter, unlike the Mistral in as much as it is accompanied by heavy clouds.

(iv) The *Föhn* is not really a Katabatic Wind. It is a wind blowing over a mountain ridge and down the lee slopes, and so warming adiabatically (i.e. without gaining heat). This results in a warm dry wind which thaws snow quickly. The name Föhn originated in the Alps. On the east side of the Rockies a similar wind is called *Chinook*.

(Anabatic Winds are the opposite to Katabatic Winds and are caused by the warming of a valley causing the air to rise up the slopes by convection, and a wind to blow up the valley.)

8. **(a) FOG** is atmospheric obscurity of horizontal visibility of less than 1100 yards. Generally fog consists of water particles condensed (due to cooling) on tiny nuclei of dust, smoke, or salt particles. But "dust fogs" or "smoke fogs" consisting of dust particles or smoke particles occur in desert areas or manufacturing cities respectively. The formation of an ordinary fog (water particles) depends on—

(i) The amount of water vapour present in the air (see para. 5).

(ii) The existing temperature of the air.

(iii) The temperature at which the existing amount of water vapour in the air will cause it to become saturated—and at which this vapour will therefore tend to condense into solid water particles. This temperature is called the *Dew Point*.

(iv) The existence of nuclei.

(v) The cause of the air's becoming cooled. This varies, resulting in fogs of different kinds, as follows—

(b) (i) *Radiation* Fogs occur usually in autumn and winter at night and in the morning, being worst between 2 a.m. and dawn. They are caused by moist air being cooled to its Dew Point or below by contact with the ground which has become very cold by radiation. This results in a low ground fog. This type of fog is most likely to form on a calm clear night (wind less than 8 m.p.h.) with moist air.

(ii) *Valley* Fog is a kind of radiation fog. High exposed ground cools quickly and the moist air in contact with it is cooled below its Dew Point. It then gravitates katabatically and also due to the actual weight of water particles into the surrounding valleys. The resulting adiabatic warming is not usually strong enough to disperse the fog by vaporizing its particles.

(iii) Occasionally the ground cools very quickly so that the moisture particles which condense immediately freeze, forming hoar-frost. When, in the morning, the ground is warmed again the frost is melted and tends to evaporate, so possibly raising the relative humidity to saturation point, causing fog. Of course, this fog disappears as soon as the air becomes warmed further.

(c) High Ground Fog is caused (i) merely by existing clouds being blown over high ground; or (ii) by moist air being cooled dynamically by being forced upwards over cliffs or hills.

(d) Sea Fog. (i) In spring, sea fogs are caused by warm moist air being cooled by blowing over relatively cold sea. This is a very common form of fog.

(ii) Land fogs often drift seawards, particularly in winter.

(e) An Advection Fog, of which (d) (i) above is an example, is caused by moist warm air being blown over a colder surface which by contact cools it to its Dew Point.

9. CLOUDS AND PRECIPITATION. (a) **Clouds** are the same as fog but differ in that they are above the ground and that sometimes they consist of ice, snow, or sleet, instead of water particles.

Clouds are generally formed by moist air being cooled below its Dew Point by rising. The height at which Dew Point is reached is called Saturation Level. Vertical movements have already been discussed in para. 6 of this chapter.

Clouds are classified for convenience of reference, but of course there are many doubtful cases. The international cloud classification consists of ten forms, which can be divided into three classes—

High—Cirrus, Cirro-stratus, and Cirro-cumulus.

Medium—Alto-cumulus, Alto-stratus.

Low—Strato-cumulus, Nimbus, Cumulus, Cumulo-nimbus, and Stratus.

Briefly the ten cloud forms may be described as follows—

(i) Cirrus (Ci), "mares' tails," are white fibrous clouds, of ice crystals, usually in front of a Depression. Height about 5–6 miles.

(ii) Cirro-stratus (Cs) is a thin veil of water-particles cloud, at a height similar to, or slightly lower than, that of cirrus.

(iii) Cirro-cumulus (Cc), "mackerel sky," is a cirrus cloud of small rounded masses. Unsettled weather usually follows.

(iv) Alto-cumulus (Ac) is a cloud consisting of rounded masses in groups or lines, the lumps being larger than Cc, and, of course, being lower.

(v) Alto-stratus (As) is a dense greyish sheet of cloud at a height of about 2–3 miles.

(vi) Strato-cumulus (Sc) is a large lumpy dull grey cloud, generally covering the whole sky but with occasional gaps.

(vii) Cumulus (Cu), "Wool-pack," is thick, white, rolled cloud with domed top and flat base. It is formed by convection currents of air, and is often the result of diurnal heating only.

(viii) Nimbus (Ni) is dense dark cloud giving rain, or snow. It usually has Cs or As above it.

(ix) Cumulo-Nimbus (Cn), the thunder cloud, is a towering mass of cloud causing heavy showers. At its top, which is very high, a horizontal veil (false cirrus) often forms giving the whole an appearance like the shape of an anvil (hence called anvil cloud). It is usually a region of violent vertical currents, in which there is danger of ice accretion and lightning.

(x) Stratus (St) is a uniform layer of cloud at low altitude.

(b) Precipitation. (i) **Snow.** In clouds at very low temperatures, particularly down at 0° F. and lower, water particles do not exist, but instead the cloud consists of very fine ice crystals in the form of minute needles and star-shaped discs. A snow-flake consists of many of these ice particles entangled and matted together.

Snow can only reach the surface as such provided that it does not fall through a warm region which melts it either partially into sleet or completely into rain drops.

Incidentally these two last-mentioned forms of precipitation often originate as snow in the tops of the clouds from which they fall.

(ii) **Soft Hail** probably originates as snow-flakes when falling from the top colder part of the cloud into a slightly warmer part where they become coated with opaque ice formed from a mixture of super-cooled water (i.e. below freezing-point but not frozen) and snow.

(iii) **Sleet** consists of snow-flakes of which the outer protruding ice-crystals have been melted away by falling through warmer air leaving only the more closely matted core of the flake, and leaving it in a rather wet and sticky state.

(iv) **Rain** is produced by the condensation of water vapour by cooling, or by the complete melting of snow into water drops. The speed at which a drop falls through the air depends on its size. The terminal velocity of a water drop of 0·5 mm. diam. = about 8·0 ft. per sec.; of 2 mm. diam. = 19·3 ft. per sec.; and of 5 mm. diam. = about 26·25 ft. per sec. Drops of diameters greater than about 5·5 mm. tend to fall at a speed which breaks them up into smaller drops. It can be seen from these comparatively low terminal velocities that it only requires a moderately strong upward current of air to hold up raindrops.

Rain is sometimes classified depending on the cause of the cooling which brought about the condensation.

Orographic Rain is caused by a moist wind striking a mountain slope and being deflected upwards, which causes cooling dynamically. Thus, a mountain range running at right-angles to the direction of a prevailing moisture-laden wind will consistently cause rain.

Convectional Rain is caused by moist air becoming warm, expanding, and rising convectionally. The rising causes it to cool adiabatically—and rain to form. The best example of convectional rain is that of the diurnal thunderstorm. This type of rain sometimes is extremely heavy, and is more severe than the other types.

Cyclonic Rain is caused by the low pressure system, called a Cyclone or Depression, to be dealt with more fully later.

(v) **Hail** consists of lumps of nearly clear ice usually formed from drops of rain carried up by strong convectional currents into very cold air where they freeze solid.

(vi) **Drizzle** is equivalent to very fine rain. The water particles, being extremely small, fall at a very slow speed. As, therefore, these particles could not descend against any appreciable upward movement of air, it follows that drizzle only falls from clouds of a stratus nature.

(vii) **Granular Snow** is drizzle frozen owing to low temperature. The particles as they freeze stick to each other, so forming into very small white opaque grains.

10. ICE ACCRETION. (a) The danger of ice formation on aircraft is well known, but an enormous amount has still to be learnt about this complicated phenomenon. Danger sometimes exists in conditions where some theorists would have us believe no icing is possible.

The following types of accretion are given as a guide, but, of course, there is no distinct dividing line between them.

(i) *Glazed Ice,* the most dangerous, but fortunately an infrequent type, consists of clear ice which forms, often very rapidly, when an aircraft flying in a layer of cold air (below freezing-point) enters rain which has fallen from a warmer region above. The magnitude of this type of icing makes it dangerous both because of the weight of the ice picked up and also because of the spoiling of the aerofoil shapes of the wings and airscrews.

In this type of icing, safety can often be found by climbing quickly to the warmer layer, which in theory is above. But if an early decision is made it may be discreet to reverse course to run out of the danger quickly. The climb can then be carried out and the original course resumed, due attention being paid to the air temperature.

(ii) A *partially opaque and partially glazed ice* is formed when large water particles in a dense cloud usually just below freezing-point strike the leading edges. Part of the water freezes immediately on the leading edge, and as it does so it gives out its latent heat (the latent heat of freezing) which raises the temperature of the remainder of the drop. This, as it blows aft, cools by contact with the cold aircraft and by evaporative cooling to form streaks of clear and nearly clear ice. Thus this type consists of packed ice particles on the leading edge with a layer of streaky but glazed ice running aft from it. It is of considerable danger, and is more common than (i) above

(iii) Another type, not often mentioned, but one which can be a menace, is simply *Packed Snow.* Dry snow alone (i.e. very cold), or ice crystals, will not stick to an aircraft regardless of the speed of the aircraft or of the frontal area to be impinged upon. But dry snow mixed with super-cooled water will cause icing on leading edges—

the snow-flakes impinging on the water drops at the moment of solidification and so becoming stuck to it on the leading edges. Similarly, wet snow, or snow and sleet, or just sleet will, through natural stickiness, become packed on the leading edges. This type never extends far aft along the chord, but its danger lies mainly in the destruction of lift due to spoiling the aerofoil section.

(iv) A white opaque formation, also confined to the leading edges and usually not very thick, is formed from super-cooled water particles, very small and generally very cold. They form into small independent ice particles immediately on impact. The coating, being of an aerated nature, is fairly soft. It is generally known as *Rime*.

(v) A type of deposit which is of no great importance can be formed in a clear atmosphere. This is done by the aircraft flying at a height where it becomes cooled to well below freezing-point and then it descends quickly into warm moist air. The cold surfaces of the aircraft condense the vapour in contact with them and freeze the resultant water particle instantaneously. The result is a very *thin semi-crystalline* coating.

(b) The following remarks concerning the icing properties of the various cloud types generally apply: The cirrus types consist of cold dry ice crystals and therefore cannot cause ice accretion. Alto-cumulus and alto-stratus are very cold clouds but often consist of super-cooled water particles, highly prone to form into ice on an aircraft. But these clouds are of a thin nature and therefore ice accretion is slow.

Strato-cumulus, a very common winter cloud often of great extent, frequently causes icing, generally of a moderate degree, of a type between (a) (iii) and (a) (iv) above, when the temperature is suitable.

Nimbus types, being regions of heavy precipitation will cause heavy ice formation on aircraft, particularly at temperatures just below freezing.

Cumulus and cumulo-nimbus, being convectional clouds, hold up large water particles. In the former, ice accretion is not usually serious and the clouds themselves are usually comparatively small, but the latter type often causes very dangerous icing, particularly in its middle and upper parts.

Stratus when below 32° F. causes Rime.

(c) In the avoidance of ice accretion the following points may be noted—

(i) Greatest ice accretion occurs between 32° F. and 20° F. (0° C. and − 7° C.). Below about 10° F. (− 12° C.) it is practically never serious nor is it above 34° F. (*Note.*—Ice does sometimes persist even slightly above normal freezing-point.)

(ii) With a knowledge of the temperatures where danger of ice exists a pilot should maintain a regular watch on the temperature of the air in which he is flying. The present thermometers used for this purpose could with advantage be replaced by an instrument which would record graphically both temperature and height against time, to provide the pilot with a permanent record.

(iii) Flying in cloud or through precipitation should be avoided when at a height at which the temperature is suitable for ice formation. The rate of ascent or descent through layers in which ice formation may be possible should be as quick as possible compatible with passengers' comfort.

(iv) Be prepared, navigationally, for unexpected and, theoretically, improbable ice accretion.

SECTION 2

MEASUREMENT OF THE ELEMENTS OF THE WEATHER

11. THERMOMETERS for reading air temperature must be situated so that they are protected from direct heat rays, and therefore give accurate readings of the heat of the air in contact with them.

(a) The Mercury Thermometer used for most meteorological purposes is simply a thin glass tube of uniform bore enlarged at the bottom to a small bulb. A certain amount of mercury is inserted and the tube sealed. Expansion of the mercury with rise of temperature causes its upper level to move up the tube in proportion to the rise. A scale adjoining the tube reads temperature direct. It must be noted that mercury freezes at about − 40° F. and therefore cannot be employed for thermometers to be used below that value.

(b) The Maximum Thermometer is designed to indicate the maximum temperature reached during a given period.

In the vertical type a mercury thermometer has its bulb at the upper end, and immediately below the bulb is a constriction. Mercury will only pass out through this constriction under the expansion force of the mercury when its temperature rises. This mercury forced out then falls to the bottom and the height of the column so formed is read off against a scale of temperature. To reset the thermometer it is inverted and swung sharply, forcing mercury back into the bulb. It is then righted and the amount of mercury still in the tube should indicate the existing temperature.

In the horizontal type the principle of the constriction is the same, but instead of reading from the bottom of the tube upwards the length of the mercury is measured from the constriction horizontally. Clinical thermometers employ the same principle.

(c) The Minimum Thermometer indicates the minimum temperature reached during a given period. A glass tube with a bulb contains alcohol which expands and contracts with temperature change. Usually the tube is mounted horizontally. Inside the tube and in the alcohol, touching the boundary between the alcohol and the vapour, is a small glass Index piece. As the temperature falls the alcohol contracts, and as the light Index is unable to break through the surface tension of the alcohol it is drawn along the tube to the position of minimum temperature reached.

(d) The Thermograph is an instrument which actually records the temperature on a graph which is moved by clockwork.

(i) The Mercury type has a large bulb of mercury the expansion and contraction of which causes variations in pressure in a spiral tube which actuates a pen over the graph.

(ii) The Bi-metallic Spiral type has a spiral of two metals of differing Coefficients of Expansion anchored at one end and at the other end connected through levers to a pen.

12. BAROMETERS are of two types, the Mercury Barometer and the Aneroid Barometer. The former is generally used for accurate work, and the principle of the latter is employed in self-recording instruments, in barometers for the layman, and for approximate work, and in altimeters.

(a) The Mercury Barometer indicates the atmospheric pressure by the length of a column of mercury which the pressure will support. If a glass tube about 3 feet long and sealed at one end is completely filled with mercury and inverted with its open end in a small cistern of mercury, then the top of the mercury in the tube will stand at about 30 inches above the level of the mercury in the cistern. This height will, of course, vary with atmospheric pressure. Above the mercury in the tube the space is filled with mercury vapour, and not with a vacuum as was supposed in old days.

The height of the mercury column is read against a scale which in modern barometers is in millibars, but in older models may be in inches or millimetres. A slider with a vernier scale on it is usually provided to obtain accurate readings. The bottom of the slider is brought coincident with the top of the curved upper surface of the mercury in the tube. The slider goes right round the tube, and by sighting, so that both the near and the far side of the bottom are in line with the top of the mercury, parallax error is avoided. Variation in the level of the mercury in the cistern is automatically allowed for in the Kew pattern barometer, but in other types this level must first be adjusted to the zero of the scale.

Accurate readings, such as for synoptic purposes, must be corrected for or to the following—

(i) Latitude. As the weight of a given mass of mercury increases from the Equator to the pole some standard latitude must be chosen. 45° is the Latitude to which all mercury barometer readings are corrected.

(ii) Index Error. Errors in construction are found and must be allowed for. Index Error is not a constant error (due to such things as varying diameter of the tube) but varies with the reading obtained.

(iii) Mean Sea-level. So that the readings of two stations can be compared on a common basis the readings are corrected for the height of the instrument above sea-level (or some other arbitrary level).

(iv) Temperature. The weight of a given volume of mercury decreases with rises of temperature, and vice versa. Also the scale probably expands a little. A Temperature correction is therefore necessary. (*Note.*—This is for the temperature of the room where the barometer is installed, and not the outside temperature. A small thermometer is therefore usually mounted on the barometer for convenience.)

Then, the *Standard Temperature* for a particular barometer is that at which the algebraic sum of Temperature correction, and Index Error is zero.

The *Fiducial Temperature* of a barometer is that at which the algebraic sum of Latitude correction, Temperature correction and Index Error is zero.

The *Adjusted Fiducial Temperature* of a barometer is that at which the albegraic sum of the Latitude, the Height, and the Temperature corrections and Index Error is zero.

(b) The Aneroid Barometer has a thin air-tight corrugated metal capsule, usually partially exhausted of air, anchored at one side and attached at the other through a system of levers to a pointer moving over a scale. Variations in pressure cause the capsule to move in and out. A number of capsules in series are often used. In accurate instruments compensation for expansion of the parts due to temperature is provided.

(c) The Altimeter used in aircraft is simply an aneroid barometer (see Chapter III, Section 3) with a scale of heights instead of pressure.

There are two different assumptions used in calibrating altimeters.

(i) The Isothermal calibration assumes that the air temperature remains constant at 10° C. (50° F. or 283° A.). Hence readings of altimeters calibrated by this law must be corrected. Computers for this purpose are available, or the approximate rule—"Subtract about $\frac{1}{500}$th of the height indicated for every degree below 50° F." —may be applied. That is, the Error when temperature falls below

50° F. = about $\dfrac{h}{500 \text{ ft.}}$ per 1° F., approximately where h = height;

or $- h \dfrac{\text{diff. of Temp. A}}{\text{Temp. A}}$.

(ii) The I.C.A.N. calibration assumes 288° A. (15° C.) at sea-level, and a uniform Lapse Rate of 6·5° C. per kilometre. The actual law is $\dfrac{p_0}{p} = \left(\dfrac{288}{288 - 6 \cdot 5\,h}\right)^{5.256}$, where h is in kilometres, p_0 is surface pressure, and p is pressure at the height.

The International Standard Atmosphere on which this is based is given in Table I.

TABLE I

DATA UP TO 11,000 METRES FOR THE INTERNATIONAL STANDARD
ATMOSPHERE

Ht. in Km.	Degrees, Absolute	Degrees, Centigrade	Degrees, Fahrenheit	Pressure in Millibars	Density in Grammes per Cubic Metre
0	288·0	15·0	59·0	1,013·2	1,226
1	281·5	8·5	47·3	898·6	1,112
2	275·0	2·0	35·6	794·8	1,007
3	268·5	− 4·5	23·9	700·9	909
4	262·0	− 11·0	12·2	616·2	819
5	255·5	− 17·5	0·5	540·0	736
6	249·0	− 24·0	− 11·2	471·6	660
7	242·5	− 30·5	− 22·9	410·4	590
8	236·0	− 37·0	− 34·6	355·8	525
9	229·5	− 43·5	− 46·3	307·2	466
10	223·0	− 50·0	− 58·0	264·1	413
11	216·5	− 56·5	− 69·7	226·1	364

(See also Appendix IV.)

(d) Barographs are self-recording barometers, giving a continuous record of pressure readings.

(i) The Aneroid Barograph (Aneroidograph) has a series of aneroid cells connected by suitable levers to actuate a pen.

(ii) The Mercury Barograph records photographically on a moving sensitive paper the height of a column of mercury.

13. HYGROMETERS are of two kinds; firstly those which indicate the Relative Humidity, and secondly, those which indicate Absolute Humidity (the actual amount of water per unit volume of air).

(a) The Dew Point Hygrometer finds the absolute humidity by measuring the temperature at which moisture from the air under consideration condenses out on to a polished surface which is artificially cooled. Condensation indicates saturation point. Then the amount of water in saturated air at various temperatures is as follows—

At 32° F.	−	5 grammes of water vapour per cubic metre.					
40° F.	−	7	,,	,,	,,	,,	,,
50° F.	−	9	,,	,,	,,	,,	,,
60° F.	−	13	,,	,,	,,	,,	,,
80° F.	−	25	,,	,,	,,	,,	,,
100° F.	−	45	,,	,,	,,	,,	,,

(b) The Chemical Hygrometer finds the absolute humidity simply by absorbing the moisture from a given volume of the air. The difference in the weight of the chemical before and after is the weight of water vapour extracted.

(c) The Wet and Dry Bulb Hygrometer (Psychrometer) relies on the facts that evaporation causes cooling, and that evaporation is proportional to the Relative Humidity. Two similar thermometers are mounted side by side and therefore under similar conditions. But one is uninfluenced, while the other has a muslin cloth around its bulb which is kept wet by a wick from a small water container. Thus, air temperature and "temperature of evaporation" are found. By entering these two values in tables compiled for the purpose Relative Humidity is found.

(d) The Hair Hygrometer relies on the fact that human hair expands with increase of Relative Humidity. A human hair is held at one end, and connected at the other end to a suitable system of levers which actuate a pointer over a dial. The hair hygrometer has the great advantage that it works above and below freezing-point. It is not very accurate. The Hygrograph which gives a continuous record of humidity is usually a recording hair hygrometer.

14. THE SOUNDING BALLOON provides a means of obtaining data of the upper air. The balloon lifts a very light meteorograph up to a height of about 12 miles where the balloon breaks. The meteorograph then falls to the ground and as it is attached to a very light bamboo frame the impact with the ground does no harm to it, even without a parachute. A label attached requests the finder to forward the meteorograph to the meteorological station concerned.

The Dines's Meteorograph consists of an aneroid capsule coupled to a recording scriber, a recording bi-metallic thermometer, and sometimes a recording hair hygrometer. The scribers scratch their records on a very small silver plate about the size of a postage stamp.

Much very useful information of the upper atmosphere has been obtained by this means.

The more modern form of sounding balloon, called the Radio Sonde, consists of a small wireless which transmits indications of pressure, temperature, and humidity.

15. THE ANEMOMETER is an instrument for measuring wind speed. In all types the "exposure" of the instrument is of great importance. Obviously the wind near the ground is obstructed and retarded by obstacles and by general surface friction. Therefore it is necessary, for reasons of standardization, to have the anemometer in an open position and at a height of 30 feet above the ground.

(a) The Dines's Pressure Tube Anemometer is the type most generally in use. A pressure head is held head into wind by means of a wind vane. A suction tube—drilled with a series of annular holes —is mounted vertically below the pressure head. The pressure tube usually passes down the centre of the suction tube for convenience. This part of the anemometer is mounted about 30 feet high over the building which houses the recording part of the instrument. The recorder consists of an inverted bell float in a nearly air-tight tank partially filled with water. From the top of the float a rod projects through the lid of the tank and carries a pen which is in contact with a moving graph paper. Then the pressure tube is connected to the inside of the float chamber and the suction tube to the tank. An increase in wind speed will obviously cause a pressure in the pressure tube and a suction in the suction tube causing the float to rise, so moving the pen. Now the horizontal cross-sectional area of the float chamber varies from the top downwards in inverse proportion to the square of its height. Thus both pressure and suction which are proportional to the square of the wind speed cause a movement in linear proportion to the speed, allowing a constant scale on the graph paper.

A direction recorder is situated vertically below the wind vane and by suitable gearing records wind direction.

Checking should be carried out thus—

(i) Zero should be checked to the room pressure by opening the three-way cock provided.

(ii) Water level should be checked against the mark provided.

(iii) Calibration can be carried out against a water pressure gauge. Then Inches of Water $= V^2 \times$ Factor of the Instrument.

(b) The Robinson Windmill Anemometer has four semi-spherical cups carried on four metal arms at right angles to one another.

As the speed of rotation is not directly proportional to the speed of the air passing, a factor must be applied.

$$\text{Then the Factor of the Instrument} = \frac{\text{Distance travelled by Wind}}{\text{Distance travelled by Cups}}.$$

This is usually about 3 at 2 m.p.h. to about 2 at 25 m.p.h., etc. A Correction Table is also necessary.

(c) Other anemometers include the pressure-plate type, ordinary air-speed indicators, etc.

16. THE NEPHOSCOPE provides a means of finding the speed and direction of movement of a cloud, and therefore the W.S. and D.

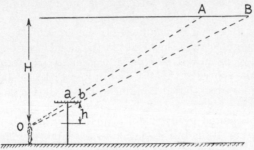

FIG. 146. THE GEOMETRY OF THE NEPHOSCOPE

at the height of the cloud. The principle is the same as that of finding the Track and G/S of an aircraft by a drift sight and timing bead observation. But in this case the observer is stationary and is looking upward instead of downward.

(a) Besson's Comb Nephoscope consists of a horizontal cross-piece fixed to a vertical rod which can be rotated in azimuth by strings controlled by the observer. The cross-piece has a number of small upright spikes at known distances apart, projecting from its upper side. The whole is mounted on a post so that the top of the spikes are at a known height above the eye of the observer. A small plate graduated in degrees is fixed to the vertical rod to indicate the direction of the cross-piece.

The operation is as follows: The observer rotates the nephoscope so that with his eye stationary (a head rest may be used) the clouds move exactly down the line of the spikes. Then the direction of the cross-piece is read on the truly oriented plate provided. The time taken for a cloud to move from one spike to another is measured by stop-watch. Then if the height of the cloud is known or estimated, its speed of movement can be found. In Fig. 146 *a* and *b* are two spikes of a nephoscope, at a height *h* above the observer's eye. The cloud, in appearing to move from *a* to *b*, actually moved from *A* to *B*.

Then from Fig. 146 it can be seen that $\dfrac{ab}{h} = \dfrac{AB}{H}$ where H is the cloud height. And Speed of Cloud movement per hour

$$= \left(\dfrac{AB \text{ in miles} \times 3600}{\text{Time in secs.}}\right) \text{m.p.h.} = \left(\dfrac{ab \times H \times 3600}{h \times \text{time in secs.}}\right) \text{m.p.h.}$$

H, of course, must be in miles, or in nautical miles if the answer is desired in knots. The values of ab and h are usually in feet, but must both be in the same unit.

(b) Fineman's Nephoscope is a portable instrument. The principle is the same, but instead of sighting directly at a cloud, its reflection is used. A horizontal disc of dark glass is mounted on a tripod stand provided with spirit levels and adjusting screws for levelling. A small vertical pointer is mounted on the edge of the glass, with a slider and height scale. The height of the cloud is set on this pointer. Then the eye is moved so that a particular part of the cloud is exactly in the centre of the disc and in line with the sliding pointer. The eye is moved so that it remains in line with this pointer and the reflection of the cloud, and its direction over the glass is noted. The disc can be oriented by means of a small dry compass needle below it. (*Note.*—Variation and deviation to be applied.) The time taken to move out to one of the concentric circles is measured. Then

$$\dfrac{\text{Velocity}}{\text{Ht.}} = \dfrac{\text{Radius moved through} \times 3600}{\text{Ht. of slider} \times \text{time in secs.}}$$

17. PILOT BALLOON. Observations by means of a theodolite are made to determine the wind speed and directions at various heights above ground level. A small rubber balloon filled with hydrogen is usually used.

(a) There are three different methods employed.

(i) The balloon is filled so that it will rise at a given rate. To do this the balloon itself is weighed and then filled with hydrogen until it has a definite lift force. This is measured by means of a filling-balance or by attaching a small weight of the required size as a test lift. The relationship of free lift required for a balloon of given weight for a certain rate of ascent is given by the formula: $V = \dfrac{kL}{(L + W)}$, and where V, the rate of ascent, is in feet per minute, W, the weight, and L, the free lift, are grammes, then k, the constant, is about 275.

Then the balloon is released and its altitude and bearing are measured by a truly set-up and oriented theodolite at intervals of one minute (by stop-watch) from the time of release. Now in Fig. 147 it can be seen that the horizontal distance d of the balloon B

from the observer $O = h$ Cot $BOA = H$ Cot Altitude, where $H =$ known rate of ascent multiplied by the time.

Then, in Fig. 147, OA is the horizontal distance of the balloon from the observer — OC is its "easting" or distance east, and OD is its "northing" or distance north (in this case, a minus quantity). OC and OD are found by simple trigonometry, having measured the direction of OA by theodolite.

Now if the distance east and the distance north are found for the

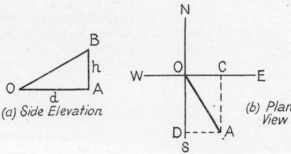

(a) Side Elevation (b) Plan View

FIG. 147. PILOT BALLOON OBSERVATION

balloon at various heights, then the average wind between any two adjoining heights can be found by simple trigonometry from the change in distance east and the change in distance north.

The method is simple and requires one theodolite and observer only. But inaccuracy results if the rate of ascent is not as assumed.

(ii) The "Tail" method is more accurate and still requires only one observer. In this the actual height is found by observing on a graticule in the telescope of the theodolite the angle subtended by a tail of known length attached to the balloon. The tail consists of cotton with a coloured paper at its lower end. A small paper half-way down the cotton may also be attached. The altitude (or angle of elevation) and the bearing are taken at one minute intervals as before, together with the graticule reading.

In Fig. 148, in the triangle ABC, $AC = AB$ Sin $ABC = l$ Sin $(90° -$ Altitude$) = l$ Cos a, where l is the length of the tail and a is the altitude.

Then if g is the graticule reading,

$$AO = AC \text{ Cosec } g = l \text{ Cos } a \text{ Cosec } g$$

and $h = AO \text{ Sin } a = l \text{ Cos } a \text{ Cosec } g \text{ Sin } a.$

The remainder of the method is as in (i). Releasing a balloon with a tail is helped by winding the cotton on a free roller. The balloon is let go and the cotton allowed to unwind. In this method of observation a "swinging" tail sometimes causes errors.

(iii) Two theodolites a known distance apart may be used to take simultaneous observations of a balloon. This method is, of course, the most accurate, but is more cumbersome.

(*Note.*—At night pilot balloon observations may be taken by attaching a very light paper lantern with a candle in it to an ordinary balloon.)

(b) To facilitate the calculations of finding wind from pilot balloon observations a special very useful slide rule has been produced, called the Pilot Balloon Slide Rule. The whole problem can be worked out quickly and accurately on this rule.

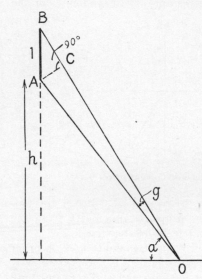

FIG. 148. PILOT BALLOON WITH TAIL

SECTION 3

WEATHER MAPS

Note.—The syllabus for First-class Navigators requires the navigator to have not only a good theoretical knowledge of meteorology but also thorough practical ability in meteorological observations and work generally. Amongst other things the navigator must be able to produce in reasonable time from coded messages complete synoptic weather charts, and forecasts therefrom. To do this requires considerable practice. This syllabus ensures a thorough understanding and appreciation of the processes of forecasting and observing.

18. SYNOPTIC CHARTS, SYMBOLS, AND CODE MESSAGES.

(a) One of the most successful and by far the most practised methods of forecasting the weather is by the use of synoptic charts or weather maps. On a synoptic chart the existing weather conditions at a large number of observing stations at a particular time are plotted together with, in some cases, indications of changes.

(b) In order to plot a very large amount of data for each station over a reasonably large area and at the same time to keep the chart reasonably small it is obviously necessary to have a code of symbols. As it is impracticable to memorize all these symbols the best procedure is to make out a card showing all the symbols against their meanings and/or code numbers (see Table II). Then this card is kept in front of the plotter when making the chart. The positions of the various symbols in relation to the position of the station of observation are shown in Fig. 151.*

(c) In order to collect data from outstations and to broadcast it from a central office a good signal organization is necessary and

Scheme of Arrangement of Information around the Position of the Station

Station Model. The circle denotes the position of the station. *In the Station Model the letters have the following customary meanings :*

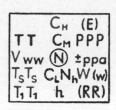

Station Model.

PPP = Pressure. pp = Tendency.
TT = Temperature. T_1T_1 = Sea Temperature.
ww = Present Weather. W = Past Weather.
a = Characteristic. E = State of Ground.
$C_LC_MC_H$ = Form of Low, Medium and High Cloud.
T_ST_S = Dew Point Temperature.
N = Total Amount of Cloud. V = Visibility.
N_h = Amount of Low Cloud. RR = Rainfall.
h = Height of Low Cloud.

Also (w) = That part of ww which refers to the last hour but not to the time of observation.
U = Humidity is alternative to T_ST_S.

Where lack of space necessitates a modification of the Station Model a deformation of it without permutation of the places allotted to the individual elements, is permissible.

If only one colour is used it should be black. If two colours, black and red, are used then red should be used for one or more of the following :—

(1) For C_H (2) For W (Past Weather)   (3) For TT, T_ST_S (4) For V
(5) For pp *when pp is negative.*

Red should *not* be used for PPP, ww, C_M, C_L, T_1T_1, N_h, h.

FIG. 149. PLOTTING ELEMENTS OF THE WEATHER AT A STATION

suitable codes must be employed. A Meteorological Office (British Air Ministry) publication called "Wireless Weather Messages" or more usually "MO 252" gives details of the organization, times and types of messages, names, etc., of stations and codes used for reports in Great Britain, Gibraltar, Malta, Middle East, and 'Iraq. The navigator should be in possession of this publication. MO 2459 gives details of the codes and plotting symbols (Price 1s.

* This illustration, and Tables II and III which appear on pp. 320 and 321, are reproduced from *Instructions for the Preparation of Weather Maps with Tables of the Specifications and Symbols* (Air Ministry Meteorological Office Form 2459) by kind permission of the Controller of H.M. Stationery Office.

TABLE II

Symbols for Present Weather (ww)

The vertical stroke | means "has increased" if placed before a symbol, and "has decreased" if placed after a symbol.

The sign () means "within sight of the station".

The sign] means that the phenomenon has been observed within the last hour but is not occurring at the time of observation.

In 21, 41, 91, etc., the bracket sign may be omitted where the time of occurrence is clear from the position of the symbol on the chart (see note, p. 7, para. 1).

In 42 the space between the middle and bottom lines should be black from the left for approximately one half of the whole length.

In 43, etc., the opening in the horizontal stroke should be about one-third of the length, i.e. equal to each of the short strokes,

In 30, 40, etc., the circle may be omitted if desired.

In 23, 70, 71 . . . , 80, 90, etc., the horizontal stroke is to be clearly shorter than the horizontal stroke in 41, etc.

In 10, 20, 80, 93, 95, 97 use either ● or ✳ unless in doubt.

In 25, 80, etc., the angle at the lower point of the shower symbol must be smaller than the other two angles, i e. it must be appreciably less than 60°.

In 27, 88, 89, 94, 96, 99 the angles of the hail symbol are 60°; the angles in 78 are also 60°.

In ww = 66 or 76 the elementary signs ● or ✳ shall be arranged in form of a rhomb, the vertical diagonal of which is clearly longer than the horizontal one.

As a rule the symbols for ww = 00–03 will be used only when the cloud amount N_h is not available.

Symbols in series horizontally denote "sequence".
Symbols in series vertically denote "Co-existence".

TABLE II (*contd.*)—

Symbols for Cloud, Barometer Tendency, Sea and Swell. Past Weather and State of Ground.

	N	C_L	C_M	C_H	C	a	K	A	W
0								0	
1								12	
2								24	
3								50	
4								>60	
5								12	
6								24	
7								50	
8								>60	
9									

at H.M.S.O.) For details of foreign meteorological organizations and the international interchange of weather messages which is carried out over practically the whole of the northern hemisphere, reference must be made to "Les Messages Synoptiques du Temps," printed unfortunately in French only, and published in five parts by the Secretariat de L'Organisation Météorologique Internationale, De Bilt, Holland.

(d) Now, to make a synoptic chart, the messages which have been collected by Air Ministry for a large number of stations at a particular time and broadcast, are received by wireless. These are decoded and plotted against their respective stations on the chart. Then, lines joining places of equal barometric pressure (in each case reduced to sea-level and corrected to Lat. 45° and for temperate, etc.) are drawn on the map. These lines are called Isobars, and are usually drawn at one or two millibar intervals. They show at a glance the pressure distributions, and as particular forms of pressure distribution are usually associated with particular weather, they constitute one of the greatest aids in forecasting from a weather map. Of course, the other factors, such as movement of the pressure system, whether it is developing or decaying, the clouds, rain, etc., the past weather, the winds, the temperatures, etc., all indicate something and must be taken into account.

19. TYPES OF PRESSURE DISTRIBUTION. There are various forms of distribution. Eight types are given hereafter together with remarks concerning the weather usually associated with each. The first four given are Low pressure types, the next three are High pressure types, and the last cannot be classified. Pressure systems generally move eastwards, low pressure areas moving much more than high pressure areas, but the direction and speed of movement is very variable and must be carefully watched. Movement of a system on a chart can be deduced from the barometric changes, and/or by reference to a previous but very recent chart. The descriptions which follow refer to the northern hemisphere, and it must be remembered that reciprocal conditions for a similar pressure distribution will occur in the southern hemisphere. Thus winds blow around the other way, etc. The figures given for the northern hemisphere will apply for the southern hemisphere if held upside-down in front of a mirror.

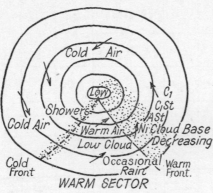

FIG. 150. A CYCLONE OR DEPRESSION

(a) The Cyclone or Depression (or "Low") is an area with a Low pressure centre, as illustrated in Fig. 150, usually of approximately the form shown. The extent of a Low varies from about 50 miles diameter in tropical cyclones, to as much as 2000 miles in large mild temperate depressions. Generally, low pressure systems are much more virile than high pressure systems, and are more active in the Tropics than in temperate zones. But their intensities and speeds of movement (average about 25 m.p.h.) vary very much. The theory of the cause or causes of low pressure systems is not by any means certain.

(i) The more modern theory is that a stream of polar air moving

towards the Equator is deflected by Geostrophic deflection so that in
the northern hemisphere it is blowing from the NE. Also a stream
of hot equatorial air from the south is deflected so that it flows from
the SW. (in northern hemisphere). Thus two streams of air blowing
in opposite directions are, of course, subject to frictional forces at the
boundary or Front. The simplest way of looking at it is that this
frictional force between the two causes an eddy motion of large

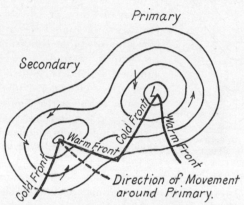

FIG. 151. A SECONDARY DEPRESSION IN THE
NORTHERN HEMISPHERE

scale, and sometimes considerable intensity. (*Note.*—A Front is
the boundary between two different streams of air. See para. 20.)

(ii) The older theory is that an area of surface air becomes heated
and rises, so leaving an area of low pressure. The air which therefore tends to rush in from the sides is deflected by Geostrophic
deflection to form the rotation wind of a cyclone.

It is probable that the first and generally accepted theory gives
the cause of the depressions of temperate zones, but it seems equally
probable that the second theory is applicable to the cyclones of the
Tropics.

(b) A Secondary Depression (see Fig. 151) is a smaller depression
which develops within the area of a primary depression. Usually it
appears first as a bulging of the isobars of the primary, and then
gradually takes the circular form of a separate depression. Usually
a secondary tends to move around its primary, clockwise in the
northern and anti-clockwise in the southern hemisphere. It often
develops rapidly while its primary decays.

(c) A V-shaped Depression (see Fig. 152) is a deep trough of low
pressure usually extending outwards from a depression. It is
really the highly-developed cold front of a low pressure system.

Usually it causes a very severe and sudden squall accompanied by heavy rain, called a Line Squall because of a long line of dark turbulent cloud along the line of the V travelling broadside on.   As the line squall passes, the wind veers suddenly from about S. or SW. to NW. or N. (in northern hemisphere) and the temperature falls.

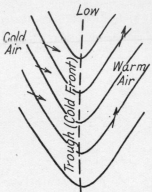

FIG. 152.   A V-SHAPED DEPRESSION (TROUGH)

(d) A Col (see Fig. 153) is the extension of a low pressure ridge between two areas of high pressure. It usually indicates unstable conditions—with fog in winter, thundery conditions in summer, and fairly sudden changes.

(e) An Anticyclone (or "High") is an area with a High pressure centre. Anticyclones usually cover areas much larger than depressions, move more slowly, and are generally of a quiet and settled nature.   It will be noticed (see Fig. 154) that the surface winds blow slightly outwards across the isobars.   In winter time anticyclonic areas are liable to radiation fog—due to the clear skies and lack of winds of any appreciable

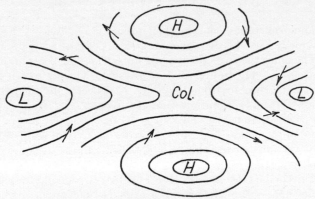

FIG. 153.   A COL

strength.   Sometimes a sheet of dull cloud covers the sky in an anticyclone, resulting in "Anticyclonic Gloom."

(f) An Anticyclonic Wedge is a V-shaped High pressure "wedge" extending from a High pressure area, between two Lows. (See Fig. 155.)   Usually a "wedge" gives a period of fine weather between the rainy unsettled conditions of two depressions.

(g) An Anticyclonic Ridge (see Fig. 156) is a line of high pressure running from one High to another between two Low pressure areas. It is similar in form to a Col, but has its High pressure areas on each

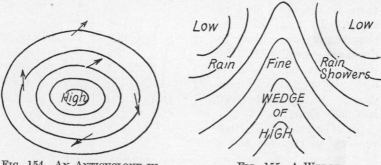

FIG. 154. AN ANTICYCLONE IN THE NORTHERN HEMISPHERE

FIG. 155. A WEDGE

side closer together and the centre strip is of predominantly "High" characteristics. Like the "wedge" it usually gives a period of fair

FIG. 156. A RIDGE

weather but the influence of the following depression soon becomes effective.

(h) Straight Isobars occur when the nearest centre of High or Low pressure is a long way away and the curvature of the isobars is practically nil. If there is a considerable rate of change of pressure it indicates that there is a different pressure system approaching and that its effect will soon be felt. But if there is no indication of this, then the following will probably apply—

(i) If there is Low pressure to the east and High to the west, as in Fig. 157, cold and sometimes squally winds result. In winter there is sometimes sleet or snow. In the summer thunderstorms are likely to develop—generally in the early afternoon, which is also the period of most clouds. At night the sky is usually clear.

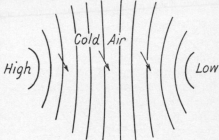

FIG. 157. STRAIGHT ISOBARS

(ii) If there is a High pressure to the east and a Low pressure to the west, as in Fig. 158, variable conditions usually result. The wind is generally warm. If it has blown over the sea and has picked up moisture, sea fogs or high ground fogs may occur when it reaches cold sea, or hills or high coast respectively.

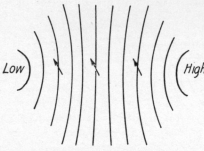

FIG. 158. STRAIGHT ISOBARS

20. As already mentioned, a **Front** is the boundary between two different streams of air, differing in characteristics such as temperature, humidity and density, and sometimes in direction of movement. These differences, particularly temperature difference, constitute a source of great potential energy sufficient to cause the development of active weather phenomena.

(a) Frontal Zones of a general nature exist on the Earth's surface. Of them the one most distinct and of most practical importance is the *polar frontal zone* which is the boundary between the tropical air and polar air. The frictional forces between these two air streams (the polar stream moving from the west while the tropical stream is easterly) cause large scale eddy motions which, together with the temperature differences between the streams, form what we know as depressions. The best example of this is in the southern hemisphere where, uninfluenced by land masses, the south polar frontal zone causes the depressions which move around the Earth in the latitude of the Roaring Forties. In the northern hemisphere the polar frontal zone is well marked across the Atlantic from the United States towards Norway, and in a similar latitude band across the Pacific.

(b) Fronts which are far smaller but are nevertheless well-defined occur within air systems. Of these the fronts in a depression are the most important. As can be seen in Fig. 150 there is usually a sector of warm air on the equatorial side of a depression, while the remainder of the air is cold. The boundary between the leading edge of the warm sector and the cold air ahead of it is called the Warm Front, and between its trailing edge and the cold air cutting in behind, it is called the Cold Front.

(i) At the warm front the warm lighter air tends to rise and so climb over the cold heavier air ahead of it. Thus the warm front slopes forwards. At the high, leading part of the front cirrus and cirro-stratus clouds form. Behind them come alto-stratus, lower and becoming denser, finally merging into the increasing nimbus of the lower part of the front where continuous rain falls. The intensity of this rain depends on the strength of the depression. It extends usually in a wide band along the front, to a position on the polar side of the centre of the depression. (See Fig. 150.) The wind behind a warm front veers in relation to the wind ahead of it in the northern hemisphere, and backs in the southern hemisphere.

(ii) At the cold front the warm lighter air is undercut by the cold heavier air coming in behind it, so that the boundary surface slopes backwards. But the cloud of the cold front slopes forward owing to the fact that, as the warm air is forced upwards to form the cloud, it is carried forward by the oncoming cold air which generally increases its speed with height. The cloud of cold front is usually alto-cumulus in the upper leading part, and nimbus on the front itself. It is far less extensive than the clouds of the warm front. The rainfall of the cold front is usually a fairly narrow band along the front and a little ahead of it. The wind veers when passing across the front from the warm to the cold sector in the northern hemisphere (and backs in the southern hemisphere). This change is often quite sudden and very considerable. In a sharply defined cold front where the cold undercutting air is forcing the warm air up at a big ascentional velocity the black turbulent line of cloud which is characteristic of the Line Squall is formed. In these conditions the passage of the front is marked by squally winds and a sudden veering of the wind.

(iii) An Occluded Front or Occlusion occurs when in an advanced stage of the development of a depression the warm air is finally undercut completely by cold air so that there is no front at the surface. In such a case the warm sector still exists but does not extend down to the Earth's surface. The weather of an occluded front is similar to a warm or a cold front, depending on whether the undercutting of the cold air has been strongest from the front of the warm front or from the rear of the cold front.

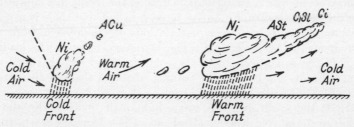

FIG. 159. SECTION ACROSS THE WARM SECTOR OF A DEPRESSION

21. AIR MASSES. (a) History of an Air Mass. The atmosphere as a whole appears to have a tendency to develop more or less distinct masses of air within itself, each having characteristics and properties differing from those of neighbouring masses. An enormous amount of information for use in forecasting can be derived from a study of the characteristics (particularly temperature and humidity) of the air mass or masses of which the weather system under consideration consists. While many of these characteristics prevailing at a particular moment can be observed and reported, there is also much to be learnt from a more prolonged study of the air masses.

In order to deduce the properties which characterize an air mass it is necessary to consider three main points—

(i) The *Source* where it has picked up its fundamental properties. Obviously the mass will not assimilate any appreciable intensity of a property from its source unless it remains stationary or moves but slowly over that source. Therefore the air mass in an anticyclone or other high pressure type is more likely to assume the properties attributable to the surface at its source. The humidity gained at the source will depend on whether it is land which gives off no moisture or sea which gives off considerable moisture. The temperature picked up at the source depends on the temperature of the surface and its radiation characteristics.

(ii) The *Path* over which it travels. Just as the source gives particular fundamental properties of humidity and temperature to a mass, so also in the same way the influence of the path over which it travels will be felt by it. Obviously, the slower the speed, the greater is the influence of the path.

(iii) The *Age* of the mass. The source and path which make and modify respectively the properties of an air mass are surface influences. Obviously, when an air mass is young its properties are confined to a comparatively shallow layer near the surface which, with time, will gradually extend upwards due to convective mixing of the air, etc. Therefore, the age of the mass must be borne in mind, particularly as an indication of the vertical extent of the mass.

(b) Types of Air Mass. In naming air masses three main points are usually expressed. These are the source, and the relative temperature and the moistness or aridity of its source and path, of which the latter two are the more important.

(i) There are two main types of sources—

The subtropical anticyclones and the doldrums which generate *Tropical air masses;* and

The high latitude anticyclones and the polar caps which generate *Polar air masses.*

(ii) Classification according to relative temperature divides air masses into two—

Cold air masses which are colder than the surface over which they pass; and

Warm air masses which are warmer than the surface over which they pass.

(iii) The amount of moisture present entails the necessity for a further division—

Maritime air masses which have derived considerable moisture from contact with the sea; and

Continental air masses which are comparatively dry due to contact with the comparative aridity of large land masses.

Thus, for example, if an air mass had its source in high latitudes over the North Atlantic in winter and then drifted over the colder land of northern Europe it would be described as a "warm mass of maritime polar air."

(c) Properties of Air Masses. (i) Cold Masses usually bring weather of a convective nature. When a cold mass forms it is cooled from below which forms a stratified layer of cold air on the surface—a stable state, as cold air is heavy. When this cold layer then travels over a warmer surface it is warmed from below and the warm rising causes convective currents. If the air travels over sea it will pick up considerable moisture which, when raised by convection, will condense out to form clouds. Thus, Maritime Cold Masses are usually characterized by cumulus and cumulo-nimbus clouds, abrupt showers, increasing humidity and temperature, etc.

A Continental Cold Mass is also a convective type, but having a much smaller moisture content the cloudiness is much less; there is no increase in humidity, and the temperature increase only takes place during hours of sunlight.

(ii) Warm Masses usually bring stability in the lower layers of the atmosphere. When a warm mass derives its heat a fairly deep layer of warm air is formed (due to convection). When this moves over a surface which is colder than itself the lower layer only becomes cooled (by contact), and as this cooler heavier air has no tendency to rise it forms a stable layer with a temperature inversion above. If it is a maritime warm mass with an appreciable moisture content fog may form, or if wind causes surface turbulence stratus cloud will result with possible drizzle. The relative humidity will be high and visibility generally poor. A continental warm mass similarly has its stable, stratified, cool, lower layer but the lack of moisture will obviate the tendency towards fog, stratus and poor visibility.

There are multitudinous complications in types and properties of air masses far beyond the scope of this book. Study of the subject even to a moderate degree is proportionately worth while.

22. D/F OF THUNDERSTORMS. A valuable aid to meteorologists in locating storm centres and following their movements has recently been developed by Watson Watt at Slough and carried on in a practical way in Australia and South Africa, to which countries it has obvious value.

Practically all atmospherics originate from discharges in the nature of lightning which occur in storm areas. By fixing the position of the discharges the storm area itself is located. In ordinary D/F the direction of an incoming wave is found by swinging a loop or rotating a search coil in a goniometer. This method is completely impossible for use on atmospherics owing to the fact that a single impulse only emanates from a flash of lightning, so that there is no time to turn a loop or coil. The method used consists of two ordinary directional loops (N.-S. and E.-W.) connected through matched amplifiers to deflecting elements (also 90° apart) in a Cathode Ray Oscillograph. An incoming impulse from an atmospheric discharge is picked up by the coils according to their normal directional properties and its final effect on the cathode ray is to deflect the electron bombardment so that the spot of light which is usually in the centre of the fluorescent screen is deflected away from the centre in a particular direction. This is read off a suitably graduated scale of angles.

Two stations or more can then co-ordinate the bearing obtained to plot the actual positions of disturbances. In order to do so it is necessary to identify the disturbances, and this is done by using a land-line between stations to observe for synchronism of impulses received.

The scheme is by no means perfect as yet, but it appears to be a valuable aid well worthy of considerable attention, particularly in countries where thunderstorms are prevalent.

APPENDIX I

INTERNATIONAL LEGISLATION

IT is necessary for a navigator to have a good understanding of the legal position, both international and national, applying to the operation of aircraft. A brief outline of the Conventions, Acts, Orders, and Rules applying to aviation is given below. All are obtainable from H.M. Stationery Office, with the exception of the International Air Convention which is obtainable from Air Ministry, London. A detailed study of each is, of course, necessary.

1. "The **Convention relating to the Regulation of Aerial Navigation** dated 13th October, 1919," usually referred to briefly as the International Air Convention, is an international agreement by which the following are provided—

(i) General principles of the sovereignty of the air, but providing for the grant of freedom of passage over territories (excepting prohibited areas), are laid down.

(ii) Special agreements between Contracting States with Non-contracting States are permitted, provided that there is no infringement of the Convention.

(iii) Provisions for airworthiness, competency, and licences are laid down.

(iv) Rules for flying over foreign territory are made.

(v) Carriage of arms, etc., prohibited.

(vi) State aircraft are defined.

(vii) The International Committee of Air Navigation (I.C.A.N.) is provided for and representation and its duties laid down.

(viii) The co-ordination and co-operation of States in meteorology, maps, wireless, etc., are agreed upon—and provisions for Customs arrangements.

(ix) Arrangements for arbitration in case of disagreement between two States in connexion with the Convention are made.

Then a number of Annexes give details of registration, markings, log-books, C.s of A., lights, signals, rules, licensing, medical requirements, maps, meteorological arrangements, customs, etc.

The International Air Convention while enforcing the inconvenient restrictions, etc., and causing expense and trouble for the Contracting State, has at the same time done enormous good in the development of aviation. Unfortunately States not party to the Convention have reaped benefit from it without suffering its apparent disadvantages.

2. The **Air Navigation Act, 1920,** makes the International Air

Convention legally effective in Great Britain and applies its provisions to both international and internal flying. It authorizes Orders in Council to be made by His Majesty to cover various matters, and also Directions to be made by the Secretary of State for Air to cover details.

It embraces many subjects not laid down by the Convention.

3. The **Air Navigation (Consolidation) Order,** 1923, as amended by various Orders, provides regulations under the Air Navigation Act, 1920.

4. The **Air Navigation Order** relating to **Wreck and Salvage** of aircraft provides under the Act, 1920, for the application of Section 557 of the Merchant Shipping Act, 1894—with certain provisions.

5. The **Air Navigation (Investigation of Accidents) Regulations,** and various Air Navigation Directions giving detailed rules, etc., are made by the Secretary of State for Air under the Act, 1920.

6. The **Convention** for the unification of certain rules relating to **International Carriage by Air,** 12th October, 1929, lays down arrangements for the carriage of passengers, luggage, freight, etc., and defines the liabilities of the carrier.

7. The **Carriage by Air Act, 1932,** gives effect to the above Convention in Great Britain and applies its rules. It also provides for Orders in Council to be made for any extensions or modifications necessary.

8. The **International Sanitary Convention for Aerial Navigation,** 1933, is an agreement laying down precautions and regulations to prevent the spreading of disease germs by carrying them by aircraft from infected parts, etc.

APPENDIX II

CIVIL AIRCRAFT NAVIGATORS' LICENCES—FIRST CLASS

GENERAL INFORMATION AND CONDITIONS OF EXAMINATION

1. Examinations for First Class Navigators' Licences are normally held in London, and occupy five days, but special arrangements for examinations at overseas centres are also made in accordance with the programme notified annually in Notices to Airmen. Normally only the written papers may be taken abroad, and the oral examination must be taken at the London centre at a later date, which must be within twelve months of taking the written papers.

2. Applications to sit for the First Class Examination will only be considered in the case of candidates who have held a Second Class Licence for at least six months.

3. Formal application for a licence must be made on C.A. Form 2 C (1) and together with the prescribed fees of five guineas for the Technical examination, one guinea for the Medical examination, if required (see application form), and five shillings for the Licence, must have been received by the Under Secretary of State, Air Ministry (CH3), Adastral House, Kingsway, London, W.C.2, on or before the closing date of entry for each examination. Full details are contained in the Notice to Airmen announcing the programme of examinations.

4. Candidates should give with their formal application full details of any qualifications and experience they already possess.

5. Before a First Class Licence can be issued, candidates will be required—

(a) to have been the holder of a Second Class Aircraft Navigators' Licence for a period of not less than one year;

(b) to pass or be exempted from the Technical examination (see paras. 6, 10 and 11);

(c) to produce proof of having the requisite air and navigational experience (see paras. 7 and 8);

(d) to pass the prescribed medical examination.

6. The Technical Examination comprises oral and practical tests as well as written papers in the subjects specified below, except that there is no written paper for Signalling.

	Subject	Total marks allotted
1.	International and United Kingdom Air Legislation .	200
2.	Form of the Earth; Maps and Charts, Tides . .	400
3.	Meteorology	400
4.	Dead Reckoning and Radio Direction Finding Navigation	400
5.	Earth's Magnetism and Compasses	400
6.	Astronomical Navigation	500
7.	Signalling	Pass or Fail
		2300

The syllabus for these subjects is set out fully hereafter.

In order to obtain a pass candidates will be required to gain not less than 90 per cent of the possible marks for Signalling, not less than 60 per cent of the marks for any one other subject, and not less than 70 per cent *of the total marks for all subjects*, excluding Signalling.

7. Air Experience. Candidates will be required to produce proof, in the form of log books or other equivalent evidence, of having had at least four years' air experience, and at least 600 hours' air experience, of which not less than 100 hours must include navigational experience and of which not less than 15 hours shall have been obtained in connection with cross country flights made between two hours after sunset and two hours before sunrise.

Note.—By "Air Experience" is meant experience as pilot or navigator.

8. Navigational Experience must have included the taking of at least nine astronomical observations, two by day and seven by night, the details of which are as follows—

(a) *By Day.* Two observations of the Sun.

(b) *By Night.* (i) Two observations.

(ii) An estimated position obtained from two observations giving a running fix, the time of run being at least one hour. The resulting position lines should give a "cut" of at least 60°.

(iii) A fix from three simultaneous or nearly simultaneous observations of different bodies.

Note.—(1) Of the four observations required under (a) and (b) (i) above, one should be chosen to check the track of the aircraft, and one to check the ground speed of the aircraft.

(2) At least one of the sights specified in (b) (i)–(iii) should be an observation of the Moon.

(3) The results of all astronomical observations should be plotted on squared paper or suitable forms, and applied to the navigation of the aircraft.

(4) The flights during which astronomical observations were taken should be clearly marked in the Pilot's Log Book.

9. Astronomical sight books or forms should be produced together with the Pilot's Log Book in support of the astronomical air navigational experience, and the sights specified in Para. 8 should be certified by some responsible authority as having been taken *and worked out* in the air.

10. Exemption. Applications for exemption from any part of the First Class examination, except on the basis set out in paragraph 11 below, will not under any circumstances be considered.

11. Royal Air Force personnel who have obtained a satisfactory pass in the Specialist Navigation Course, and who have kept in close touch with practical navigational duties, may apply for exemption from all or any of the subjects 2–6 set out in paragraph 6 above. Each application will be treated on its merits, but a detailed knowledge of the civil radio and D.F. organization and procedure will be checked by a supplementary examination.

To obtain a pass for the purpose of this paragraph, candidates must in any case have gained at the R.A.F. passing-out examination not less than 60 per cent of the total marks allotted for *any one subject* or group of subjects, and not less than 70 per cent of the marks allotted *for all subjects*.

12. Candidates are required to provide themselves with all drawing and calculating instruments. All standard tables are provided at the examination, but candidates may, subject to the permission of the presiding officer in each case, bring any alternative or auxiliary tables or forms with which they may be familiar into the examination room. (See Appendix III, para. 6 (*h*).)

(APPENDIX III)

AIRCRAFT NAVIGATORS' LICENCES—FIRST CLASS

SYLLABUS FOR THE TECHNICAL EXAMINATION

1. International and United Kingdom Air Legislation. As set out in Appendix I, for the Second Class syllabus, but a more detailed knowledge and a broader outlook on the object of such Regulations will be expected. The latest list of Air Navigation Regulations in force, given periodically in Notices to Airmen, should be consulted.

2. (*a*) **Form of the Earth.** As for the Second Class syllabus, with the addition of Spherical Trigonometry and with particular reference to : The geometry of the sphere ; properties of spherical triangles ; the special cases of spherical triangles, e.g. polar triangles, right angled and right sided and oblique angled spherical triangles ; the solution of spherical triangles by the sine, cosine, natural haversine, log haversine and cosecant formulae ; Napier's Analogies and

Napier's Rules; the Sailings—parallel, mercatorial, Great circle and composite.

(b) **Maps and Charts.** As for the Second Class syllabus, with the addition of—

(i) The principles of construction and the properties of tho following projections—

Cassini, Conical Orthomorphic with two Standard Parallels (Lambert's second), Simple Conic, Conic with two standard parallels, Bonne's, Polyconic, International Modified Polyconic, Mercator, Gnomonic, Stereographic, Orthographic, Zenithal Equidistant (Polar case).

(ii) The actual construction of the graticule, on any given scale, of any of the following projections—

Simple conic, Conic with two standard parallels, Simple polyconic, Mercator, Polar Gnomonic and Polar Stereographic.

(c) **Tides.** Elementary theory of tide generating forces, the combination of lunar and solar tidal waves; terrestrial effects in the formation of tide; general theory of the harmonic constants.

Arrangement and method of use of Admiralty Tide Tables. Conventional signs for tidal streams as employed on Admiralty charts, and tidal information available on Admiralty charts and plans.

Definitions.—Terms employed in the study of the Theory of Tides, and employed in the Admiralty Tide Tables and similar publications. (Examples: Age of tide; lunitidal intervals; stand of the tide; single day tide; H.W.F. & C.; M.L.W.S.; M.T.L.; Chart datum, bore; flood stream; etc., etc.) Tidal Prediction with the aid of tables, including the harmonic method.

3. Meteorology. As for the revised Second Class syllabus, with the following additions—

Elementary inferences from observations of temperature, pressure and humidity in the upper atmosphere; importance and calculation of air-density; general conditions in the stratosphere.

Average conditions (including upper wind) and special weather phenomena affecting the weather conditions over the world (official reference books will be supplied).

Meteorological organization over the world (reference books will be provided in the examination).

Analysis of synoptic charts; in particular, recognition of different air-masses, fixing the positions of fronts, methods of estimating the probable development and movement of pressure systems and fronts.

Candidates will be required

(1) To plot on a partially completed chart a number of coded weather reports—in accordance with current symbolic methods;

(2) To insert isobars and enter fronts on this chart. (A completed chart for the preceding standard hour of observation will be provided.)

(3) To interpret, either orally or in writing, the figures and symbols used in plotting and the significance of the chart with particular reference to the fronts.

4. (a) **Navigation by Dead Reckoning.**
   (b) **Navigation by Radio Direction Finding.**

As for the Second Class syllabus, but more difficult problems will be set and more importance will be attached to speed and accuracy.

5. **Earth's Magnetism, Compasses.** As for the Second Class syllabus, but candidates will be expected to display a more advanced knowledge, e.g. calculation of the deviation from the approximate coefficients for any course, calculation of changes in the deviation due to change of magnetic latitude, the general principles of design of aircraft compasses. Coefficients Lambda and Mu, but the actual computation of the latter coefficient is not required.

6. **Astronomical Navigation.** (a) *The Celestial Sphere.* The solar system, movements of the earth, moon and planets.

The stars, constellation (designation of bright stars, magnitudes of stars). Recognition of stars, and planets.

Circles of reference in the celestial sphere. Position of heavenly bodies.

Representations of the celestial sphere on various planes, e.g. the plane of the observer's meridian, the plane of the observer's celestial horizon.

(b) *Time.* Apparent annual motion of the sun.

Apparent daily motion of the heavenly bodies.

Apparent and mean solar days, Hour angles of true and mean sun. Equation of Time, Civil Time, Greenwich Mean Time, change of time with longitude, Zone Time, Standard Time, Greenwich date. Greenwich Hour Angle. Greenwich Hour Angle of the first point of Aries.

Sidereal day and sidereal time. Sidereal Hour Angle. Right ascension of the mean sun. Hour angle of a heavenly body. Calculations of times and of rising, setting and of transit.

(c) *Air Almanac.* Arrangement and use. *Note:* Candidates who prefer to use the Nautical Almanac will not be penalized.

(d) *Azimuth Tables.* Arrangement and use.

(e) *Position Line derived from observation of a heavenly body.*

Calculation of the zenith distance at the estimated position. Correction of observed altitude. True zenith distance. Geographical Position of a heavenly body. Circle of Position. Position Line.

Mark St. Hilaire (intercept) method of obtaining a position line. The value of a single position line.

(*f*) *Position by Astronomical Position Lines.* Positions from two or more observations, transferring position lines; various causes and magnitudes of errors in position lines and fixes.

(*g*) *Special cases of the astronomical position line.* Altitudes of Polaris; the relationship between observations of bodies on or near the meridian, and on or near the prime vertical, and the determination of latitude and longitude respectively; the selection of celestial bodies suitable for checking (1) the track and (2) the ground speed.

(*h*) *Reduction of Sights by Special Tables, Graphical Methods and Instruments.* In Part I of the written paper candidates will, in at least one question, be expected to compute the calculated zenith distance using the natural haversine formula, and to determine the azimuth from azimuth tables. Candidates are expected to be familiar with the general principles governing the application of "Napier's Rules for Circular Parts" to the spherical triangle as employed in the majority of the present-day abbreviated methods for the determination of Zenith Distance or Altitude.

Special tables (Weems's Line of Position Book, Dreisonstock's Tables, $a.\beta.\gamma$. Tables, Aquino's Tables, Gingrich's Tables, etc.), graphical methods (e.g. Weems's Star Curves, Nomograms) and Calculating Instruments (e.g. the Position Line Slide Rule (Bygrave)) may, however, if candidates so desire, be employed for the purpose of answering any of the remaining questions of Part I, or for the whole of Part II.

Candidates must nevertheless obtain the permission of the presiding officer before bringing any private tables, diagrams or star curves into the examination room unless previous general instructions have been given allowing any type of tables, forms or instruments to be used.

(*i*) *Instruments.* The Marine Sextant, Bubble Sextant. Care and use of the sextant; index error determination.

The Chronometer and Chronometer Watch, care and use; rate; time signals.

Care and use of Deck Watches, Stop Watches, Second-setting Watches.

Errors and limits of accuracy of the above instruments in aircraft; conditions affecting accuracy.

(*j*) *Definitions.* Terms employed in the Theory and Practice of

Astronomical Navigation. (Examples: Celestial Sphere; Equinoctial; Zenith Distance; First Point of Aries; Azimuth; Amplitude; Hour Angle; Superior Transit; Mean Time; Apparent Time; Sidereal Time; Equation of Time; Obliquity of Ecliptic; etc., etc.)

7. Signalling. As for the Second Class syllabus.

8. General Note. Candidates for the First Class Examination will be expected to display a more advanced knowledge than is required for the Second Class Examination of the theory of the subjects as set out above, in so far as the syllabus is common to both examinations, but nevertheless practical work will carry weight in the examination.

Neatness, speed and accuracy will be expected, and credit will be given for any methods which serve to eliminate unnecessary work in the air. Errors in computation, of whatever nature, will be heavily penalized, as will failure to return all rough working.

CIVIL AIRCRAFT NAVIGATORS' LICENCES—
SECOND CLASS

General Information and Conditions of Examination

1. Examinations for Second Class Civil Aircraft Navigators' Licences will be held in London in accordance with the programme notified annually in Notices to Airmen. Examinations are also held concurrently with the London examinations, in April and October, in Egypt, Malta, India, 'Iraq, and Singapore, provided there is a sufficient number of candidates for examination at these centres.

2. Formal application for licences must be made on C.A. Form 2C (2) and together with the prescribed fees of two guineas for the technical examination, one guinea for the medical examination, if required (*see* application form), and five shillings for the licence, must have been received by the Under-Secretary of State, Air Ministry (CH3), Adastral House, Kingsway, in the case of candidates for the London examination, or by the authorized representatives abroad, in the case of candidates at centres abroad, on or before the closing date of entry for each examination. Full details are contained in the Notice to Airmen announcing the programme of examinations. *Under no circumstances will late applications be considered.*

3. Candidates should give with their formal application full details of any qualifications and experience they already possess. Before a licence can be issued, candidates in addition to passing the technical examination must have—

(i) passed a medical examination;

(ii) produced proof (in the form of log books or other equivalent evidence) of having had at least two years' air experience, during which at least 300 hours must have been carried out as pilot or navigator of an aircraft.

4. It should be clearly understood that if candidates elect to take the technical examination before satisfying the prescribed conditions as to air experience, the Air Ministry reserves the right to require a further examination before the issue of a second class licence.

5. The technical examination comprises oral and practical tests, as well as written papers in the subjects specified below, except that there is no written paper for signalling.

Subject	Total marks allotted
(i) International and United Kingdom Air Legislation .	100
(ii) Form of the Earth, Maps and Charts . . .	200
(iii) Meteorology	200
(iv) Dead Reckoning and Navigation by Radio Direction Finding	300
(v) Earth's Magnetism and the Compass . . .	200
(vi) Signalling	Pass or Fail
	1000

The syllabus for these subjects and details of practical tests are set out fully in Appendix I. Notes on books for study are given in Appendix III.

6. The examinations occupy three days and conform approximately to the following time table—

Date	Time	Subject
1st day .	0930–1030	International and United Kingdom Air Legislation.
	1100–1300	Form of the Earth, Maps and Charts.
	1430–1630	Earth's Magnetism and the Compass.
2nd day .	0930–1230	Dead Reckoning and Radio D.F. Navigation.
	1400–1630	Meteorology.
One other day	0930–1300 and 1415–1700	Signalling Tests. Practical Tests in other subjects.

7. In order to qualify, candidates will be required to obtain not less than :—

(i) 90 per cent in signalling ;

(ii) 60 per cent in any other subject ; and

(iii) 70 per cent of the total marks for all subjects (excluding signalling).

Note.—Re-examination for candidates who fail in signalling only can be arranged at the examination centres of the Mercantile Marine Department of the Board of Trade at London, Liverpool, Hull, Newcastle-on-Tyne, Glasgow, and Cardiff. Application should be made on C.A. Form 2C (2) and together with a fee of ten shillings forwarded to the Under-Secretary of State, Air Ministry (CH3), Adastral House, Kingsway, W.C.2.

8. Exemption from certain subjects of the technical examination may be granted to officers and non-commissioned officers of the Royal Air Force, in accordance with the conditions laid down in A.M.O. A.349/1938.

9. Candidates are required to provide themselves with all necessary writing materials (including a supply of black ink and red ink) drawing and calculating instruments, but logarithmic and other necessary tables will be provided at the examination.

Except where otherwise stated candidates may only make use of private books or tables with the express permission of the presiding officer.

10. Candidates should be in attendance at least 10 minutes before the scheduled times for the commencement of each paper.

(APPENDIX I)
AIRCRAFT NAVIGATORS' LICENCES—SECOND CLASS
SYLLABUS FOR THE TECHNICAL EXAMINATION

1. International and United Kingdom Air Legislation. (*a*) A *detailed knowledge* of the regulations contained in the following publications—

(i) The International Convention for the Regulation of Air Navigation; the articles and the contents of Annex D.

(ii) The Air Navigation Consolidation Order, 1923 (with subsequent amendments); paras. 15, 16, 17, 18, 31, 33, schedule 2 (paras. 8, 9, 9A, 10), schedule 4, schedule 7, schedule 8, schedule 9.

(iii) The Air Navigation Directions, 1936 (A.N.D. 13 amended); paras. 23, 57A, section 8, section 11, section 16.

(iv) Air Ministry Notices to Airmen, containing regulations affecting navigation or radio procedure.

(v) The Air Pilot; Great Britain and Ireland, parts 1, 2 and 4 with particular reference to organization and regulations.

(vi) Regulations for the Prevention of Collisions at Sea.

(*b*) A *general knowledge* of the arrangements and contents of the following publications—

(i) The International Convention for the Regulation of Air Navigation; The Air Pilot, Great Britain and Ireland; The "Q" Code (Air Publication 1529); The list of Air Navigation Regulations published in part 1, para. 1, of the Air Pilot, Great Britain and Northern Ireland and from time to time in Air Ministry Notices to Airmen.

Note.—The above-mentioned publications are required for the written paper in this subject and must be supplied by the candidates.

(c) A *general knowledge* of the application and the practical use of the following publications—

(i) The Air Pilot, Great Britain and Ireland.

(ii) Air Ministry Notices to Airmen.

(iii) The Air Regulations Handbooks.

(iv) The Berne List.

(v) The Admiralty List of Lights, Fog Signals and Visual Time Signals.

(vi) The Admiralty List of Wireless Signals.

(vii) Admiralty Sailing Directions.

(viii) Admiralty Notices to Mariners.

Note.—The above publications are supplied by the examiners. Reference to the relevant publications will be permitted for the purpose of answering questions in respect of sections (b) and (c) above.

2. Form of the Earth, Maps and Charts. (a) *Form of the Earth.* Definitions: Sphere, Spheroid, Axis, Poles, Equator, Parallel of Latitude, Meridian, Rhumb line, Great Circle, Small Circle, Latitude, Longitude, Diff. Latitude, Diff. Longitude, Mid. Latitude, Departure, Meridional Parts, Prime Meridian, Nautical Mile, Statute Mile.

Dimensions of the earth; use of sexagesimal geographical coordinates in fixing position; solution of triangles by plane trigonometry; logarithms and their use in simple cases, including tables of the trigonometrical ratios (five or six figure tables).

The calculation of courses and distances by both the Middle Latitude and the Mercatorial formulæ. The Traverse Tables and their application to the solution of triangles.

Apparent annual motion of the sun; apparent and mean Solar Days; Hour angle; Declination; Azimuth; Equation of Time; GAT; GMT; LMT; ZT; ST. Change of time with longitude; apparent daily motion of heavenly bodies; the stars; principal constellations; recognition of stars and planets.

Determination of sunrise and sunset, moonrise and moonset; use of ephemeral tables.

(b) *Maps and Charts.* British Ordnance Survey Maps (Civil Air Editions); Admiralty Charts (Mercator and Gnomonic); International 1/1,000,000 Maps; International Aeronautical Maps; general knowledge of maps covering different countries and suitable for navigation purposes.

Properties of the projections of the above maps and charts and the precautions required in their use. Units of distance and angles; conventional signs and abbreviations (with particular reference to methods of indicating height); scales; technical topographical terms.

Measurement of distance and direction; preparation of maps for flights; description of country from topographical maps; plotting of bearings.

3. Meteorology.

(The syllabus for the Second Class Navigators' Examination as shown below, will come into force shortly: the precise date will be notified in Notices to Airmen. For the present, examinations in this subject will be based on the old syllabus as given in Appendix II hereto.)

(a) *Meteorological Observations.* How observations are made and principles of the instruments in general use for—

Pressure, temperature, humidity, cloud, precipitation, visibility, observed from the ground; wind (surface and upper).

(b) *General meteorology and physical principles. Pressure.*— Variation with height, altimeter corrections for pressure and temperature.

Temperature.—Radiation, convection, variation of temperature with height, inversions, stability and instability, diurnal variations.

Winds.—Surface and in upper atmosphere, relation with isobars. Wind structure in troposphere, turbulence, gusts, squalls, bumpiness, vertical currents, diurnal variations.

Water vapour and water in the atmosphere.—Absolute and relative humidity, dew point, condensation. Cloud; types, heights, thicknesses. Precipitation; rain, drizzle, snow, sleet, hail, thunderstorms. Dew, hoarfrost, glazed frost, rime.

Visibility.—Causes of bad visibility, formation of fog and mist, effect of smoke, dust and sand.

Topographical effects.—Local variations in the above factors due to topography: altitude, mountain ranges, hills, valleys, rivers, coasts, land and sea.

Ice-formation on aircraft.

(c) *Meteorological Organization.* (Reference books will be supplied if necessary in the examination.)

(i) International meteorological organization involved in the preparation of synoptic charts.

(ii) Meteorological information available for civil aviation, and the Regional organization in Europe* for the exchange of meteorological information for civil aviation.

Exact knowledge of time tables, wavelengths of broadcasts, and observation stations are not required, but only the broad outline.

* Candidates at overseas centres will be expected to know the Regional organization for the corresponding area instead of the European organization.

The times for which charts are drawn and the main centres supplying information for aviation should, however, be known.

(d) *Synoptic Meteorology.* Construction and interpretation of synoptic charts. Depressions, anticyclones and subsidiary pressure systems.

Meteorological conditions associated with different types of pressure systems; estimating the movement of these systems in simple cases; elementary knowledge of conditions associated with fronts; movement of fronts. Effect of orographical features on the development of weather. Candidates will be required—

(1) to plot the reports from a number of stations in accordance with current symbolic methods;

(2) to insert isobars and simple fronts on a chart on which the reports from stations have already been plotted. A completed chart for the preceding hour of observation will be provided;

(3) to interpret, either orally or in writing, the figures and symbols used in plotting, and the significance of the chart.

(e) *Climatology.* General distribution and seasonal variations of meteorological elements over the globe—pressure, temperature, winds near the surface, precipitation, without detailed knowledge of local conditions. More detailed knowledge of average conditions over Europe, including upper winds, clouds, fog.

Note.—Account will be taken in marking papers of a candidate's knowledge of the application of meteorology to air navigation and of the weather conditions likely to be a source of danger to aviation.

4. Dead Reckoning Navigation and Radio D.F. Navigation.

(a) *Dead Reckoning Navigation.* Course (true, magnetic and compass); track, track angle (true and magnetic); drift; drift angle; measurement of air speed and ground speed; units of speed.

Triangles of velocities; methods of solution for determination of track angle, drift angle, course, ground speed, wind speed and direction, and interception.

Drift sights, course and distance computer; principles of construction and errors of the air speed indicator, methods of calibrating; the air speed computer; principles of construction and errors of the altimeter, methods of calibrating; the common slide rule.

Determination of position by means of bearings and transits. Problems connected with aircraft endurance, common to charter work. Preparation for flights; calculations dealing with fuel and payload.

(b) *Navigation by Radio Goniometry.* Elementary knowledge of the various systems of guiding by radio-electric means applicable to the use of aircraft (apparatus in aircraft and ground installations).

Value of the various systems in the practical conditions of operation. Methods of fixing the position of an aircraft by means of direction finding bearings and radio-beacons, with the application of the necessary corrections; knowledge of the organization and methods of radio-electric orientation, including the practical use and knowledge of the Navigational groups of the "Q" Code; possible causes of error in radio-goniometric bearings; Night Effect, Coastal Refraction, etc.

Method of working and laying off bearings with particular reference to the charts and maps detailed in 2 (b) above: position lines and fixes, lines of equal bearing, head and tail bearings; convergency of meridians, conversion angle.

5. Earth's Magnetism and the Compass. Elementary Magnetism; Earth's Magnetic Poles, Magnetic Variation, Changes of Variation (Secular Change), Dip, Earth's Horizontal and Vertical Force, Isogonal and Isoclinal Lines.

Principles of construction of magnetic compasses, with reference to common types in use; various methods of reading; fitting of compasses; care and maintenance of compasses.

Deviation, causes and effects; compass compensation; the Micro-Adjuster; determination of deviation by means of Amplitude and Azimuth Tables; preparation and analysis of deviation tables; approximate coefficients, A, B, C and D. Northerly turning error; Acceleration and deceleration errors; elementary principles of the gyroscope, causes of precession; the directional gyro.

Practical Test. The test may include the actual compensation of the compass of an aircraft or the compensation of a compass by means of a model aircraft.

6. Signalling. (i) Semaphore—Ground. Ability to send and receive accurately messages made in plain language at a speed equivalent to 10 words per minute.

(ii) Flashing—Ground. Ability to send and receive accurately messages made either in plain language, coded groups, or numeral groups at a speed equivalent to 8 words per minute.

(iii) Aural Morse (Sound)—Ground. Ability to send and receive accurately messages made either in plain language, coded groups, or numeral groups at a speed equivalent to 4 words per minute.

(iv) International Code of Signals—Ground. Ability to recognize and record accurately (when displayed), the names of the flags, pendants, or substitutes used in the International Code of Signals. Normally 30 seconds will be allowed for recording each flag, pendant or substitute displayed for test purposes. Candidates must understand the correct method of reading signals when hoisted.

(v) Detailed knowledge of the *essential* procedure necessary to ensure the rapid correct exchanging of simple messages by the above methods (i), (ii) and (iii).

Note.—A word is taken as consisting of five letters for the purpose of calculating speeds.

(Appendix II)

AIRCRAFT NAVIGATORS' LICENCES—SECOND CLASS

Syllabus for the Technical Examination

Meteorology. (*The Syllabus shown below will be superseded shortly by that given in Section 3 of Appendix I of this pamphlet: the precise date will be notified in Notices to Airmen*).

(*a*) **General Meteorology.** Pressure of the atmosphere; the barometer; reduction of pressure to mean sea level.

Winds; Buys Ballot's Law; relation of wind to pressure gradient; wind measurement; Beaufort scale; anemometers; variation of wind with height; diurnal variation; local winds.

Temperature; scales in use, Fahrenheit, Centigrade, Absolute; measurement of air temperature.

Water in Atmosphere; relative humidity; general account of formation of mist and fog, clouds; rain, hail, and snow; classification of cloud forms; diurnal and seasonal variation of fog; conditions affecting visibility.

Weather Maps; types of pressure distribution and associated weather features.

(*b*) **Application of Meteorology to Air Navigation.** Meteorological observations at single reporting stations; preparation of coded reports; dissemination and collection of meteorological reports.

Construction and interpretation of synoptic charts; weather forecasting; development of local weather due to orographical features.

(*c*) **Climatology.** General distribution of meteorological elements over the globe; climatic conditions on any air route known to the candidate.

(Appendix III)

EXAMINATION FOR AIRCRAFT NAVIGATORS' LICENCES—SECOND CLASS

Notes on Books for Study

No one book contains the whole of what is required in the examinations; in many cases there are alternatives to those given in the list, and it should be borne in mind that a wider reading gives a wider view-point.

The books printed in capital letters are recommended as forming a useful nucleus for candidates taking up the study of air navigation *ab initio.*

INTERNATIONAL LEGISLATION

(1) "INTERNATIONAL CONVENTION FOR THE REGULATION OF AIR NAVIGATION" (Air Ministry, C.A. Information Bureau, post free).

(2) { "THE AIR PILOT, GREAT BRITAIN AND IRELAND" (H.M.S.O., 15s.).
AIR PILOT MONTHLY SUPPLEMENTS, 5s. annually post free.

(3) THE AIR NAVIGATION REGULATIONS which are listed in "The Air Pilot" (No. (2) above) and (H.M.S.O.) from time to time in Notices to Airmen (No. (4) below).

(4) AIR MINISTRY NOTICES TO AIRMEN.

Note.—These Notices are issued free to purchasers of the Air Pilot Monthly Supplements.

(5) THE AIR REGULATIONS HANDBOOKS (obtainable through Air Ministry C.A. Information Bureau, 6d.—1s. per copy).

(6) THE "Q" CODE (Air Publication 1529) (H.M.S.O., 1s. net).

(7) { The Berne List.
The Admiralty List of Lights, Fog Signals and Visual Time Signals.
The Admiralty List of Wireless Signals.
The Admiralty Sailing Directions (Pilots).
The Admiralty Notices to Mariners.

Note.—The agent for the sale of Admiralty Sailing Directions, Admiralty Lists of Lights, etc., is J. D. Potter, 145 Minories, London, E.C.3. Admiralty Notices to Mariners may also be obtained through this agent.

AIR NAVIGATION (GENERAL)

(8) "MANUAL OF AIR NAVIGATION," Vol. I. (With Amendments), Air Publication No. 1234 (H.M.S.O., 6s. net).

(9) Martin's Air Navigation, C. W. Martin (Eversley Press, Ltd., 21s.).

(10) "Avigation," Harvey B. Holland (McGraw-Hill Publishing Co., Ltd., 15s. post free).

(11) "Glossary of Navigation" (Third Edition), J. B. Harbord (Brown, Son & Ferguson, Ltd., 7s. 6d.; post free, 7s. 10d.).

These books, especially Nos. (8) and (9), give a useful introduction to the Second Class Navigators' syllabus. No. (10) is a good general summary of American methods of air navigation. Candidates should omit those portions of Nos. (10) and (11) which deal with astronomical navigation. No. (11) as its title implies gives an alphabetical list of terms used in navigation with full explanations.

The following Summary gives the principal sources of information, *in addition to the above,* grouped under the various subjects of the examination.

FORM OF THE EARTH

(12) "ADMIRALTY MANUAL OF NAVIGATION," Vol. I, 1928 (H.M.S.O., 6s.; post free, 6s. 9d.).

(13) "Nautical Almanac" (Abridged Edition). (H.M.S.O., Published Annually, 2s. 6d.; post free, 3s.)

(14)   Tables of Sunrise and Sunset, Moonrise and Moonset (H.M.S.O., Published Annually, 1s. 6d. net).

(15)   "INMAN'S NAUTICAL TABLES" (J. D. Potter, 24s., post free, 24s. 9d.).

or

(16)   "NORIE'S NAUTICAL TABLES" (Imray, Laurie, Norie & Wilson, 21s.; post free, 21s. 9d.).

or

(17)   BURTON'S NAUTICAL TABLES (George Philip & Son, Ltd., 14s. 6d.).

(18)   "Modern Navigation," Wm. Hall (University Tutorial Press, 10s. 6d.; post free, 10s. 11d.).

MAPS AND CHARTS

(—)   "ADMIRALTY MANUAL OF NAVIGATION," Vol. I, 1928. (*See* No. (12) above.)

(—)   "MANUAL OF AIR NAVIGATION," Vol. I (H.M.S.O., 6s.). (*See* No. (8) above.)

(—)   "INTERNATIONAL CONVENTION FOR THE REGULATION OF AIR NAVIGATION." Annex F. (*See* No. (1) above.)

(19)   "An Introduction to the Study of Map Projections." J. A. Steers (University of London Press, Ltd., 8s. 6d.; post free, 9s.).

(20)   "A Little Book on Map Projection." W. Garnett (G. Philip & Son, Ltd., 4s. 6d.; post free, 4s. 10d.).

(21)   "Manual of Map Reading, Field Sketching and Air Photography" (H.M.S.O., 3s.; post free, 3s. 4d.).

(22)   "Map Projections" (2nd edition, 1921), R. Hinks (Cambridge University Press, 7s. 6d.; post free, 8s.).

(—)   Conventional Signs Sheets for British Ordnance Survey Maps, International Million Series, Admiralty Charts. (Obtainable from agents for maps and charts, *see* note below.)

Note.—The agents for the sale of Ordnance Survey Maps (Civil Air Editions) and International Aeronautical Maps are—

E. Stanford, Ltd., 43 Whitehall, London, S.W.1.

Sifton, Praed & Co., 67 St. James Street, London, W.1.

T. Fisher Unwin, 1 Adelphi Terrace, London, W.C.

Wm. & A. K. Johnston, Ltd., Master Road, Edinburgh.

Philip, Son & Nephew, 20 Church Street, Liverpool.

The agent for the sale of Admiralty Charts is J. D. Potter, 145 Minories, London, E.C.3.

METEOROLOGY

A. ORGANIZATION

(23)   Wireless Weather Messages (M.O. 252) (H.M.S.O., 1s. 6d.).

(—)   Admiralty List of Wireless Signals, Vols. I & II. Hydrographic Dept., Admiralty. (H.M.S.O., Vol. I, 8s.; Vol. II, 5s.). (*See* No. (7) above.)

(—)   International Convention for the regulation of Air Navigation (Annex G). (*See* No. (1) above.)

(—)   THE AIR PILOT, GREAT BRITAIN AND IRELAND. (*See* No. (2) above.)

B. GENERAL METEOROLOGY: CLIMATOLOGY

(24)   *METEOROLOGY FOR AVIATORS (Sutcliffe). M.O. 432 (H.M.S.O.).

* To be published shortly.

(—)   MANUAL OF AIR NAVIGATION, Vol. I. (*See* No. (8) above.)
(25) A SHORT COURSE IN ELEMENTARY METEOROLOGY (Pick). M.O. 247 (H.M.S.O., 2s. 6d.).
(26) THE WEATHER MAP (M.O. 225 (i)) (H.M.S.O., 3s.).
(27) THE METEOROLOGICAL GLOSSARY (M.O. 225 (ii)) (H.M.S.O., 4s. 6d.).
(28) ICE ACCRETION ON AIRCRAFT. Professional Notes, No. 82 (H.M.S.O., 3d. net).
(29) The Meteorological Observers' Handbook (M.O. 191) (H.M.S.O., 5s.).
(30) The Climates of the Continents. W. G. Kendrew, M.A. (Oxford University Press, 21s.).
  C. PLOTTING
(31) Instructions for the Preparation of Weather Maps with Tables of the Specifications and Symbols—M.O. Form 2459. (H.M.S.O., 1s.).

FLIGHT BY DEAD RECKONING AND INSTRUMENTS

(—)   "MANUAL OF AIR NAVIGATION," Vol. I. (*See* No. (8) above.)
(—)   "ADMIRALTY MANUAL OF NAVIGATION," Vol. I, 1928. (*See* No. (12) above.)
(32) "GENERAL INSTRUMENT EQUIPMENT FOR AIRCRAFT." Air Publication No. 1275. (H.M.S.O., 3s. 6d. net; post free, 3s. 11d.)
(33) "Instruments," R. W. Sloley (Sir Isaac Pitman & Sons, Ltd., 5s. net; post free, 5s. 3d.).

DIRECTION AND POSITION FINDING BY RADIO DIRECTION FINDING

(—)   "ADMIRALTY MANUAL OF NAVIGATION," Vol. I, 1928. (*See* No. (12) above.)
(—)   "MANUAL OF AIR NAVIGATION," Vol. I. (*See* No. (8) above.)
(—)   "The 'Q' Code" (Air Publication 1529) (H.M.S.O., 1s. net. (*See* No. (6) above.)

Candidates should study that part of No. (6) dealing with navigation as distinct from the technical radio details.

EARTH'S MAGNETISM: COMPASSES

(—)   "MANUAL OF AIR NAVIGATION," Vol. I. (*See* No. (8) above.)
(—)   "ADMIRALTY MANUAL OF NAVIGATION," Vol. I, 1928. (*See* No. (12) above.)
(—)   "Nautical Almanac" (Abridged Edition). (*See* No. (13) above.)
(—)   Tables of Sunrise and Sunset, Moonrise and Moonset. (*See* No. (14) above.)
(34) "Deviation and the Deviascope," C. H. Brown (Brown, Son & Ferguson, Ltd., 8s. 6d.; post free, 8s. 11d.).
(35) "Davis's Tables." Revised Edition. (Davis 1.) (J. D. Potter, 20s.)
(36) "Burdwood's Tables." 2nd Edition. (Davis 2.) (J. D. Potter, 20s.)

In addition, any standard work on magnetism should be consulted by those requiring an introduction to this subject.

SIGNALLING

(37) "BROWN'S SIGNALLING." 1936 Edition. (Brown, Son & Ferguson, Ltd., Glasgow, 3s. 6d.; post free, 3s. 10d.)
      International Code of Signals. Colour Plate 2. Chapters 1 to 6. (Only those paragraphs dealing with the correct method of reading signals when hoisted.)

Semaphore	Chapter 7	With particular reference to the
Flashing	Chapter 8	essential procedure necessary
Aural Morse	Chapter 9	to ensure the rapid and correct
(Sound Signalling)		exchanging of simple messages.

(38) *AIR NAVIGATION SIGNALS BOOK. Compiled by the International Commission of Air Navigation.

Specimen Examination Papers

Copies of the papers set at previous examinations for Second Class Civil Aircraft Navigators' Licences may be obtained from His Majesty's Stationery Office, York House, Kingsway, London, W.C.2.

* To be published shortly.

APPENDIX III

BIBLIOGRAPHY

1. International Air Convention, and regulations, etc. (See Appendix I.)
2. The Manual of Air Navigation (Air Ministry), now replaced by Vol. II.
3. The Admiralty Manual of Navigation, Vols. I and II.
4. *Air Navigation*, by Lt. Cmdr. P. V. H. Weems.
5. *Nicholl's Concise Guides*, by Chas. H. Brown.
6. *Trigonometry for Navigating Officers*, by W. Percy Winter.
7. *Modern Navigation*, by William Hall.
8. Inman's Nautical Tables.
9. Norie's Nautical Tables.
10. Steer's *Study of Map Projections*.
11. Hink's *Map Projections*.
12. Manual of Map Reading, Field Sketching and Air Photography.
13. Tide Tables, Parts I, II, and III.
14. The Air Pilotage Manual (Air Ministry), now replaced by the Manual of Air Navigation, Vol. I.
15. Meteorology for Aviators, by R. C. Sutcliffe (H.M.S.O., 7s. 6d.).
16. The Weather Map (Air Ministry Met. Office).
17. The Meteorological Glossary (Air Ministry Met. Office).
18. Wireless Weather Messages (MO 252) (Air Ministry Met. Office).
19. Kendrew's *Climate of the Continents*.
20. *Handbook of Aeronautics* (Pitman).
21. Glossary of Aeronautical Terms.
22. Admiralty Manual of Wireless Telegraphy.
23. The Airworthiness Handbook.
24. The Nautical Almanac—complete and abridged editions.
25. Brown's Nautical Almanac.
26. Brown's Signalling.
27. The Air Almanac.
28. *Manual of Meteorology*, by Sir Napier Shaw.
29. Burton's Nautical Tables.

The books which may be referred to for subjects of the First Class Navigator's examination are as follows—

Subject	Books as per above list	Chapter applicable in this book
International Legislation	1	Appendix I
Forms of the Earth	2, 3, 4, 5, 6, and 7	Chap. I
Maps and Charts	1, 2, 3, 10, 11, and 12	,, II
Tides	3, 13, and 2	,, VIII
Meteorology	15, 21, 3, 16, 17, 20 and 28	,, IX
D/R Navigating	14, 2, 3, 4, etc.	Chap. V
D/F W/T	22, 14, 2, etc.	,, IV
Earth's Magnetism and Compasses	2, 3, 14, 23, and 4	,, III
Astronomical Navigation	2, 3, 4, 5, 6, 7, 8, 9, 24, and 25, etc.	Chaps. VI and VII
Visual Signalling	26	Chap. IV

APPENDIX IV

CONVERSION FACTORS, CONSTANTS, ETC.

1. Conversion Factors

To Convert	Into		
Absolute	Centigrade	Subtract	273
Atmospheres	Lb./sq. in.	Multiply by	14·70
B.Th.U.	Calories	,, ,,	·252
Calories	B.Th.U.	,, ,,	3·968
Centigrade	Absolute	Add	273
Centigrade	Fahrenheit	$= \dfrac{(C° \times 9)}{5} + 32$	
Centimetres	Inches	Multiply by	0·3937
Cubic centimetres	Cubic inches	,, ,,	0·06102
Cubic feet	Gallons	,, ,,	6·229
Cubic feet	Cubic metres	,, ,,	0·02832
Cubic inches	Cubic centimetres	,, ,,	16·388
Cubic metres	Cubic feet	,, ,,	35·31
Degrees	Radians	,, ,,	0·01745
Fahrenheit	Centigrade	$= (F° - 32)\, \dfrac{5}{9}$	
Feet	Metres	Multiply by	0·3048
Feet per minute	Knots	,, ,,	0·00987
Feet per second	Kilometres per hour	,, ,,	1·0973
Feet per second	Knots	,, ,,	·5921
Feet per second	Miles per hour	,, ,,	0·68182
Force de cheval	Horse-power	,, ,,	0·9863
Gallons	Litres	,, ,,	4·546
Gallons	Cubic feet	,, ,,	0·1605
Gallons	U.S. gallons	,, ,,	1·205
Horse-power	Force de cheval	,, ,,	1·0139
Horse-power	Foot-lb. per second	,, ,,	550
Imperial gallons	U.S. gallons	,, ,,	1·205
Inches	Centimetres	,, ,,	2·5399
Inches	Miles	,, ,,	63360
Inches of mercury	Lb. per square inch	,, ,,	0·4902
Inches of mercury	Millibars	,, ,,	33·9
Inches of water	Lb. per square inch	,, ,,	0·03615
Kilogrammes	Lb.	,, ,,	2·205
Kilogrammes per square centimetre	Lb. per square foot	,, ,,	14·22
Kilometres	Miles	,, ,,	0·62137
Kilometres	Nautical miles	,, ,,	0·5396
Knots	Feet per second	,, ,,	1·6889

To Convert	Into		
Knots	Feet per minute . .	Multiply by	101·38
Knots . . .	k.p.h.	,, ,,	1·8532
Knots . . .	m.p.h. . . .	,, ,,	1·1515
Lb. . . .	Kilogrammes . .	,, ,,	0·4536
Lb. per square inch	Atmospheres . .	,, ,,	0·0680
Lb. per square inch	Kilogrammes per square centimetre	,, ,,	0·0703
Lb. per square inch	Inches of water . .	,, ,,	27·6625
Lb. per square inch	Inches of mercury . .	,, ,,	2·040
Lb. per square inch	Millibars . . .	,, ,,	68·93
Litres . . .	Cubic inches . . .	,, ,,	61·025
Litres . . .	Gallons . . .	,, ,,	0·220
Metres . . .	Inches	,, ,,	39·37
Metres per second .	Feet per second . .	,, ,,	3·281
Metres per second .	m.p.h.	,, ,,	2·2369
Miles per hour	Kilometres per hour .	,, ,,	1·6093
Miles per hour	Knots	,, ,,	0·8684
Miles per hour	Feet per minute . .	,, ,,	88
Miles per hour	Feet per second . .	,, ,,	1·4667
Miles per hour	Metres per second . .	,, ,,	0·447
Millibars . .	Inches of mercury . .	,, ,,	0·0295
Millibars at S.L. .	Height in feet . .	,, by	27·25
Millibars . .	Lb. per square inch .	,, ,,	0·0145
Millibars . .	Millimetres of mercury .	,, about	0·7501
Millimetres . .	Inches	,, by	0·03937
Radians . .	Degrees . . .	,, ,,	57·2958
Square centimetres	Square inches . .	,, ,,	0·155
Square feet .	Square metres . .	,, ,,	0·0929
Square inches .	Square centimetres .	,, ,,	6·4516
Square kilometres .	Square miles . .	,, ,,	0·3862
Square metres .	Square feet . . .	,, ,,	10·76
Square miles .	Square kilometres . .	,, ,,	2·589
U.S. gallons .	Imperial gallons . .	,, ,,	0·830
Yards . . .	Metres	,, ,,	0·9144

2. Miscellaneous Values

WATER, PETROL, AND OIL WEIGHTS*

1 gal. of Fresh Water = about 10 lb. = 4·53 Kg.
1 gal. of Sea Water = about 10·26 lb. = 4·65 Kg.
1 gal. of Petrol = about 7·6 lb. = 3·45 Kg.
1 gal. of Mineral Oil = about 9·7 lb. = 4·39 Kg.
1 cub. ft. of Fresh Water = about 62·43 lb. = 28·31 Kg.
1 cub. ft. of Sea Water = about 64 lb. = 29·02 Kg.

(Sea Water averages about 1 ton per 35 cub. ft.)

* Weight of a given volume varies with density which in turn varies inversely as the temperature.

Velocity of Sound in air at $t°$ C. $= 33240 \sqrt{1 + 0.0037\,t°}$ cm. per sec.

$\qquad\qquad\qquad\qquad\qquad = $ about 1100 f.p.s.

Velocity of Light in vacuo $\qquad = 3 \times 10^{10}$ cm. per sec.

$\qquad\qquad\qquad\qquad\qquad = $ about 9.843×10^{8} f.p.s.

3. Formulae

(a) Mensuration Formulae: where $A =$ area; $S =$ surface; $V =$ volume; a, b, and $c =$ the sides of a figure; $h =$ the height; $l =$ the slant height; and R and $r =$ radii of circles.

(i) Rectangle or Parallelogram. $A = ah$.

(ii) Trapezium. $A = \frac{1}{2}(a + b)h$, where a and b are the parallel sides.

(iii) Triangle. $A = \frac{1}{2}ah = \sqrt{s(s - a)\,(s - b)\,(s - c)}$, where $s =$ semiperimeter.

(iv) Regular Polygon. $A = \dfrac{na^2}{4} \times \text{Cot}\dfrac{180°}{n}$, where $=$ number of sides.

(v) Circle. Circumference $= 2\pi r$; $A = \pi r^2$.

(vi) Ellipse. $A = \pi ab$, where a and b are the semi-axes.

$\qquad\qquad$ Circumference $= \pi\,(a + b)$ *approx.*

(vii) An Irregular Figure (by Simpson's Rule). $A = \dfrac{s}{3}(X + 4Y + 2Z)$,

$\qquad$ where $s =$ distance between two consecutive ordinates; $X =$ sum of first and last ordinates; $Y =$ sum of even and $Z =$ sum of odd ordinates.

(viii) Rectangular Prism. $\quad S = 2(ab + bc + ac)$; $\quad V = abc$; $\quad$ Diagonal $= \sqrt{a^2 + b^2 + c^2}$.

(ix) Cylinder. $S = 2\pi rh + 2\pi r^2$; $V = \pi r^2 h$.

(x) Cone. $S = \pi rl + \pi r^2$; $V = \frac{1}{3}\pi r^2 h$.

(xi) Sphere. $S = 4\pi r^2$; $V = \frac{4}{3}\pi r^3 = 0.5236 d^3$.

(xii) Ring. $S = 4\pi^2 Rr$; $V = 2\pi^2 r^2 R$.

(xiii) Spheroid. $V = \dfrac{4}{3}\pi ab^2$, where a and b are the major and minor axes.

(b) Mechanics; where $v =$ final velocity; $u =$ initial velocity; $f =$ acceleration; $t =$ time; and $s =$ space or distance.

In a straight line,

$\qquad$ (i) $v = u + ft$.

$\qquad\qquad s = ut + \frac{1}{2}ft.^2$

$\qquad\qquad s = \frac{1}{2}(u + v)t$.

$\qquad\qquad v^2 = u^2 + 2fs$.

$\qquad\qquad P = mf = \dfrac{w}{g}f$.

In a curved path,

$\qquad\qquad$ Centrifugal Force $= P = \dfrac{mV^2}{r}$, where $m =$ mass;

$\qquad\qquad\qquad\qquad\qquad\qquad\qquad\qquad v =$ velocity;

$\qquad\qquad\qquad\qquad\qquad\qquad\qquad\qquad r =$ radius of curvature.

Time of Swing of Pendulum, $t = 2\pi\sqrt{\dfrac{l}{g}}$

NOTE: Trigonometrical formulae are summarised in para. 24 of Chapter I.

4. The International Standard Atmosphere.

Standard Sea Level Conditions—

Temperature = 15 Centigrade.
Pressure = 1013·2 millibars.
Specific Weight = 0·07651 lb. per cub. ft.
Gravity = 32·1740 ft. per sec.
Density = 0·002378 slugs (lb./ft./sec.).

Height above Sea Level		Rel. Density	$\sqrt{\sigma}\left(=\dfrac{IAS}{TAS}\right)$	Air-speed Factor $\dfrac{1}{\sqrt{\sigma}}\left(=\dfrac{TAS}{IAS}\right)$	Temp.	Rel. Pressure
Feet	Metres					
− 1,000	− 305	1·0296	1·0147	·986		1·0367
0	0	1	1	1	15° C.	1
1,000	305	0·9710	0·9862	1·014	13	0·9644
2,000	610	0·9428	0·9718	1·029	11·1	0·9298
3,000	914	0·9151	0·9569	1·045	9·1	0·8962
4,000	1219	0·8881	0·9425	1·061	7·1	0·8636
5,000	1524	0·8616	0·9285	1·077	5·1	0·8320
6,000	1829	0·8358	0·9149	1·093	3·1	0·8013
7,000	2134	0·8106	0·9008	1·110	1·2	0·7716
8,000	2438	0·7859	0·8865	1·128	− 0·9	0·7427
9,000	2743	0·7619	0·8726	1·146	− 2·9	0·7147
10,000	3048	0·7384	0·8593	1·164	− 4·8	0·6876
11,000	3353	0·7154	0·8458	1·182	− 6·8	0·6614
12,000	3658	0·6931	0·8325	1·201	− 8·8	0·6359
14,000	4267	0·6499	0·8062	1·241	− 12·75	0·5873
16,000	4877	0·6088	0·7802	1·281	− 16·7	0·5418
18,000	5486	0·5698	0·7548	1·324	− 20·7	0·4992
20,000	6096	0·5327	0·7299	1·369	− 24·65	0·4594
22,000	6706	0·4974	0·7053	1·418	− 28·6	0·4222
24,000	7315	0·4640	0·6812	1·468	− 32·6	0·3874
26,000	7925	0·4323	0·6575	1·522	− 36·55	0·3550
28,000	8534	0·4023	0·6343	1·577	− 40·5	0·3248
30,000	9144	0·3740	0·6116	1·634	− 44·45	0·2968

APPENDIX V

DEPARTURE CORRECTION FACTORS (LOG OF) FOR THE TERRESTRIAL SPHEROID

For the sphere—

Departure = d. Long. × Cos Mid. Lat.

= d. Long. × Cos (Mean Lat. + Correction).

This correction is given in Inman's and in Norie's Tables (Workman's Table).

But for the terrestrial spheroid—

Departure = d. Long. × Cos Mid. Lat. × Corr. Factor

= d. Long. × Cos (Mean Lat. + Corr.) × Factor.

or Log Dep. = Log d. Long. + Log Cos Mid. Lat + L. Corr. Factor

(As given below.)

The following table is based on the Clarke 1880 Figure of the Earth, and has been calculated *de novo* by the author after a vain search to find such a table. It is based on the simple formula—

$$\text{Factor} = \frac{\text{Length of } 1' \text{ of Long. in Feet on the spheroid}}{6080 \text{ Cos Lat.}}$$

Lat.	L. Corr. Factor	Lat.	L. Corr. Factor	Lat.	L. Corr. Factor
0°	0·00051	26°	0·0008	51°	0·0014
1°	0·00051	27°	0·00081	52°	0·00142
2°	0·00051	28°	0·00083	53°	0·00145
3°	0·00051	29°	0·00085	54°	0·00148
4°	0·00052	30°	0·00087	55°	0·0015
5°	0·00052	31°	0·00089	56°	0·00152
6°	0·00052	32°	0·00091	57°	0·00154
7°	0·00053	33°	0·00094	58°	0·00157
8°	0·00053	34°	0·00096	59°	0·0016
9°	0·00054	35°	0·00099	60°	0·00162
10°	0·00055	36°	0·00101	61°	0·00164
11°	0·00056	37°	0·00104	62°	0·00166
12°	0·00057	38°	0·00107	63°	0·00168
13°	0·00059	39°	0·0011	64°	0·00171
14°	0·0006	40°	0·00112	65°	0·00173
15°	0·0006	41°	0·00114	66°	0·00176
16°	0·00062	42°	0·00116	67°	0·00178
17°	0·00063	43°	0·00119	68°	0·00179
18°	0·00064	44°	0·00121	69°	0·0018
19°	0·00066	45°	0·00124	70°	0·00182
20°	0·00068	46°	0·00127	71°	0·00183
21°	0·0007	47°	0·0013	72°	0·00184
22°	0·00072	48°	0·00132	73°	0·00185
23°	0·00073	49°	0·00134	74°	0·00187
24°	0·00076	50°	0·00137	75°	0·00189
25°	0·00078				

INDEX

361

MADE IN GREAT BRITAIN AT THE PITMAN PRESS, BATH
D—(A.31)

PITMAN'S BOOKS
on
AVIATION
and
AERONAUTICAL
ENGINEERING

LONDON
SIR ISAAC PITMAN & SONS, LTD., PITMAN HOUSE, PARKER ST., KINGSWAY, W.C.2
BATH   ASSOCIATED COMPANIES   MELBOURNE
Pitman Publishing Corporation, New York and Chicago
Sir Isaac Pitman & Sons (Canada), Ltd., Toronto (Incorporating The Commercial Text Book Co.)
Wholesale Agents for India: A. H. WHEELER & CO., BOMBAY, CALCUTTA, AND ALLAHABAD

THE AIR ANNUAL OF THE BRITISH EMPIRE, 1938

Founder and First Editor, SQUADRON-LEADER C. G. BURGE, O.B.E., A.R.Ae.S.I. This well-known annual provides up-to-date and interesting information relating to the progress, development and activities of British Aviation. Crown 4to, cloth gilt, 616 pp., illustrated. **21s.** net.

PILOT'S " A " LICENCE

Compiled by JOHN F. LEEMING. Everything the pilot must know and do in order to satisfy the requirements of the examiners awarding a Flying Certificate is described in this useful handbook. Crown 8vo, cloth gilt, 88 pp. Eighth and Revised Edition. **3s. 6d.**

LEARNING TO FLY

By FRANK A. SWOFFER, M.B.E. A standard guide for all who are taking flying lessons, as well as a useful source of reference to details of engine working and maintenance for pilots. Crown 8vo, cloth gilt, 152 pp., illustrated. Fourth Edition. **7s. 6d.** net.

FLYING AS A CAREER

By OLIVER STEWART, M.C., A.F.C. Air enthusiasts who wish to find out all they can about the life and work of airmen should read this book. Crown 8vo, cloth, 84 pp. Second Edition. **3s. 6d.** net.

THE ROYAL AIR FORCE
Careers and How to Join

By T. STANHOPE SPRIGG. This book gives a clear idea of the numerous careers within the R.A.F., and the methods of entry, together with details of pay, promotion, pensions, etc. Demy 8vo, cloth gilt, 136 pp. Third Edition. **5s.** net.

HOW TO FIND YOUR WAY IN THE AIR

By G. W. FERGUSON, M.C., A.F.C., M.I.Loco.E. The text of this book is based on the instruction methods adopted by the author after long experience of teaching cross-country flying. Crown 8vo, cloth, 80 pp. Second Edition. **3s. 6d.** net.

ASTRONOMICAL NAVIGATION MADE EASY

By G. W. FERGUSON, M.C., A.F.C., etc. Explains in a simple and comprehensive manner the calculations necessary for navigation by astronomical means. Demy 8vo, cloth, 72 pp. **5s.** net.

THE AUTOGIRO AND HOW TO FLY IT

By REGINALD BRIE. This book tells how the autogiro originated and how it has been developed and indicates the immense possibilities in the future for this type of aircraft. Demy 8vo, cloth gilt, 116 pp., illustrated. Second Edition. **5s.** net.

PRACTICAL AIR NAVIGATION
Simply Explained

By WING-COMMANDER J. K. SUMMERS, M.C., A.F.C. This book deals with the problems met with in everyday air navigation, and is strongly recommended to all who have mastered map-reading and to all others interested in the subject. Crown 8vo, cloth, 57 pp., illustrated. **2s. 6d.** net.

AIRPORT MANAGEMENT

By MAJOR L. F. RICHARD. The author explains the responsibilities of the airport manager from beginning to end—from the organization and management of the airport to the actual working of the control tower. Medium 8vo, cloth, 150 pp. **5s.** net.

AERODROMES (Air Transport Series)
Their Location, Operation, and Design

Translated from the German. An important volume of research into air transport ground organization, embracing the study of (i) the location of aerodromes in air transport systems and (ii) the design of aerodromes with a view to the flight and routine operations performed there. Demy 8vo, cloth, 129 pp. **10s. 6d.** net.

STRATOSPHERE AND ROCKET FLIGHT (Astronautics)

By C. G. PHILP. Explains the scientific principles and the general and practical details of rocket flight, and describes significant experiments which have recently taken place. Crown 8vo, cloth gilt, 126 pp. Third Edition. **3s. 6d.** net.

THE CONQUEST OF THE STRATOSPHERE

By C. G. PHILP. This book tells the story of the principal stratosphere flights of recent times. Compiled from the original records, diaries and reports of the actual experiences of the participants, it provides virtually a first-hand account of each flight. Crown 8vo, cloth, 216 pp. **7s. 6d.** net.

A SIMPLE STUDY OF FLIGHT

By J. D. HADDON, B.Sc., F.R.Ae.S. A straightforward treatment of the theory of flight, filling the gap between the very elementary books and the advanced mathematical works which are too involved for the beginner. Medium 8vo, 88 pp., illustrated. **3s. 6d.** net.

THE AIRMAN AND THE AIR

By A. B. FIELDING. A simple and interesting explanation of the "Why and Wherefore" of what happens in the air. Demy 8vo, cloth, 152 pp. **5s.** net.

THE COMPLETE AIR NAVIGATOR

By D. C. T. BENNETT. This book covers the syllabus for the Air Ministry First Class Air Navigator's Licence. The full syllabus of the First Class Air Navigator's Licence is given in an Appendix. Demy 8vo, cloth, 280 pp. **15s.** net.

AEROBATICS

By OLIVER STEWART, M.C., A.F.C. Contains simple explanations of aerial evolutions, such as looping the loop, rolling, spinning, etc. A very interesting and instructive book. Crown 8vo, cloth, gilt, 86 pp., illustrated. **5s.** net.

HYDRO- AND AERO-DYNAMICS

By S. L. GREEN, M.Sc. Written for students of aeronautics and physics, providing a sound introduction to the theory of the motion of fluids, including modern developments. Demy 8vo, cloth, 166 pp. **12s. 6d.** net.

AIRMANSHIP

By JOHN McDONOUGH. This book describes the construction and use of every part of the machine, and gives instruction in practical flying and overhauling. Demy 8vo, cloth gilt, 128 pp., illustrated. **7s. 6d.** net.

AEROPLANES AND ENGINES (Airsense)

By W. O. MANNING, F.R.Ae.S. An excellent introductory manual for pilots, ground engineers, and students of aeronautics. Written in a simple style throughout, it will appeal to all who wish to obtain a good general understanding of the theory of flight and the technicalities of flying. Demy 8vo, cloth, 83 pp. Second Edition. **3s. 6d.** net.

WIRELESS TELEGRAPHY. Notes for Students

By W. E. CROOK. This book covers the Postmaster-General's Air Licence for W/T operators, and represents the theoretical part of the Wireless Course given for this purpose at Air Service Training Ltd. Demy 8vo, cloth, 185 pp., illustrated. **7s. 6d.** net.

THE MATERIALS OF AIRCRAFT CONSTRUCTION

By F. T. HILL, F.R.Ae.S., M.I.Ae.E. This practical handbook embraces the complete range of materials used in the modern practice of aeronautical engineering. Demy 8vo, cloth gilt, 422 pp. Third Edition. **20s.** net.

METAL AIRCRAFT CONSTRUCTION

By M. LANGLEY, M.I.Ae.E., A.M.I.N.A. A review of the modern international practice on the construction of metal aircraft, compiled with the assistance of leading international aircraft manufacturers. Demy 8vo, cloth gilt, 364 pp., illustrated. Third Edition. **15s.** net.

MARINE AIRCRAFT DESIGN

By WILLIAM MUNRO, A.M.I.Ae.E. Describes the individual types of marine aircraft, and the details of design in aircraft ranging from 3,000 lb. to 20,000 lb. all-up weight for flying boats and from 1,500 lb. to 5,000 lb. for float seaplanes. Demy 8vo, cloth gilt, 240 pp., illustrated. **20s.** net.

METAL AIRCRAFT FOR THE MECHANIC
(Aeronautical Engineering Series)

By J. HEALEY. This book presents a clear account of modern operations and processes dealing with work on metal aircraft. It is recommended to metal riggers, ground engineers, fitters, etc. Demy 8vo, 95 pp. **5s.** net.

THE STRESSES IN AEROPLANE STRUCTURES

By H. B. HOWARD, B.A., B.Sc., F.R.Ae.S. Discusses those portions of the theory of structures that are of special importance in aeroplane design. Demy 8vo, cloth gilt, 264 pp., illustrated. **20s.** net.

4

SEAPLANE FLOAT AND HULL DESIGN
(Aeronautical Engineering Series)

By MARCUS LANGLEY, M.I.Ae.E., A.M.I.N.A. This up-to-date book deals thoroughly with the latest trends in flying boat design. Medium 8vo, cloth gilt, 136 pp., illustrated. **7s. 6d.** net.

INTERNATIONAL INDEX TO AERONAUTICAL TECHNICAL REPORTS, 1937

Prepared by the Society of British Aircraft Constructors, Ltd. A complete annual reference to the Technical Reports, Memoranda, and Papers issued during the past year relating to every branch of aeronautics and aeronautical engineering. Demy 8vo, cloth gilt, 126 pp. **5s.** net.

AIRCRAFT PERFORMANCE TESTING

By S. SCOTT HALL, M.Sc., D.I.C., A.F.R.Ae.S., and T. H. ENGLAND, D.S.C., A.F.C., A.F.R.Ae.S., R.A.F. (Ret.). This book is written primarily for the constructor who wishes to put his aircraft through an adequate programme of tests on modern lines. Demy 8vo, cloth gilt, 206 pp., illustrated. **15s.** net.

LIGHT AERO ENGINES

By C. F. CAUNTER. A practical manual describing the chief types of light aero engines, with instructions for their maintenance. It will appeal to the owner-pilot, the ground engineer, and the manufacturer. Crown 8vo, cloth gilt, 304 pp., illustrated. **12s. 6d.** net.

PRACTICAL PERFORMANCE PREDICTION OF AIRCRAFT

By LIEUT.-COL. J. D. BLYTH, O.B.E., A.F.R.Ae.S., M.I.Ae.E. This book enables students and members of design office staffs to investigate and predict the performance of aeroplanes under all conditions of flight. Medium 8vo, cloth gilt, 80 pp., illustrated. **5s.** net.

AUTOMOBILE AND AIRCRAFT ENGINES

By A. W. JUDGE, Wh.Sc., A.R.C.S., A.M.I.Ae.E., D.I.C., etc. This volume records the results of modern scientific research into all branches of the subject. It is a recognized standard work for designers and students concerned with aero engine work. Demy 8vo, cloth gilt, 890 pp., illustrated. Third Edition. **42s.** net.

DEFINITIONS AND FORMULAE FOR STUDENTS— AERONAUTICS

By J. D. FRIER, A.R.C.Sc., D.I.C. Every student of aeronautical engineering and everyone connected with aeronautical practice will find this a most useful source of essential formulae and data. Pocket size, 36 pp. **6d.**

SMALL TWO-STROKE AERO ENGINES
(Aeronautical Engineering Series)

By C. F. CAUNTER. Every type of two-stroke engine at present in use or projected for use in light aircraft is described in this book. Medium 8vo, stiff boards, 96 pp., illustrated. **6s.** net.

SMALL FOUR-STROKE AERO ENGINES
(Aeronautical Engineering Series)

By C. F. CAUNTER. A companion volume to SMALL TWO-STROKE AERO ENGINES. Photographic illustrations of most of the models described and of interesting features are included. The book is a fascinating study of a progressive branch of the aircraft industry. Medium 8vo, stiff boards, 91 pp., illustrated. **6s.** net.

AIR TRANSPORTATION COSTING (Air Transport Series)

By CAPTAIN N. T. MACLEOD, M.C., D.C.M. This book, by a well-known Canadian authority, describes the most accurate costing methods for concerns engaged in commercial and passenger flying. Medium 8vo, 98 pp., illustrated. **7s. 6d.** net.

ECONOMICS OF AIR TRANSPORT (Air Transport Series)

By S. J. NOEL-BROWN, F.A.I.A., A.C.I.S., M.S.M.A. Gives a complete statement of cost of air line operation. Detailed explanations, supported by figures, are given of airframe, engine and airscrew overhauls and maintenance. Medium 8vo, cloth, 74 pp. **6s.** net.

THE CONSTRUCTION OF WOODEN AIRCRAFT

By S. F. WILKINSON, A.R.Ae.S.I. This is a book for practical aircraft workers and aeronautical students. Every process in the creation of the complete aeroplane, from the selection of suitable timber to the installation of the engine, is explained in detail from the standpoint of the individual craftsman, and illustrated with complete drawings. Size 8⅝ in. × 11 in., stiff boards, 112 pp., illustrated. **10s. 6d.** net.

HOW TO BUILD FLYING BOAT HULLS AND SEAPLANE FLOATS (Aeronautical Engineering Series)

By J. STREETER. This book deals fully with every operation in the actual construction of a seaplane float and hull, and gives a detailed account of repairing methods, general workshop practice, riveting, etc. Medium 8vo, cloth, 104 pp., illustrated. **6s.** net.

RIGGING AND AIRFRAMES

By J. CAMPBELL CORLETT, A.R.Ae.S.I. This book contains particulars of the constructional principles of the latest types of metal aircraft, describes the materials and tools employed and gives complete information on repairs, upkeep, and the checking of common faults. Medium 8vo, cloth, 116 pp., illustrated. **5s.** net.

PRACTICAL AIRCRAFT STRESS ANALYSIS

By D. R. ADAMS, A.F.R.Ae.S. This is a practical, detailed study, augmented by diagrams and tables, of the methods used in the stress analysis of aircraft components. Demy 8vo, cloth, 160 pp., illustrated. **8s. 6d.** net.

SEAPLANES
Maneuvering, Maintaining, Operating

By DANIEL J. BRIMM, JNR., M.A. This book, by a well-known American engineer and pilot, with an unrivalled knowledge of seaplanes and flying boats, provides comprehensive guidance on all aspects of seaplane flying. Demy 8vo, cloth, 140 pp., illustrated. **10s. 6d.** net.

THE AIR MARINER

By a FLYING BOAT PILOT. A practical handbook containing a store of essential information and advice on the flying and handling of flying boats; indispensable as an introduction and textbook for all those desirous of learning flying boat technique. Demy 8vo, cloth, 123 pp., illustrated. **6s. 6d.** net.

AIRPLANE AND ENGINE MAINTENANCE

By DANIEL J. BRIMM, JNR., M.A., and H. EDWARD BOGGESS. One of the most complete works on this subject so far produced, covering the whole of the practical work of the ground engineer and mechanic and forming a comprehensive guide to American methods. Size 6 in. × 8½ in., cloth boards, 500 pp., illustrated. **7s. 6d.** net.

AIRCRAFT MATERIALS AND PROCESSES

By GEORGE F. TITTERTON. This book brings to British aeronautical students and engineers a vast amount of information, based on American experience in the use of metal alloys and other materials, and presented by a practical expert in a form which makes it of immediate utility to everyone concerned in aircraft design and manufacture. Demy 8vo, cloth gilt, 328 pp., illustrated. **15s.** net.

AIRCRAFT RADIO (Air Transport Series)

By D. HAY SURGEONER, A.F.R.Ae.S. A practical illustrated handbook explaining the uses of wireless in modern aviation. It deals extensively with direction-finding and blind landing methods as used on all major air lines of the world. There is also a section on Airport Lighting. Crown 4to, cloth, 151 pp., illustrated. **12s. 6d.** net.

THE AIRPLANE SERVICING MANUAL

By LIEUT.-COLONEL VICTOR PAGE. A complete work of reference for all interested in inspection, maintenance, rigging and repair of airplanes. Size 6 in. × 9¼ in., cloth gilt, 1,000 pp. **25s.** net.

MACHINE DRAWING FOR STUDENTS
(Aeronautical Engineering Series)

By F. J. PRYER, B.Sc. Provides useful instruction in machine drawing for students of aeronautical engineering. Crown 4to, cloth, 141 pp. Third Edition. **7s. 6d.** net.

AIR AND AVIATION LAW (Civil Aviation)
Being an Exposition of the Statute and Case Law Affecting Air Navigation.

By WM. MARSHALL FREEMAN. Demy 8vo, cloth gilt, 176 pp. **7s. 6d.** net.

GROUND ENGINEERS' TEXTBOOKS

A series of Nine Books covering the requirements of the Ground Engineers' Licences.

AERO ENGINES. Inspection of Before Flight
By R. F. Barlow. "C" Licence. 36 pp. **2s.** net. Second Edition.

AERO ENGINES. Inspection of During Manufacture, Overhaul and Test
By A. N. Barrett, A.M.I.A.E. "D" Licence. 123 pp. **3s. 6d.** net. Fifth Edition.

INSTRUMENTS
By R. W. Sloley, M.A., B.Sc. "X" Licence. 120 pp. **5s.** net. Third Edition.

ELECTRICAL AND WIRELESS EQUIPMENT OF AIRCRAFT
By S. G. Wybrow, A.M.I.E.E., A.M.I.M.E. "X" Licence. 132 pp. **5s.** net. Third Edition.

INSPECTION OF AIRCRAFT AFTER OVERHAUL
By S. J. Norton, A.M.Inst.C.E., A.F.R.Ae.S. "B" Licence. 92 pp. Third Edition. **3s. 6d.** net.

THE RIGGING, MAINTENANCE, AND INSPECTION OF AIRCRAFT
By W. J. C. Speller. "A" Licence. Second Edition. 130 pp. **3s. 6d.** net.

NOTES ON SUPERCHARGING FOR GROUND ENGINEERS
By C. E. Jones. 32 pp. **3s.** net.

THE DEVELOPMENT OF SHEET METAL DETAIL FITTINGS
By William S. B. Townsend. 42 pp. Second Edition. **2s. 6d.** net.

THE AIRCRAFT BENCH FITTER
By William S. B. Townsend. 72 pp. **3s. 6d.** net.

HANDBOOK OF AERONAUTICS

Third Edition. Published under the authority of the Royal Aeronautical Society. This work is a standard source of authoritative technical information among aircraft manufacturers and designers all over the world. It is compiled by leading specialists, and is published in three volumes comprising over 1,500 pages and hundreds of illustrations.

Volume I. Aerodynamics—Performance—Construction—Materials—Meteorology —Instruments—Air Survey and Photography—Design and Construction of Sailplanes. Med. 8vo, 722 pp. **30s.** net. The sections on Aerodynamics and Performance are obtainable as separate books, price **6s.** net each.

Volume II (Aero Engines: Design and Practice). By A. Swan, B.Sc., A.M.Inst.C.E., A.F.R.Ae.S. Med. 8vo, 400 pp. **25s.** net.

Volume III. Design Data and Formulae—Aircraft and Airscrews. 243 pp. **20s.** net.

AN INTRODUCTION TO AERONAUTICAL ENGINEERING

A series of textbooks dealing with the theory underlying modern practice in aeronautical engineering. Each in demy 8vo.

Volume I. Mechanics of Flight

By A. C. Kermode, B.A., A.F.R.Ae.S. 231 pp., illustrated. **6s. 6d.** net. Third Edition.

Volume II. Structures

By J. D. Haddon, B.Sc., F.R.Ae.S. 150 pp., illustrated. **6s.** net. Third Edition.

Volume III. Properties and Strength of Materials

By J. D. Haddon, B.Sc., F.R.Ae.S. 181 pp., illustrated. **8s. 6d.** net. Third Edition.

MADE IN GREAT BRITAIN AT THE PITMAN PRESS, BATH
(D.6300)